Operant Procedures

in Remedial Speech

and Language Training

Edited by **HOWARD N. SLOANE, JR.**
UNIVERSITY OF UTAH

BARBARA D. MAC AULAY
UNIVERSITY OF NEVADA

HOUGHTON MIFFLIN COMPANY · BOSTON

New York   Atlanta   Geneva, ILL.   Dallas   Palo Alto

FOREWORD

This book is a partial answer to the critics of psychology who allege that psychologists have little interest in applying the scientific knowledge derived from basic research. It shows that in some areas, at least, the myriad of experiments in psychology can assist a teacher in the methods of teaching.

The techniques of operant conditioning are a direct application of much psychological knowledge. And it has been found that in general teachers are eager to adopt systematic teaching procedures based on experimentally derived principles and laws that are applicable to their task.

This book, then, with its compilation of techniques for shaping or modifying behavior in remedial speech and language should be welcomed by teachers. Its concentration is not on "why" a child or adult cannot speak, or speaks incorrectly, but on "how" he can be helped to emit adequate speech. The application of operant procedures to speech defectives is not concerned with the etiology of the individual's difficulty so much as with systematic principles of reinforcement that can be used to assist him in becoming more adequate.

The authors have not confined themselves to remedial speech or speech re-education, but have included theoretical as well as systematic procedures for the shaping of attention and controlling classroom behavior of retarded children, methods of recording and evaluating behavior, programs for teaching speech and reading, and programs for rehabilitating aphasics, stutterers, and other speech deficient individuals. The step-by-step description of actual methods that have been successful with particular children or adults have direct application to other similar persons.

This book should be a valuable guide to the speech therapist. Its description of operant procedures should appeal to teachers remediating speech defectives as well as to teachers of the mentally retarded and other teachers who have such problems in their classrooms.

SAMUEL A. KIRK

PREFACE

In the last 25 years, scientific data concerning the modification of human behavior has been accumulating at an increasing rate. This has led to an expansion of interest in the application of laboratory findings to clinical problems. One specific area of application that has concerned many is that of remedial speech and language training. Much of the research on behavior modification in speech and language has been published in journals not readily available to those most directly concerned with speech and language problems, while a large percentage of this research has not been published at all. However, those who deal directly with these problems are the persons who will ultimately determine whether or not new procedures gain common usage and whether any particular procedure is practical in the "real-life" situation in which it must be used. Thus, it is very important for speech and hearing correctionists and special education teachers to be familiar with these new developments. The purpose of this book is to bring together a collection of papers that summarize current progress.

Traditional approaches to the modification of inadequate speech and language are often based upon assumed neurological processes, upon inferences stemming from "cognitive" models of behavior, or upon hypothetical "dynamic" personality variables. Critics have often questioned the meaningfulness, the usefulness, and the degree of empirical validity of these approaches, as well as expressing concern over derived methods of training. These criticisms have generated various alternative models for both remediation and theory.

In the laboratory, contemporary research using operant conditioning has become quite sophisticated since the primitive activities of the 1920 behaviorists. A wide range of human activity has been studied, and complicated problems are analyzed with the help of more powerful and refined techniques, rather than by insisting that all behavior fit the simple reflex paradigm. As research has confronted more complex behavioral repertoires, conditioning procedures have inevitably become concerned with that most intricate of human performances, speech and language. Often these endeavors have been characterized by a laboratory rather than a clinical interest, and by the fact that the personnel involved have been from professional disciplines outside the speech and language area. Thus, the special skills and knowledge that the individual trained in special education or remedial speech and language training might contribute to operant approaches have often not been available, and the results and implications of such research, as well as knowledge of the particular procedures, have not obtained wide circulation in the pertinent clinical communities. This lack of communication is most unfortunate, for there is much evidence to suggest that the direct application of operant conditioning procedures to the problem of modifying speech and language behavior holds the promise of a soundly based and effective remedial technology.

This book contains a collection of reports on speech and language modification attempts that have utilized operant conditioning procedures, as well as several papers on background topics. We hope that the reader will come to share our excitement over the implications of these articles for the development of more effective remedial procedures in the area of speech and language.

HOWARD N. SLOANE

BARBARA D. MACAULAY

CONTENTS

Foreword   v

Preface   vii

PART I

General and Theoretical Background

1. H. N. SLOANE and B. D. MACAULAY, Teaching and the
   Environmental Control of Verbal Behavior   3

2. J. BIRNBRAUER, M. WOLF, J. KIDDER, and C. TAGUE, Classroom Behavior of Retarded Pupils with Token Reinforcement   19

3. M. JOHNSTON and F. R. HARRIS, Observation and Recording of Verbal Behavior in Remedial Speech Work   40

4. R. PETERSON, Imitation: A Basic Behavioral Mechanism   61

PART II

Instituting Speech in Severely Impaired Children

5. H. N. SLOANE, M. K. JOHNSTON, and F. R. HARRIS, Remedial Procedures for Teaching Verbal Behavior to Speech
   Deficient or Defective Young Children   77

6. B. D. MACAULAY, A Program for Teaching Speech and Beginning Reading to Nonverbal Retardates   102

7. O. I. LOVAAS, A Program for the Establishment of Speech
   in Psychotic Children   125

PART III

Echolalic Speech

8. T. Risley and M. Wolf, Establishing Functional Speech in Echolalic Children   157

9. M. Johnston, Echolalia and Automatism in Speech   185

PART IV

Rehabilitating Speech in Aphasics

10. A. Holland and A. Harris, Aphasia Rehabilitation Using Programmed Instruction: An Intensive Case History   197

PART V

Reinstating Speech in Mute Children and Adults

11. J. G. Sherman, Use of Reinforcement and Imitation to Reinstate Verbal Behavior in Mute Psychotics   219

12. J. Straughan, The Application of Operant Conditioning to the Treatment of Elective Mutism   242

PART VI

Articulation Difficulties

13. A. Holland and J. Matthews, Application of Teaching Machine Concepts to Speech Pathology and Audiology   259

14. J. McDearmon, Programmed Learning Instruction in Phonics   282

15. D. E. Mowrer, R. L. Baker, and R. E. Schutz, Operant Procedures in the Control of Speech Articulation   296

PART VII

Stuttering

16. R. MARTIN, The Experimental Manipulation of Stuttering
    Behaviors   325

17. I. GOLDIAMOND, Stuttering and Fluency as Manipulatable
    Operant Response Classes   348

PART VIII

Conclusions

18. F. KANFER, Issues and Ethics in Behavior Manipulation   411

19. L. ULLMANN, Some Implications of Current Research   424

    Index   431

OPERANT PROCEDURES IN REMEDIAL

SPEECH AND LANGUAGE TRAINING

PART I

General and Theoretical Background

The papers in Part I are not directly concerned with remedial speech and language training, but provide background information to make the other sections of the book more meaningful. Following a brief introduction, Chapter 1 reviews in condensed fashion what is currently known about operant behavior and the environmental variables that control it. It is a selective review; topics are included or excluded depending on their pertinence to the subject matter of the book. For those unfamiliar with what now is often called "reinforcement theory," it is hoped that this chapter will serve as an introduction to concepts and terminology used in the other chapters.

Chapter 2, by Birnbrauer *et al.*, on the use of token reinforcement (incentives) in the classroom management of retarded pupils, follows directly from Chapter 1. Individuals working with speech defective children often express concern over non-speech problems such as maintaining attention, "motivation," and avoiding undesirable behavior. One solution to this kind of problem for one particular setting is presented in Chapter 2. It is based quite directly on the analysis of behavior presented in Chapter 1. Although Birnbrauer *et al.* are concerned in their chapter with retarded pupils in one specific kind of academic classroom, the general procedures and rationale presented are applicable to a multitude of "management" problems. In some of the later chapters on particular speech problems, similar procedures are "built in" to general programs.

A factor common to nearly all of the papers in the book is the emphasis upon objective data, both for purposes of evaluation of procedures and for the guidance of remedial work. The important subject of objective data is given specific treatment in Chapter 3 by Johnston, who discusses its value in research and clinical settings, as well as the technology of recording and observing verbal behavior itself.

Chapter 4 presents a functional analysis of imitative behavior and its relationship to speech and speech training. Peterson's dual interest in the general phenomena of imitation and the practical problems of behavior modification is reflected here. In remedial work, imitation is often the "stepchild" who is expected to do the work but rarely receives explicit attention. Children who do not imitate usually present extremely difficult problems for the speech correctionist or special education teacher. Due to general lack of knowledge concerning variables that develop and maintain imitative behavior, these problems often become insurmountable. Peterson presents an excellent theoretical discussion of imitation and related empirical studies, a practical discussion of the ways in which imitation can be used in speech training, and a discussion of the development of imitative behavior in nonimitative individuals.

Howard N. Sloane, Jr.
Barbara D. MacAulay

Teaching and Environmental Control of Verbal Behavior

Approaches to remedial speech and language training traditionally have been based upon conceptual models that were not developed specifically as theories of speech and language, but reflect more general attempts to understand human development and behavior. Different approaches suggest different answers to the basic questions that all behavior modification rationales must answer: What is the problem? What types of conditions lead to the development of such problems and maintain them? What should the correctionist or teacher do? Remedial approaches based upon neurological considerations view speech and language problems as due to deficiences in brain function, resulting from historical accidents in development (e.g. Hebb), or due to structural or functional brain deficiencies that, other than at moment of origin, are ahistorical (e.g. Strauss, Goldstein). Absent or defective speech is thus a symptom of this underlying neurological problem, and modification must involve retraining neural structures, or "circumventing" them.

Remediation based upon "dynamic" personality theories (e.g. psychoanalysis) also conceives of speech difficulties as symptoms of more fundamental problems, problems that concern the arrangement of, or interrelationship among, "intrapsychic" forces or constructs, or symptoms of mentalistic hypothetical constructs such as "anxiety." Modification is therefore directed towards the manipulation of these internal variables, with the assumption that the speech symptom will disappear when the underlying problem is alleviated. A variety of models of speech and language are based upon communications systems research, and conceptualize verbal behavior in terms of hypothetical functions derived by analogy with machine systems, or in terms of mathematical models such as information theory. Disorders of speech are seen in terms of disturbances of these functions. Remedial procedures are selected on the basis of assumed breakdown of particular communications processes. Various approaches stressing normative data see many speech problems in terms of slow development or lack of "readiness"; and amelioration may often consist merely of waiting for the slow developer to "catch up," or providing environmental "stimulation" to accelerate development.

Behavior modification approaches consider the speech defect the problem itself, rather than a symptom of some "underlying" difficulty. All behavior, including speech, is seen as developing out of the interaction between the current behavior of the organism, however primitive or limited, and the environmental antecedents and consequences of behavior, as well as the history of such interactions (see later in this chapter). Speech modification therefore proceeds by a functional analysis of the behavior-environment interactions and the development of a program to modify the environment and thus change the behavior. Such an approach treats speech, as well as all other behavior, from a "natural science" point of view.

What, however, does such a viewpoint mean by "behavior"? Is the "act of talking" behavior? Is "being afraid" behavior? Stated informally, behavior refers to something observable that a person does. The aspect of this definition that is most often misunderstood is the term "observable," with its positivistic implications. To be observable, an event must produce some effect that can be reduced to simple sensory impressions to which other humans can respond. This does not mean that all behavior must be visible to the untrained naked eye. Changes in muscle tonus are not usually visible, but through instruments can be converted to meter deflections about which observers can reliably agree. Various "emotional" changes of an electrical or glandular nature can be similarly treated. Forming pencil marks in certain locations on a test score sheet is also behavior. The major requirement is that with or without intervening instruments, different observers (perhaps after training) be able to agree as to whether or not an instance of the supposed behavior occurred. Human behavior of interest may be very simple (pushing a button) or very complex (writing "Hamlet").

It is usually useful to assume that behavior is controlled by two sets of variables. One is related to the structure of the person, and is a function of genetics, past history (prenatal conditions, nutrition, disease, etc.), and current conditions that may affect structure, such as drugs, fatigue, temperature, nutrition, and disease. The second set of variables, often called "psychological," consists of the behavioral history of the individual (i.e. what he did under what conditions and what happened) and the current environment. Treating structural and psychological (environmental) variables as separate is largely pragmatic, and the difference is difficult to define if pushed too hard. In fact, psychological events ultimately must act through, or be reduced to, structural, biochemical, or electrical changes.

In practice, the correctionist, teacher, or parent is usually in a position to vary environmental (psychological) factors much more easily than structural variables, which may not be accessible or available for manipulation. Therefore, it is our belief that approaches to understanding speech and language must be based upon an environmental analysis in order to have any direct implication for remedial work.

It will be noted that the analysis of behavior so far described has two major characteristics. The first is that the dependent variable has been defined as observable behavior rather than as some mentalistic concept or hypothetical construct. The second major emphasis has been to suggest that behavior be viewed as a function of environmental factors. However, behavioral analyses of speech and language behavior are often proposed that essentially correlate certain behaviors with other behaviors, but do not relate behavior to environmental events that may influence it, or that refer behavior to some mentalistic construct. Thus, atypical speech patterns called "stuttering," high scores on a test scale labeled "anxiety," and periods of pacing up and down, with tremors, fidgeting, and sweating, all of which interfere with other behavior, may be noted in a young man. These all may be described quite objectively. The behaviors may then be interpreted under the rubric of "anxiety." Sometimes this term is merely intended as a shorthand way of referring to all the behaviors noted; they may all be labeled "anxious behaviors." However, the term also may be used in such a manner as to suggest that it refers to something beyond the observed behaviors and has some "explanatory" value. The individual problems noted may be said to be *due to* anxiety, a state or condition of which the noted behaviors are symptomatic. In this latter case one may question whether the analysis has remained behavioral, as well as whether the implied causality "explains" anything. In the former case, where the term "anxiety" was used merely to describe the young man's stuttering, responses to test items, and general fidgeting, one may be able to predict the future probability of such behaviors, relative to population norms, at a better than chance level. However, no information has been gained that may be useful in helping the individual to change. One has merely shown that there is a correlation among various different behaviors, and perhaps among similar behaviors over time. This is fundamentally the "trait" approach to understanding behavior, and it typically allows good prediction of future behavior, but does not suggest methods of intervening to change behavior. This appears to be due to the fact that this sort of attempt to understand speech and language says little about the independent variables of which the verbal behavior is a function, although it may accurately describe the dependent variable, other behaviors with which it correlates, and the stability of these behaviors over time. It answers the question, "What is the problem?" but stops there.

Suppose, though, that the investigation of this young man were pursued further, and it was found that certain antecedents, such as the presence of attractive young women, were followed by an increase in stuttering and fidgeting behavior. Suppose it were further found that other people tended to respond differently to the young man upon noting these "anxious" behaviors. Without becoming further enmeshed in this hypothetical case, let us observe that relating these behaviors to the environmental situations in which they occur suggests, if vaguely, a strategy for changing the behavior: change the environmental antecedents and/or the consequences of the behavior, either in the laboratory or clinic, or in the everyday environment. The major portion of this book is concerned with making this strategy more specific.

Reinforcement Operations

We have suggested that behavior may vary as a function of its consequences. Behavior controlled by its consequences is called *operant* behavior (as opposed to reflexes), and specific responses are often referred to as *operants.*

Most learning situations require strengthening some behavior, that is, increasing the probability that desired behavior will occur or become more frequent. Stimuli following a response are defined in terms of their effect upon the future frequency of that response. If the response rate increases as a function of the presentation of some stimulus after a response, the response-contingent presentation of that stimulus is called *positive reinforcement,* and the stimulus is called a *positive reinforcer* (S^r).

The use of positive reinforcement is not, however, the only way in which behavior is strengthened. If the response rate increases as a function of the *removal* of some stimulus after a response, the response contingent termination of that stimulus is called *negative reinforcement,* and that stimulus is called a *negative reinforcer.* Thus, positive reinforcement and negative reinforcement both refer to operations that strengthen (increase the frequency of) behavior. If a child's "thank you" is strengthened by the resulting adult smile, the presentation of the smile after this verbal operant is an example of positive reinforcement. If John's response, "I'm sorry," is strengthened by the termination of Mary's "nagging," the cessation of the stimulus called "nagging" is an instance of negative reinforcement. The "smile" is a positive reinforcer and the "nagging" a negative reinforcer. Notice that reinforcers are defined in terms of their effect upon the frequency of behavior. A consequence that does not affect response frequency is not called a reinforcer, no matter how pleasant, rewarding, painful, or aversive it may appear to be on the basis of subjective or cultural considerations. These terms merely describe or label observed functional relationships between the frequency of particular behaviors and certain aspects of the environment; the terms have no "explanatory" function.

Behavior can also be weakened by consequences. After an individual performs some act, a positive reinforcer may be removed or a negative reinforcer presented. This is usually found to decrease the future probability of the behavior, and is called *punishment*. Loss of allowance as well as the application of the hand to the seat of the pants are well known punishments. A *"time out from positive reinforcement"* is a punishment procedure that involves presenting a negative reinforcer. In this procedure, as used in training, a stimulus that has been associated with non-reinforcement is delivered after an undesirable response. Thus, if a child starts laughing, giggling, or wandering about the room during a speech session, the teacher may shut his eyes and drop his head on his chest for a brief interval of time. During this interval, the teacher will neither respond to the child nor provide any other opportunity for reinforcement. Eventually the sight of the teacher shutting his eyes and dropping his head in this manner will punish any responses of the child that immediately preceded the time out (*TO*). Obviously, these behaviors on the part of the teacher will not be a *TO* if the teacher's usual attentive behavior is not correlated with a relatively high frequency of reinforcement to the child; the *TO* must be a time out *from reinforcement*.

In the environment in which most people live, it is very unlikely that a particular response will be reinforced every time it is emitted, although it is possible. If every instance of a particular behavior is followed by reinforcement, the *schedule of reinforcement* is called *continuous* reinforcement. If only some occurrences of a response are followed by reinforcement, the schedule of reinforcement is said to be *intermittent*. Most "non-laboratory" behavior is maintained by intermittent reinforcement. In the initial stages of teaching a new behavior, learning progresses faster with continuous reinforcement. It is often inconvenient, however, to continue to reinforce every response, and intermittent reinforcement may be programmed once new behaviors are established. Since abrupt changes in the schedule of reinforcement are usually disrupting, it is most efficient to switch from continuous reinforcement to a rather intermittent schedule in a series of gradual steps. This is accomplished by first occasionally requiring two responses before reinforcement, then sometimes requiring three, and so forth.

Immediate consequences are more effective than delayed consequences, most rapid learning and the strongest control of behavior occurring when reinforcement is nearly instantaneous. Not only is delayed reinforcement less potent than immediate reinforcement, but other behavior that occurs in the delay interval will be closely followed by the reinforcing stimulus, and thus will be strengthened or weakened. If Mother postpones spanking a young child for misbehaving until "Daddy gets home" the spanking may have little effect on the "naughty" behavior due to the long delay. Furthermore, other behavior, such as coming to Daddy when called, may be more directly punished, if it immediately precedes the spanking. As many of the chapters to follow point out, immediate reinforcement is most important with young or slow learners, and in most of the procedures used with such populations, social reinforcers, such as "Good," and a token or candy are given at once following correct responses. "Explanations" and other verbal interchanges at these points serve mostly to weaken the effect of the reinforcer by adding a delay between the correct response and reinforcement.

Once behavior is learned, its continued performance requires at least occasional reinforcement. If reinforcement is discontinued, the frequency of a response will revert to the pre-reinforcement level. This is called *extinction*. Extinction after continuous reinforcement is very rapid compared with extinction after intermittent reinforcement, other factors being equal.

Certain consequences, called *unconditioned* or *primary* reinforcers, appear to have reinforcing characteristics as a function of the biological make-up of the organism. Thus, food will reinforce crying in a non-satiated baby, and responses that terminate painful stimuli are usually strengthened. Stimuli that are originally neutral, that is, originally have no reinforcing characteristics, can acquire reinforcing characteristics by being paired with reinforcing stimuli, and are then called *conditioned reinforcers*. Much of human behavior is maintained by conditioned reinforcers — social consequences, such as smiles, frowns, praise, criticism, and attention — produced by the behavior of other people, which are often paired with primary reinforcers. Physical objects may also acquire conditioned reinforcer characteristics; tokens, such as money, are an example.

Some stimuli become more reinforcing if certain conditions called *motivating operations* have occurred. Thus, food is more reinforcing after food deprivation, and aspirin is more reinforcing after excess alcohol ingestion. A conditioned reinforcer that has been paired with a single unconditioned reinforcer will be controlled by the motivating operations for that unconditioned reinforcer. The sign MEN may have become a conditioned reinforcer for an individual through a history of being paired with the termination of aversive stimuli. However, it is unlikely that the men's room sign will be very reinforcing except after particular motivating conditions (fluid intake and time). Some conditioned reinforcers may have been paired with several primary reinforcers. For instance, for an infant, mother's voice may have been paired with food, warmth, and the removal of various physically unpleasant stimuli. Such reinforcers become independent of any single motivating operation, and are called *generalized reinforcers*.

Shaping

Reinforcement operations that strengthen or weaken behavior are defined by the functional relationship between a response and the environmental consequences (stimuli) that follow. It might appear that a response that is not already in the individual's repertoire (however weak it may be) cannot be learned, because to be reinforced it must first be emitted. However, there are several ways in which new behavior can be acquired. One of these is by shaping, which involves the use of differential reinforcement and successive approximations to develop new behaviors. For example, when a child is learning to produce the sound /s/, certain responses that he currently produces resemble the desired terminal response more than others, even though the best match may be exceptionally crude. If only those variants of the child's speech that more closely resemble /s/ are reinforced, and other variants are placed on extinction, the range of speech sounds produced will shift in the direction of /s/. Providing *differential reinforcement* only for those response variants in the existing repertoire that more closely approximate the desired terminal behavior produces new response variations that were not previously emitted. The teacher may then change the criteria for acceptable responses, differentially reinforcing only responses that match the desired production even more closely, and thus again shift the distribution of responses emitted. This may be repeated many times in training until the desired terminal form of response is regularly produced. The gradual change in reinforcement criteria as the procedure is repeated is described as the use of *successive approximations*.

Much "new" behavior, of course, does not involve learning new responses, but demands relating existing responses to each other in particular ways. Most verbal academic skills are of this nature. Much human behavior is learned not by direct shaping but through imitation. Because imitative learning is so important in speech, this topic is discussed separately in Chapter 5.

Stimulus Control

The consequences that follow a response usually vary with the situation in which it is emitted. The infant's "mama" may bring smiles and physical contact when spoken in mother's presence, but have no consequences in her absence. If a response is reinforced in the presence of a particular stimulus and not reinforced in its absence, the stimulus is called a *discriminative stimulus* (S^D). With continued discrimination training (i.e., continued exposure to the three-part relation in which (1), a particular stimulus, called a discriminative stimulus, is the occasion in which (2), a particular response, (3), is followed by the reinforcement, while other stimuli are the occasion for non-reinforcement), the frequency with which the response occurs becomes much higher in the presence of the discriminative stimulus than in its absence. Thus, behavior becomes appropriate to the different situations in which different consequences occur. After discrimination training, response likelihood will be highest in the presence of the S^D, and higher in the presence of stimuli that more closely resemble the S^D than in the presence of stimuli that are quite different. The degree to which this *stimulus generalization* occurs depends upon several factors. One of the major factors is the degree to which the stimuli that were the occasions for the non-reinforcement in initial discrimination training resemble the S^D.

Often, in the beginning of discrimination training, *added stimuli*, which increase the probability of the correct response being emitted, may be used to facilitate learning. Thus, in a children's reading primer, initial letter discriminations may be facilitated by the addition of color cues that accentuate letter differences. These additional cues are later *faded* (gradually removed) until the child must discriminate one letter from another on the basis of form alone. If the fading process is done correctly, the control exerted by the added stimuli is slowly transferred to the other stimuli in the situation. However, care must be taken to fade all additional stimuli that will not be present in the situation in which the terminal performances must occur.

To understand verbal behavior under stimulus control, as with any discriminated behavior, three events must be taken into account: an antecedent discriminative stimulus; the verbal response in question; and the consequent reinforcement. Verbal responses for which an object, event, or some characteristic of an object or event are discriminative are called *tacts*. The statements "it's raining," "car," and "pretty flower" are usually tacts. Although it is common to talk of the tact as if it "names" something in the environment or "refers to" something in the environment, this, as will be seen, neither differentiates it from other types of discriminated verbal operants nor is necessarily true. The statement, "Glad to meet you," does not name or refer to something specific, but certain social events are the occasions for such a response's being reinforced. It is thus a tact. Tacts are usually reinforced by the "listener," who presents the "speaker" with some generalized social reinforcer. A specific tact is not characteristically followed by a particular reinforcer.

Specific consequences usually do follow certain types of verbal responses, at least within a given verbal community. "Pass the butter!" "Come here!" "Water!" or "Shut up!" produce characteristic reinforcements (butter, somebody's presence, water, or quiet). Responses that thus "specify" their reinforcement are called *mands*. Tacts are mostly controlled by the object or event that is discriminative for them. A mand, which "specifies" its reinforcer, is mostly controlled by the motivating operation (usually some deprivation, or aversive stimulation) that makes that reinforcer effective. The presence of some other person who may provide the reinforcement also exerts discriminative control. Such a person sets the occasion for the mand's being reinforced.

In *echoic* or *imitative* verbal behavior, a prior verbal response, either of the speaker himself or of some other person, is discriminative for a verbal response of similar form. The reinforcement for echoic behavior is often of an "educational" nature; that is, adults reinforce children and other adults for echoic behavior as a way of teaching something. Echoic behavior may be reinforced also by its effects upon the later behavior of the speaker himself, as in repeating instructions or a question, both of which allow time to "think," "plan," or "remember." Social convention may also lead others to reinforce some echoic behavior. Thus, repetition of part of a question in the answer may be reinforced, e.g., "Q: Who is the father of our country? A: The father of our country is . . ." The reinforcement for echoic behavior is not always clear, and under certain conditions it often appears as if the sound of the repeated echoic or imitative stimulus is in itself reinforcing. The alleged "circular reflex" in infants, a concept used to explain the maintenance of repetitive babbling at certain ages, could be interpreted in this manner. Echoic behavior plays a significant role in the development of speech and language, as well as in remedial procedures. This topic is discussed in greater length in Chapter 5, on imitative behavior.

In *textual* verbal behavior (reading), a written text is discriminative for the verbal response. Like echoic behavior, textual behavior is usually first learned with "educational" reinforcement. Textual behavior is often reinforced as a function of the reinforcement obtained by other behavior it helps to produce (as in reading instructions, advertisements, signs, etc.). Other behavior already conditioned to the textual material may also provide "automatic" conditioned reinforcement.

In textual and echoic behavior some previous verbal behavior exerts discriminative control, and the speaker's response resembles this previous verbal behavior. Verbal responses that show no similarity to the verbal responses that are discriminative for them are called *intraverbals*. In reciting memorized material, such as a poem, earlier units serve as discriminative stimuli for later units; in arithmetic behavior "one plus one" is discriminative for "two." "Fine" may be a trivial response for which "how are you" was the discriminative stimulus. The reinforcement for such responses is often a function of the larger verbal units in which they are incorporated, and that may have various characteristics.

It is important to note that verbal responses are labeled in terms of their functional characteristics, not their semantic content or linguistic characteristics. Thus "it is warm" may be a tact for which temperature is discriminative, and that usually receives some generalized social reinforcement of the "attention" type; in some other situation it may be a mand — for instance, if it is characteristically followed by one's spouse getting up and turning on the air conditioner. In the latter case, the content "disguises" the mand characteristics. It is also clear that much social behavior usually not labeled "verbal" may be functionally equivalent to the verbal responses described.

Chaining

The analysis of discriminated verbal operants (tacts, mands, etc.) utilized units that were usually larger than single speech sounds, and often larger than single words. A person does not usually say a single phoneme, word, phrase, or sentence in isolation from other speech. Like all behavior, verbal behavior usually is emitted in some ongoing pattern in which many units are related to other units. Discriminative stimuli often acquire dual functions that "organize" behavior. As discriminative stimuli correlate with the availability of reinforcement, it is not surprising that discriminative stimuli may also acquire the functional characteristics of conditioned reinforcers. If a person's history has been such that crossing the street when the light is green has been followed by positively reinforcing consequences, while crossing when the light is red has not, pressing a button on the traffic lamp post that changes the traffic light from red to green will be reinforced by the appearance of the green light. That is, the person will learn to press the button when the light is red, and will emit this behavior in appropriate circumstances as a consequence of the stimulus change the response produces. If the button ceases to be operative and no longer produces the green light, the behavior will extinguish in time, showing that the green light is indeed the reinforcer. As with all conditioned reinforcers, the green light will be a conditioned reinforcer only when the opportunity to cross the street is reinforcing.

Note that the green light plays two roles in controlling the behavior of the individual: as a conditioned reinforcer it strengthens the behavior that produces it (pressing the button), and as a discriminative stimulus it controls the probability of the street-crossing response that follows it. Thus, we have two "units" of behavior that are interrelated by the stimulus that occurs after one response and before the next. This is called a *response chain*. Nearly all speech is emitted as response chains. When an individual talks he is not only a speaker but also a listener, in that he can hear and respond to his own verbalizations. His own speech is not only a response, but produces auditory and proprioceptive stimuli that may exert control over his behavior.

Speech is chained into longer units as the sound of an individual's own speech acquires both reinforcing and discriminative functions. A child says, "Want cookie please." Saying the final word, "please," may be immediately followed by a cookie — the reinforcement is obvious. The sound of his own voice saying the next-to-last word, "cookie," exerts discriminative control over his saying "please"; that is, the probability that the child will say "please" is higher after his saying "cookie." Why? His history has been such that "please" has been followed by a cookie more often when "please" is said after he hears his own production of "cookie" than in the absence of this stimulus. The sound "cookie," as a discriminative stimulus, also acquires conditioned reinforcer characteristics. As the sound "cookie" (a conditioned reinforcer) follows the production of the first word, "want," it reinforces that response.

Chaining control is often obvious in certain rote serial verbalizations, particularly in early learning. A child may learn "1–2–3–4–5" as a serial production. If he is stopped before finishing, or asked to start at other than the beginning, he may be unable to do so. Why? Each unit (after the first) may depend very strongly upon the discriminative control exerted by the sound of the previous number. Thus, many persons can recite long poems, lines in a play, or memorized lists only if they say them in the correct order and from the beginning, unless the necessary S^Ds are presented by a "prompt" from another person or by textual material. Most speech units, whether they are blends, words, or sentences, are learned as chains composed of shorter units.

Attending Behavior

A particular type of behavior chain that is often of special concern in educational settings is called *attending behavior*. Why should a child "watch the board" while the teacher writes on it, rather than engage in some competing behavior? What kind of variables maintain (sometimes) such behavior? In practice, such behavior is often maintained by negative reinforcement (the teacher stops "bugging" the child when he attends) or by punishment of competing behavior, however subtly this is done. Is this the only alternative? Of course not.

If a teacher provides clear and immediate reinforcement, such as praise, grades, tokens, or candy for correct answers, a child will watch the board to the extent that what is written on it is discriminative for correct responses to questions. Here is a chain in which watching the board allows the child to see the stimuli presented on the board, these stimuli being discriminative for the correct verbal response that is then reinforced. The stimuli seen on the board may thus, as conditioned reinforcers, maintain watching the board. Of course, the entire sequence will occur only if the final consequences are actually reinforcing, if the children are frequently given the opportunity to respond, and if what is written on the board is in fact essential to answering the questions. Of course, "watching," whether in a classroom or a tutorial speech session, is only part of a larger chain that involves coming into the room, sitting down, and so forth, all of which may or may not be essential to the desired performance.

It was previously noted that the reinforcement following the last response in a chain is essential for maintaining the response chain as a whole. To insure that this reinforcement occurs, chains are often taught in "reverse order." The last response in a sequence, the one that is followed by the eventual reinforcement, is taught first, then the next to last, and so forth. Thus, a teacher interested in teaching children to "attend" better might first reinforce answering very simple questions. Then the questions might be changed to ones that could be answered only if the student had listened to (or looked at) some material presented immediately prior to the question. Then the teacher might change the procedure and present such material only if the students were behaving well — sitting and quiet.

This "reverse order" of teaching responses in the chain is not always possible, however. A "hyperactive" retarded child initially may never sit long enough to allow the teacher to reinforce any verbal behavior in a remedial speech situation. In such cases, in initial sessions the individual components of the chain may be separately taught and reinforced by shaping techniques. Thus, entering the room might be taught first, using ice cream as a reinforcer; then specific shaping to sit in the chair. These discrete responses can later be put under chain control by omitting the separate reinforcement for earlier units in the chain in successive stages. In some cases a behavior sequence can be learned as a series of unrelated responses and then chained together.

Progressions and Programs

If certain prerequisite behaviors under specific kinds of stimulus control are required to learn each stage of a skill, these must be sequenced in training so that at each stage the learner has the necessary repertoires to advance. Words cannot be produced, whether under echoic or other control, until a speech sound repertoire is learned. Learning to tact events or objects in the environment usually presupposes that the words to be learned can already be evoked under echoic control. Learning to tell jokes at cocktail parties usually requires all of these repertoires, and a bit more. An overall teaching *strategy*, therefore, must be based upon an analysis of the terminal behavior to be taught, the initial repertoire, and the skills required for each step in training. The *tactics* that are required by a consideration of the particular behaviors required at each stage of learning have already been discussed under headings such as shaping, adding and fading stimuli, and the development of behavior chains.

A program that incorporates very powerful and precise reinforcement contingencies, but does not give due consideration to a behavioral analysis of the progressions required, will not teach effectively, nor will a good progression with poor reinforcement contingencies. It is interesting to speculate about the number of failures to learn due to programs that are inadequate in one or the other of these requirements.

REFERENCES

Greenspoon, J., Verbal Conditioning and Clinical Psychology. In A. J. Bachrach (Ed.), *Experimental Foundations of Clinical Psychology*. New York: Basic Books, Inc., 1962.

Holz, W. C., and N. H. Azrin, "Conditioning Human Verbal Behavior." In W. K. Honig (Ed.), *Operant Behavior: Areas of Research and Application*. New York: Appleton-Century-Crofts, 1966.

Krasner, L., "Studies of the Conditioning of Verbal Behavior," *Psychol. Bull.*, 1958, 55, 148–170.

Lane, H. L., "Temporal and Intensive Properties of Human Vocal Responding under a Schedule of Reinforcement," *J. exp. anal. Behav.*, 1960, 3, 183–192.

Lane, H. L., and P. G. Shinkman, "Methods and Findings in an Analysis of a Vocal Operant," *J. exp. anal. Behav.*, 1963, 6, 179–188.

Portnoy, S., and K. Salzinger, "The Conditionability of Different Verbal Response Classes: Positive, Negative, and Nonaffect Statements," *J. gen. Psychol.*, 1964, 70, 311–323.

Rheingold, H. R., J. L. Gewirtz, and H. W. Ross, "Social Conditioning of Vocalizations in the Infant." In A. W. Staats (Ed.), *Human Learning Studies Extending Conditioning Principles to Complex Behavior*. New York: Holt, Rinehart and Winston, 1964.

Salzinger, K., S. Portnoy, P. Zlotogura, and R. Kleisner, "The Effect of Reinforcement on Continuous Speech and on Plural Nouns in Grammatical Context," *J. verbal Learn. and verbal Behav.*, 1963, 1, 477–485.

Salzinger, K., R. S. Feldman, and S. Portnoy, "The Effects of Reinforcement on Verbal and Non-verbal Responses," *J. gen. Psychol.*, 1964, 70, 225–243.

Salzinger, S., K. Salzinger, S. Portnoy, J. Eckman, P. Bacon, M. Deutsch, and J. Zubin, "Operant Conditioning of Continuous Speech in Young Children." In A. W. Staats (Ed.), *Human Learning Studies Extending Conditioning Principles to Complex Behavior*. New York: Holt, Rinehart and Winston, 1964.

Salzinger, K., "Experimental Manipulation of Verbal Behavior — a Review," *J. gen. Psychol.*, 1959, 61, 65–94.

Verplanck, W. S., "Unaware of Where's Awareness: Some Verbal Operants — Notates, Monents, and Notants." In A. W. Staats (Ed.), *Human Learning Studies Extending Conditioning Principles to Complex Behavior*. New York: Holt, Rinehart and Winston, 1964.

2

J. S. Birnbrauer
M. M. Wolf
J. D. Kidder
Cecilia E. Tague

Classroom Behavior of Retarded Pupils with Token Reinforcement[1]

It was the practice in an experimental programmed instruction classroom to reinforce correct responses with knowledge of results, verbal approval, and tokens. The tokens, check marks, were exchanged at the end of each class for an item from an array of edibles, inexpensive toys, and school supplies. To determine if the token reinforcement was essential to the relatively high levels of accuracy and rates of studying maintained by the retarded pupils, tokens were not dispensed for a period of at least 21 days and were then reinstated. Daily

[1] Paper read by the senior author at the American Psychological Association Convention, Los Angeles, September, 1964. This research is part of a project sponsored by Rainier School (C. H. Martin, Superintendent), the White River School District (Paul Webb, Superintendent) located at Buckley, Washington, and the University of Washington. It was supported in part by NIMH project grant MH–01366 and research grant MH–2232. We are indebted to Mrs. Eileen Argo and to Miss Josephine Grab for their services as assistant teachers, to Mr. John Nonnenmacher for collating the data, and to Dr. S. W. Bijou for his support and advice.
Reprinted from JOURNAL OF EXPERIMENTAL CHILD PSYCHOLOGY, Vol. 2, No. 2, June 1965. Copyright © 1965 by Academic Press Inc.

records of items completed, percentage of errors, and disruptive behavior were kept. During the no-token period three general patterns of results were obtained: (1) Five of the 15 pupils showed no measurable change in performance. (2) Six pupils increased either markedly in over-all percentage of errors or sufficiently to reduce progress in the programs. (3) Four pupils showed an increase in percentage of errors, a decline (or considerable variability) in amount of studying, and an increase in disruptive behavior. Baseline performance was recovered in these 10 pupils when token reinforcement was reinstated.

Recommendations for maintaining the motivation of pupils to study usually are limited to (1) preparing materials which are intrinsically reinforcing, i.e., are "interesting," "meaningful," and so on (e.g., *Kirk and Johnson, 1951*, pp. 270–271); (2) using materials and procedures which combine interest value and high probabilities of success, e.g., Montessori methods (*Standing, 1962*), Moore's "Responsive Environments" (*Pines, 1963*), and programmed instruction (*Porter, 1957; Skinner, 1958*); and (3) presenting social and/or symbolic reinforcers, e.g., teacher approval, grades, and stars. Although these methods may provide adequate incentives for many pupils, they probably do not for many others (*Brackbill and Jack, 1958*), for example, retarded readers (*Walters and Kosowski, 1963*), school drop-outs, and so-called chronic behavior problems. They did not appear adequate for the retarded pupils attending an experimental programmed instruction classroom (*Birnbrauer, Bijou, Wolf, and Kidder, 1965*). Had the pupils not been retarded, the poor classroom behavior and academic progress would have been attributed to the teachers, their methods, and/or low motivation.

In the experiment described here, it was assumed that the last of these was the case, and a token reinforcement system was introduced. Token reinforcers are tangible objects or symbols which in and of themselves probably have little or no reinforcing power. However, they may be exchanged for a variety of other objects which are reinforcing. Therefore, they should become generalized reinforcers (*Skinner, 1953*). The tokens in the present study were check marks which the teachers inserted in booklets that the pupils carried. When a pupil accumulated enough check marks in his booklet, he exchanged them for candy, a small toy, or other item of his choice immediately after he finished his work for the day. Thus, all of the pupils were reinforced in the same way during class and yet individual preferences were considered by maintaining a variety of items for exchange. The effectiveness of token systems has been demonstrated in laboratory studies by Staats, Staats, Schutz, and Wolf (1962) and by Heid (1964), and their practical advantages and other features have been discussed by Birnbrauer and Lawler (1964) and by Staats, Minke, Finley, Wolf, and Brooks (1964).

The purpose of this study was to determine the effects of discontinuing the token system for a relatively long period and subsequently reinstating it. Throughout the study, the teachers gave approval for appropriate behavior in the manners that were natural to them; they could remove a pupil from class for disruptive behavior; the pupils studied a variety of subjects in each session; and there were opportunities for peer interaction. These conditions made the experimental setting more like ordinary classrooms than laboratories for studies of reinforcement.

Method

Subjects

All of the 17 pupils enrolled in the Rainier School Programmed Learning Classroom took part in this study. Fourteen were residents (two were diagnosed as mongoloid; three, familial; and nine, brain-damaged) and three commuted (no clinical diagnoses available). They were all mildly or moderately retarded and were selected for this class because they performed at the first-grade level or below in academic achievement in spite of up to 5 years of previous education at Rainier School.

The characteristics of the pupils were: CA, 8 to 14 years; Peabody Picture Vocabulary Test Mental Age, 4–2 to 8–11; IQ, 50 to 72; California or Metropolitan Achievement Test Grade Equivalents, no score to 1.6 in reading and no score to 1.8 in arithmetic. Nine pupils were first enrolled in this class in September of the year in which this study was conducted; eight had been enrolled during the preceding academic year. Four of the second-year pupils and all of the first-year pupils attended in the morning; the other four second-year pupils attended in the afternoon.

Experimental Design

The study, a within-S design, consisted of three conditions: baseline (B), experimental (NT), and return to baseline (B2), in that order. Since a token reinforcement system had been used during the preceding academic year with eight of the Ss, the baseline conditions (B and B2) included dispensing of tokens; the experimental condition (NT) did not. During B and B2, the following conditions were in effect: (1) Social approval and tokens followed cooperative behavior and correct responses to the instructional materials. (2) Social extinction — i.e., no teacher response — followed incorrect responses and inappropriate, but not disruptive, behavior. (3) A brief time-out period (removal from the classroom) followed disruptive behavior or refusal to comply with instructions. Although no tokens were dispensed during NT, the teachers continued to deliver approval and to administer the time-out procedure in the same fashion as in B and B2.

NT lasted 21 days for the 13 pupils who attended class in the morning and 35 days for the afternoon group of four. (Originally, the study was to be conducted with just the afternoon class to minimize the effects of the study upon other aspects of the research project.) Reinstatement took place on the same day, seven days after the Christmas vacation, for all pupils.

Although we use the expression "days," each pupil attended this class for one to two hours per day. The data include percentage of errors (accuracy), number of items completed on the academic programs (productivity), and the amount of time spent in time-out (index of disruptive behavior).

Classroom Description and General Procedures

Each pupil attended the experimental classroom for one to two hours according to a schedule which ensured that no more than six pupils were present at a time. There was no group instruction or classes as such. Instead, each pupil was given assignments in such areas as sight vocabulary, phonics, reading comprehension, cursive writing, addition, and time-telling. (Most pupils attended other classes in arts and crafts, music, and physical education. This study pertains to their performance in the programmed learning class, the only class in which token reinforcers were dispensed and data collected.) He completed his assignments independently of the activities of the other pupils, either in the classroom proper or in one of the three individual study rooms located at one end of the room.

All of the material was prepared by the staff and was constantly being evaluated and revised as necessary. The pupils' assignments were planned every day on the basis of the previous performance of each individual, with changes being made when the error rate exceeded about 10%. In some programs the pupil was required to repeat sets when this occurred; in others, a simpler form of the program was presented, or the program was dropped temporarily until the difficulty could be found and corrected. In all cases, the teachers attempted to increase the amount of work accomplished per day.

Immediate knowledge of results was built into most programs; in others, it was delayed until the assignment was completed. Assignments required from 5 to 45 minutes. Social reinforcement and token reinforcement (during B and B2 only) were dispensed in either of two ways: (1) When a child studied independently, he indicated that he was finished by raising his hand, and the appropriate reinforcers were given as the teacher scored the work with the pupil. (2) When the program required a teacher's being present — e.g., in sight vocabulary, at the beginning of all programs, and where the type of response or other aspect of a program was changed — a token reinforcer and a social reinforcer were dispensed as each item was completed *correctly*. In September, the second procedure was followed most often; the proportion of independent studying time was increased on an individual basis.

The teachers were one male certified teacher and three female assistants. One assistant had a B.A. in Psychology and had worked in this classroom during the previous year; the other two were recent high school graduates who were trained in the performance of classroom duties by the teacher and the experienced assistant. The teachers applied the contingencies quite skillfully and probably as nearly alike as four humans could. Ordinarily, all four teachers were in the classroom. When they were not working with pupils, they performed such duties as recording data and preparing instructional materials. Children were not assigned to a teacher; whoever was free at the moment scored the completed work and gave the next assignment.

Token Reinforcement Procedures

Each pupil had a folder containing three sheets of paper each divided into squares, his "mark book." The token value of the pages varied according to the number of squares on them, and each folder had a combination of pages, e.g., two 2¢ pages and one 5¢ page. (Three pages of different values were filled concurrently so that the pupil always had partial scores or credit toward a tangible reinforcer.) When the pupil completed his work for the day, completely filled pages were usually exchanged for items from the assortment of back-up reinforcers, which included a variety of edibles, bubble gum, balloons, "caps," stationery and pencils, and trinkets. A few of the pupils saved the value of the pages either toward a more expensive object, which was purchased specifically for them, or toward a trip to town to spend the money. The pupils earned about 2¢ a day in token value. In actual value, they earned about $7 each during the academic year.

The teacher gave a check mark for every correct response to an item, a bonus of 10 marks if an assignment was error-free, and a few marks for being especially cooperative or doing something extra. Marks were made unsystematically on the three pages. Simultaneously, the teachers made such verbal comments as "good," "right," "you did that well." These comments were continued but no tokens or other tangible reinforcers were given in NT.

No attempt was made to formally explain this system to the pupils. Primarily, actual contact with the system was relied upon; and the teachers, especially at the beginning, made a point of saying such things as "Good, you get a mark for that," "Your 2¢ page is almost full," or "You've completed your 5¢ page today — good for you." Also, the number of squares was manipulated to ensure contact even though a pupil might have relatively low productivity. There is no evidence that pupils were aware of this. In about two weeks, it appeared that obtaining marks and particularly completing a page were reinforcing to them.

Time-out Procedures

Talking out of turn, responding incorrectly, cursing, and similar offenses usually were ignored by the teachers. However, if a pupil's offensive behavior was disruptive, he was told to stop and return to work or go "to the hall." If the warning did not result in prompt compliance, the teacher carried out the threat. The pupil was sent to the time-out area, a bare 8 × 22-foot room in the hallway, for 10 minutes, at which time, provided he had been quiet for the preceding 30 seconds, he was given permission to resume his studies. If he did not enter the classroom within 2 minutes, the door was closed for an additional 10 minutes. This practice was also in effect during NT. Examples of behavior that resulted in the application of time-out were refusal to undertake or complete an assignment, talking to or "roughhousing" with another pupil, temper tantrums, and throwing or destroying objects.

(The term "time-out" is an abbreviation of "time-out from positive reinforcement" (*Ferster and Appel, 1961*). We prefer the term because it emphasizes that our rationale for using the procedure was to ensure that disruptive behavior was *not* reinforced by peers and/or inadvertently by the teachers.)

Change from Tokens to No-Tokens (B to NT)

On the first day of NT, a teacher made the following announcement: "I wanted you in here all at one time to tell you something. There will be no more marks given. We want you to continue your good work just as you have been doing but you will not get marks." The mark folders and exchange trays had been removed previously. In response to questions the teachers merely replied that "the rules had been changed." (To our own surprise, there was little immediate reaction to this announcement though the mood of the class that day might be described as unenthusiastic. One pupil said that it was not fair and that he would not work any more, but completed his assignments anyway. Others asked teachers later why marks were not being given, but the reply, "the rules have been changed," ended the enquiry. It was as if the announcement had not been comprehended until after the pupils had experienced not receiving marks. The lack of reaction may be attributable in part to the fact that most of these children were institutionalized and in part to the teachers' long-established tendency not to reply to complaints or non-study-oriented conversation.)

On the first day of B2, the mark folders were placed in the previously familiar location. No announcement was made.

Data

The teachers maintained a daily record sheet for each pupil. This showed the assignments that the pupil was to have and contained space for recording the time that the pupil entered class, when he left, the beginning and ending of time-out periods and of each assignment, the total number of items completed, and number of errors made per assignment. Since the time data, except for time-out periods, were only good approximations of how each pupil spent his time in class, we shall present just the items completed, percentage of errors, and the duration of time-out periods.

An item was defined as any question or task culminating in a response that was scored objectively either "correct" or "incorrect." This criterion was met by all of the assigned studies except the cursive-writing exercises. Examples of items were: a sentence and a fill-in question about it; a multiple-choice discrimination problem; $2 + 2 = \Box\Box$; a picture and a set of possible matching words; and the printed direction, "Put 2 spoons in box 4," and an array of objects and numbered boxes. Over the course of this study, items increased in difficulty and tended to become longer. Thus, 100 items in January should have required substantially more and different work than 100 items in September.

Obviously, whether or not a procedure or incentive is "adequate" depends upon one's criteria. In general, we regarded 10% errors as the maximum acceptable level of performance. Although arbitrary and perhaps higher than most teachers require, 10% errors was nevertheless the level that resulted in our revising a program or classroom procedure. To take a specific example, if S exceeded 9% errors on a set in the Sight Vocabulary Program (SVP), he was required to repeat that set. If several Ss "failed" the same set, it was revised. So that the implications of the percentage-of-errors data in this class may be better understood, we shall report the ratio of the number of times SVP sets were "passed" (errors were less than 10%) to the number of times sight vocabulary was included in the pupil's daily assignments. This will be referred to as the "SVP ratio."

Results and Discussion

Although each pupil reacted to the removal and reinstatement of token reinforcement in a somewhat idiosyncratic way, three general patterns were obtained. (1) Five Ss showed, for all practical purposes, no adverse effects of NT. (2) Six Ss increased in percentage of errors in NT, but continued to cooperate and to complete the same or a greater number of items. (3) Four Ss increased in percentage of errors, accomplished less work, and became serious disciplinary problems during NT.[2] After tokens were reinstated, most of the Ss completed progressively more work and stabilized at levels of percentage of errors that were lower than at any previous time.

The four Ss described under (3) were those who attended class together in the afternoon and had been subjected to 35 days of NT. There were no discernible relationships between CA, IQ, or the type or amount of material being studied and the results obtained.

Figures 1, 2, 4, 5, and 6 show all of the applicable data for selected Ss. The total items completed (productivity), percentage of errors (accuracy), and time-out were compiled for each three-day period S attended class. The SVP ratios cover the experimental period in which shown. If the number of NT days was not divisible by three, the first NT point was obtained by counting backward from the end of NT and prorating the remainder. The B and B2 data were obtained by counting backward from the last day of B and forward from the first day of B2. Thirty days of B2 are shown. The B data includes all of the regular classes after an evaluation that required most of September but varied among individuals. Otherwise, the variability in amount of data resulted from the fact that this study was conducted in a classroom. Pupils were absent and classes were shortened so that the pupils might attend special events. We also excluded a day if the records contained incom-

---

[2] The data of two Ss were discarded. One was ill during most of the NT period; the other received a change in assignments coincident with the beginning of NT that could not be eliminated as a factor in accounting for the observed changes.

plete entries, or if a program ordinarily given was pre-empted by a test or other special activity, e.g., writing a letter. No more than five days was excluded for any pupil for these reasons.

The analysis performed was a visual comparison between each S's performance in NT and that during B and B2. It was concluded that removing token reinforcement had an effect only when there was a change of some duration in either the percentage of errors or the time-out data that would not have been predicted from the B data, *and* when at least the level of performance obtained in B was recovered in B2. The productivity data are shown primarily to indicate that changes in percentage of errors were not due to increases in amount of work. Because of our definition of an item, there was considerable variation in productivity. For example, the sharp declines at A in Fig. 1 do not indicate that S1 was working less diligently, but merely that a program containing fewer but more time-consuming items was presented more frequently. In other words, S1 completed all of the work that was assigned on those days. On the other hand, the declines in productivity during NT in Figs. 5 and 6 do mean that the Ss were not completing the work that was expected.

The data of Ss which clearly showed that there was or was not an effect are presented in Fig. 1, S1; Fig. 2; Fig. 4, S3; Fig. 5, S6; and Figure 6. Those that were difficult to classify or open to alternative interpretations are presented in Fig. 1, S2; Fig. 4, S4; Fig. 5, S7.

Figure 1 shows two of the five Ss whose performance appeared to be independent of token reinforcement. Subject 1, the more typical S of this subgroup, steadily increased in amount of studying from the middle of B through NT to the end of B2. He only once made more than 9% errors on SVP and maintained a satisfactorily low level of percentage of errors. Whether the slight rise in errors at the end of NT would have persisted with a longer NT period is, of course, not known. Note that the low point in productivity in B was preceded by a high percentage of errors. This reflects the teachers' efforts to adjust the assignments according to the pupil's performance.

Subject 2 differs from S1 in that she performed more poorly until about 12 days after the tokens were reinstated. Then, her percentage of errors stabilized at an acceptable level although the amount of work was increased. It is tempting to attribute this improvement to the reinstatement of tokens, but in the absence of an increase in percentage of errors in NT, the data are equivocal.

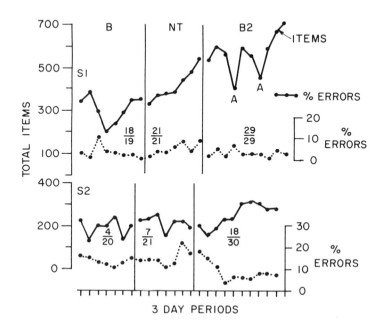

FIGURE 1

Total items completed (left ordinate, solid line) and percentage of errors records (right ordinate, dotted line) of S1 and S2, who exemplify Ss not affected by NT. The ratios are the number of times SVP errors were less than 10%, over the number of presentations of SVP in each period. Subject 2's short B period was due to an extended illness in September and October.

Subject 1 was 14 years old, diagnosed as brain-damaged, and one of the second-year pupils. The results were consistent with our impression that S1 was quite sensitive to being correct and receiving approval. Subject 2, a first-year student, was an 11-year-old mongoloid who, in addition to SVP, was receiving primarily pre-reading and pre-arithmetic instruction.

Figures 2 and 4 contain three examples of decreased accuracy during NT, but show no effect upon productivity or degree of co-operation. None of the six Ss represented required the use of the time-out procedure. The NT percentage-of-error levels were from 2 to 6 times higher than those in B and B2.

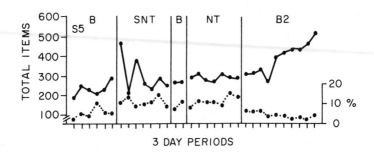

FIGURE 2

Records of S5 prepared as Fig. 1. S5 exemplifies Ss whose percentage of errors increased in NT to the borderline satisfactory level. SNT denotes token reinforcement for all work except SVP.

Subject 5 (Fig. 2) performed satisfactorily in B until he was sub-jected to a special no-token period (labeled SNT) during which he received tokens for all correct responses except while studying Sight Vocabulary. His percentage of errors immediately doubled and

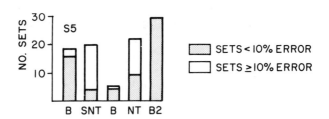

FIGURE 3

A graphic representation of S5's SVP ratios for the experimental periods in Fig. 2. No token reinforcement was delivered for studying SVP in SNT and NT.

remained at the higher level through a six-day resumption of B and through NT. In B2, S5 attained a remarkably low and stable error rate. Note the attempts by the teachers to increase the amount of work at the beginning of SNT. They were deterred by the higher error rate.

While the percentage of errors shown in Fig. 2 during SNT and NT bordered upon our acceptable 10% level, the higher level of errors had considerable effect upon progress in SVP, as can be seen in Fig. 3. When reinforced with tokens, S5 routinely made fewer than 10% errors on SVP sets. When no tokens were dispensed, he "failed" over 50% of the time.

Three other Ss showed changes in percentage of errors during NT of the order exhibited by S5. This subgroup may be thought of as border-line students. With token reinforcement they maintained at least passing records; without it, they did not.

Subject 3 and S4 (Fig. 4) yielded somewhat unique patterns.

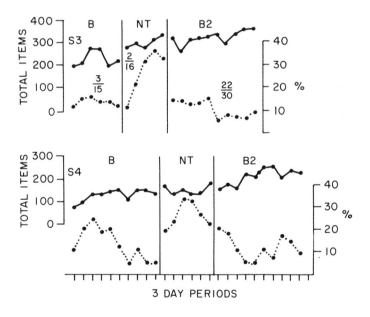

FIGURE 4

Records of Ss whose percentage of errors increased markedly in NT. Subject 3's NT period is short because of periodic absences. Subject 4 was not studying SVP.

The accuracy record of each is distinctly worse during NT. There is virtually no overlap between error scores in B (B2) and NT. However, the inverted U-shape of S4's NT data and the fact that much of the change occurred immediately suggest that S4 was affected most by the change in routine *per se* and not necessarily by the absence of token reinforcement. The possibility cannot be ruled out that baseline performance would have been regained without reinstating token reinforcement. Subject 3's data do not suffer from this ambiguity.

Subject 3 was 9 years old and had the lowest IQ of the pupils, 50. Subject 4 was 10 years old and had the highest IQ, 72. Subject 5 was 12 years old and had an IQ of 60. All were diagnosed as brain-damaged.

Figures 5 and 6 show the performance of the four second-year pupils in the afternoon class. They were 10 to 12 years old; three were brain-damaged, and the other was a nonresident who probably would be diagnosed as familial. This group had 35 days of NT. Time-out is plotted for each.

Subject 6, the nonresident, was one of the most capable pupils. This is reflected in (1) his stable 5% error rate except toward the end of NT, (2) his progress in SVP, and (3) the large number of items completed in B2. However, he occasionally required the use of the time-out procedure. During NT, he more often refused to cooperate, interacted with other pupils, particularly S7, and verbally abused the teachers. Consequently, he spent progressively more time in the time-out room and his productivity declined. During the last *three* days in NT, he completed six items, four incorrectly, yielding the terminal 66% error rate. As soon as tokens were reinstated, his former error rate was recovered and productivity increased. Time-out declined slowly to its former level.

Subject 7's data are presented because of their probable importance to the changes which occurred in S6 during NT. Token reinforcement evidently exerted little control over S7's behavior. The amount of studying was not increased during the year, and time-out was required even beyond the data shown in Fig. 5. About 15 days after tokens were reinstated, S7 went through a period of refusing to attend class, although once he was brought to class his accuracy level was exemplary.

Without token reinforcement, his behavior became worse in all

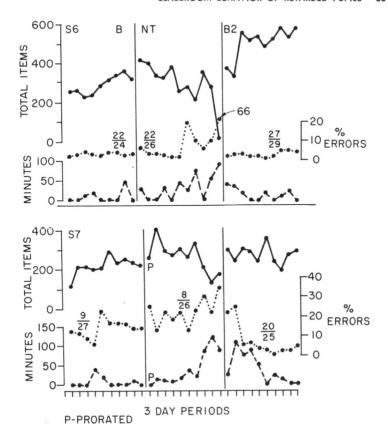

FIGURE 5

Total items completed (left ordinate, solid line), percentage of errors (right ordinate, dotted line) and time-out (left ordinate, dashed line) records of Ss 6 and 7. The final NT percentage of error level of S6 was 66%.

respects. He competed overtly with S6 to be removed from class and engaged in such behavior as hitting, chasing, and shouting at the other boys. Most often, S6 replied. That the disruptive interaction occurred mostly in NT suggests that token reinforcement provided a means whereby the teachers could effectively combat peer reinforcement. Subject 7's relatively good behavior when

tokens were being given may *not* have been due to his being reinforced with tokens. Rather, the tokens were sufficiently strong
to eliminate peer reinforcement of S7's disruptive behavior. In
fact, it was not uncommon for a pupil to tell another in effect to
"Leave me alone — I've got work to do." In other words, although
the token reinforcement system did not yield the degree of control
over S7 that was expected, it did minimize the effects that his behavior had upon other pupils.

Subjects 8 and 9 (Fig. 6) share several common features. Each

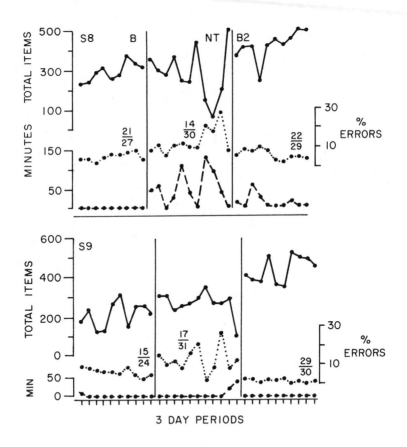

FIGURE 6

Records of Ss 8 and 9 prepared as Fig. 5.

maintained satisfactory *over-all* accuracy levels in B and B2, often failed SVP sets, were cooperative during B, and performed erratically in NT. Subject 8's unpredictability is most evident in his NT time-out record, which varies cyclically from no time in three days to as much time as S6 and S7 spent. Subject 9 varied considerably in accuracy. Subject 8's offenses most often took the form of adamant refusals to study, with unquotable verbal behavior. (During NT, the assistant teacher was reminded that S8's behavior for an entire year in a former class had been this way — "he was either an angel or a hellion. You'd never know from one day to another what to expect of him.") Clearly, Ss 8 and 9 were better students with token reinforcement than with only social and intrinsic reinforcement.

These data do not convey the entire picture of the conditions in the afternoon class during NT. The number of warnings increased; these usually sufficed for S9. Often, the time-out room was occupied when it was needed for another pupil, and placing more than one pupil in the room at a time was not a feasible alternative. Further, it became clear during NT that time-out was not aversive to some pupils and/or that it was losing its aversive properties. The competition between Ss 6 and 7 to be sent out of the room was one indication. Another was the duration of time-out per incident, which was contingent upon S's behavior in the time-out room. In B and B2, each period usually lasted the minimum 10 minutes, whereas the peaks in Figs. 5 and 6 approach the total amount of time in class for three days. It appears that removing a child from a classroom is effective to the extent that it is, in fact, time-out from positive reinforcement. Complying with classroom expectations must be more reinforcing, one way or another, than the alternatives.

The effectiveness of token reinforcement was further increased by taking away a token for each error made. The procedure used was to cross out a previously earned mark. After the page was filled, these had to be re-earned in order to exchange the page for a back-up reinforcer.

Figure 7 shows S9's accuracy level while studying sight vocabulary with and without loss of a token for each error. With loss in effect, the percentage of errors was halved, and this reduction was sufficient for him to pass the 10% criterion for advancing to the next set almost every day. Like token positive reinforcement, how-

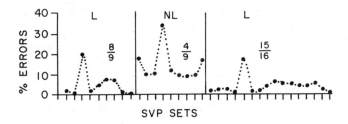

FIGURE 7

Daily percentage of errors record of S9 with token loss (L) and without token loss (NL) for errors on the Sight Vocabulary Program (SVP). SVP ratios are shown for each period. The number of items per set increased systematically from 80 to 100. These data were obtained after the 30-day B2 data in Fig. 6.

ever, loss of tokens for mistakes may not be considered a generally effective technique. Not all pupils showed a corresponding decrease in errors as did S9.

The variability in the findings is consistent with the results of studies comparing the strength of various reinforcers in children (*Brackbill and Jack, 1958; Hollis, 1965; Terrell, 1958; Terrell, Durkin, and Wiesley, 1959; Terrell and Kennedy, 1957*), and is a consequence of the inability to control the history of the pupils' experiences with the events employed as reinforcers. It is not expected that an unselected, captive group of people will be equally responsive to the same reinforcers when their individual performance is studied. Thus, for some pupils social reinforcement and/or success were sufficient; for S7, both social *and* token reinforcement were weak. The proportions of Ss like S1 and like Ss 6 and 7 undoubtedly differ widely from class to class and school to school.

There are two important points to take into account in interpreting these results. First, the teachers were accustomed to dispensing tokens and believed in their efficacy, for they had not encountered problems like those presented by Ss 6–9 since prior to the introduction of tokens a year earlier. During NT, the teachers reported that all pupils seemed to pay less attention to instructions and correction, and to react more slowly and less enthusiastically. The teachers' enthusiasm also seemed to have decreased. While it is believed that the pupils' behavior changed first, this belief cannot be documented. It would be valuable to replicate this study with teachers who do not routinely use tangible reinforcement and who do not have daily access to the data. However, we see no alternative that will preclude the teachers' changing in response to changes in the pupils' behavior. Indeed, the good teacher must behave this way.

The second factor to consider is that the pupils had received token reinforcement for studying for at least three months before NT started. One could argue that because of the frequent pairing of approval, being correct, and tangible reinforcement, the removal of tokens, i.e., extinction, should have relatively little effect for some time. This view is consistent with the fact that no effect was obtained in 21 days with five pupils, a progressive effect was observed in S3, and a delayed effect was observed in Ss 6–9.

Finally, we should emphasize that the results pertain to a situation in which something that has been a part of the reinforcement complex is abruptly omitted.

To recapitulate: (1) Five of the 15 Ss included in this analysis gave no measurable indication in 21 days that token reinforcement was necessary to maintain their cooperation and level of accuracy (Fig. 1). (2) One S (S3) steadily increased in percentage of errors during NT to a level four times that obtained in B and B2; another S (S4) also increased markedly in percentage of errors during NT but may have been responding to the change in routine *per se*. The decreases in accuracy would have been alarming by most standards (Fig. 4). (3) Four Ss declined in accuracy in NT at least to the point where the effect was educationally significant as measured by their advancing in one program, sight vocabulary (Figs. 2 and 3). (4) Three Ss (Ss 6, 8, and 9), were clearly more cooperative and more accurate with token reinforcement than without it. In fact, their disruptive behavior in NT was such that dropping them from school would have been in order under ordinary circumstances (Figs. 5 and 6). (5) The token reinforcement system and programs were not sufficient to bring another S's behavior under sufficient control for him to benefit from education (Fig. 5, S7). (6) The tokens were sufficiently powerful to contain disruptive peer interactions, substantially reducing the need for time-out procedures. (7) The effects of loss of tokens for errors ranged from no apparent effect to a considerable increase in accuracy (Fig. 7).

REFERENCES

Birnbrauer, J. S., S. W. Bijou, M. M. Wolf, and J. D. Kidder, "Programmed Instruction in the Classroom." In L. Ullmann and L. Krasner (Eds.), *Case Studies in Behavior Modification*. New York: Holt, Rinehart, and Winston, 1965.

Birnbrauer, J. S., and Julia Lawler, "Token Reinforcement for Learning," *Ment. Retardation*, 1964, 2, 275–279.

Brackbill, Yvonne, and D. Jack, "Discrimination Learning in Children as a Function of Reinforcement Value," *Child Develpm.*, 1958, 29, 185–190.

Ferster, C. B., and J. B. Appel, "Punishment of $S^\triangle$ Responding in Match to Sample by Time-out from Positive Reinforcement," *J. exp. Anal. Behav.*, 1961, 4, 45–46.

Heid, W. H., "Nonverbal Conceptual Behavior of Young Children with Programmed Material." Unpublished doctoral thesis, University of Washington, 1964.

Hollis, J. H., "Effects of Reinforcement Shifts on Bent-wire Performance of Severely Retarded Children," *Amer. J. ment. Defic.*, 1965, 69, 531–535.

Kirk, S. A., and G. O. Johnson, *Educating the Retarded Child*. Boston: Houghton Mifflin, 1951.

Pines, Maya, "How Three-year-olds Teach Themselves to Read — and Love It," *Harpers*, May, 1963.

Porter, D., "A Critical Review of a Portion of the Literature on Teaching Devices," *Harvard educ. Rev.*, 1957, 27, 126–147.

Skinner, B. F., *Science and Human Behavior*. New York: MacMillan, 1953.

Skinner, B. F., "Teaching Machines," *Science*, 1958, 128, 969–977.

Staats, A. W., K. A. Minke, J. R. Finley, M. M. Wolf, and L. O. Brooks, "A Reinforcer System and Experimental Procedure for the Laboratory Study of Reading Acquisition," *Child Develpm.*, 1964, 35, 209–231.

Staats, A. W., Carolyn K. Staats, R. E. Schutz, and M. M. Wolf, "The Conditioning of Textual Responses Using "Extrinsic Reinforcers," *J. exp. Anal. Behav.*, 1962, 5, 33–40.

Standing, E. M., *The Montessori Method — A Revolution in Education*. Fresno: Academy Library Guild, 1962.

Terrell, G., "The Role of Incentive in Discrimination Learning in Children," *Child Develpm.*, 1958, 29, 231–236.

Terrell, G., Kathryn Durkin, and M. Wiesley, "Social Class and the Nature of the Incentive in Discrimination Learning," *J. abnorm. soc. Psychol.*, 1959, 59, 270–272.

Terrell, G., and W. A. Kennedy, "Discrimination Learning and Transposition in Children as a Function of the Nature of the Reward," *J. exp. Psychol.*, 1957, 53, 257–260.

Walters, R. H., and Irene Kosowski, "Symbolic Learning and Reading Retardation," *J. consult. Psychol.*, 1963, 27, 75–82.

3

Margaret K. Johnston
Florence R. Harris

Observation and Recording of Verbal Behavior in Remedial Speech Work

The phrase "systematic observation and recording," as used in this chapter, describes techniques applicable to remedial speech work for obtaining an objective record of a subject's verbal behavior, including the antecedents and consequences of this behavior. The characteristics of these techniques, which differentiate them from other forms of observation, are that the behaviors to be studied are carefully defined, observed on a regular schedule, recorded according to a planned system, and analyzed in terms of their environmental consequences.

This method of observation has been developed in the course of recent research on behavior modification in both laboratory and field settings, and has enabled research personnel to achieve a high degree of objectivity and accuracy in the collection of data for research purposes. The records of such observations have also served as an important adjunct to the experimental treatment programs investigated in such research, serving as an indispensable tool for diagnosis, procedural planning, and evaluation of progress. In a clinical language-training program, systematic observation and recording can serve similar diagnostic and evaluative purposes, recording variables pertinent to the functional analysis of language behavior.

These techniques, their function in clinical settings, and their adaptation for clinical use are discussed in this chapter.

Values of Systematic Observational Records in a Language Training Program

Assessment and Treatment Planning

A number of tests are commonly used in the diagnosis of speech problems and deficits, often with the objective of establishing a classification or etiology of the speech disorder. While these tests give some basis for assessing the extent of a child's verbal repertoire in the test situation, they usually do not furnish usable or pertinent information about the function of this repertoire in the subject's environment, or its modification. Labeling a language disorder in terms of etiology, when no treatment for the causative factors involved is available, contributes relatively little to planning treatment procedures.

Direct and systematic observation of the child's verbal behavior does furnish pertinent diagnostic information that is immediately useful, serving to provide an objective evaluation of the subject's actual speech repertoire and the antecedent and consequent events relevant to his use of language. Such data provide a record of the speech sounds, words, phrases, and sentences that the subject uses before treatment and supply the basis for planning treatment procedures that start with the language the child already has. Observation also establishes the extent to which the child is able to attend and respond to cues and directions from the therapist, and the extent to which the subject's language is under the control of environmental stimuli.

Evaluation of Procedures and Individual Progress

When the language deficit has been analyzed and a treatment program begun, observational records serve as an adjunct to the program in three important ways: (1) they provide a record of the procedures used and their results, serving as a guide for evaluation and for planning changes in treatment design; (2) they furnish specific information about techniques that can be used in the training of other therapists; and (3) they provide a meaningful and effective evaluation of the progress of the subject and the effect of the remedial program on his use of language in other settings.

When a detailed record of treatment techniques and their results is available, the therapist can immediately evaluate which techniques should be continued or amplified and which should be modified or discarded. Changes in the subject's verbal behavior, as indicated in the observer record, provide an objective measure of progress. This information about the usefulness of various treatment methods can be used to train other therapists, contributing to the development of a behavior modification technology in the area of language training. On the basis of this information the design and goals of the treatment program can be regularly evaluated and changed in response to the progress being made.

The progress of the subject and the results of the treatment program can be studied more effectively by the techniques of systematic observation than by either subjective evaluations or presently available tests. Observational records provide an accurate measure of the responses of the child in each session. Systematic observation can be used in situations other than remedial speech sessions, and thus can be used to evaluate the generalization of newly acquired language to the subject's everyday environment. Actual use of new language in the everyday environment is the most significant measure of progress in language development.

Classes of Language Behavior To Be Observed and Recorded, Including Antecedent and Consequent Events

The classes of verbal behavior that can be observed and recorded necessarily vary from child to child during each phase of the treatment program. The first phase, assessing the initial language behaviors of the child before treatment begins, is important in establishing baseline data that can be compared with the child's speech behavior as therapy progresses. This assessment might include analysis of the following classes of verbal behavior:

1. Number of correct verbal responses to stimulus objects, or approximations to correct responses.
2. Number of correct imitations of speech sounds.
3. Correct responses to verbal cues given by the therapist.

4. Total verbal output of the subject during the period of observation.
5. Total verbal output during free speech, and types of discriminative control that appear to control his free speech.
    (a) Response to environmental events (tacting).
    (b) Free speech under intraverbal control, i.e., nonechoic responses to verbalizations.
    (c) Echoic speech, either spontaneous or on command.
6. Articulation errors, peculiar intonation, and stuttering.
    (a) Specific errors of articulation, voicing, or release.
    (b) Peculiarities in speech rhythm.
    (c) Distribution and combination of above errors in speech patterns.
    (d) Sounds or words stuttered, and environmental antecedents of stuttering.
    (e) If necessary, more detailed breakdown of stuttering into hesitations, prolongations, other non-fluencies, concomitant behaviors ("blocks"), and so forth.
7. The verbal repertoire of the child in settings outside the clinic, such as his home, school, or play room.
    (a) Frequency of words, sounds, or phrasal units used in these environments.
    (b) Length of phrases used.
    (c) Total verbal output.
    (d) Use of available language to communicate with others.
    (e) Types of discriminative control of verbal behavior in these settings.

During the second phase, when training sessions have begun, the observation is directed at recording the behavior of both the therapist and the subject, as measured by both the number and type of cues given by the therapist and the responses made by the child, and might include the following:

1. Number and kind of cues given to the subject.
2. Number of correct and incorrect responses to these cues.
3. Latency of response of the subject.
4. Response of the therapist to the subject's behavior.
5. The spontaneous verbal behavior emitted during the sessions.

In the third phase, the child's progress is evaluated by studying the extent to which language behavior learned in the training sessions has generalized to settings other than speech sessions, such as the home, classroom, and play room. Observations in these environments should be made at intervals throughout the treatment program for comparison with the baseline data collected as part of the initial assessment of language behavior, and should include information about the following classes of behavior and their antecedent and consequent events:

1. Frequency of words, sounds, or phrasal units learned in training sessions (and used in the natural environment).
2. Total verbal output.
3. Length of phrases used.
4. Use of the newly acquired vocabulary to communicate with others.
5. Articulation and intonation of verbalizations, including stuttering.
6. Types of discriminative control of verbal behavior in these settings.

It should be pointed out that in the beginning of the assessment period many measures may be taken that will not prove valuable. On the basis of these data a decision is made as to what specific behaviors are of concern for this particular subject. These behaviors are then recorded for a period prior to the institution of training procedures to provide baseline data for later comparison. During later periods, additional information may be recorded to provide information about the training procedures, along with continued recording of the behaviors observed during baseline. Progress is evaluated by comparing these later data with the baseline data. The comparison may be between initial and later verbal behavior in the remedial situation itself, or between initial and later behaviors observed at home or in the general classroom.

Observing and Recording

Although electronic equipment has been developed that can record and tabulate many kinds of behavioral information, this equipment is not yet available to most clinics or research organizations. As behavioral research progresses, a technology for automated observational methods will no doubt evolve that will provide for very accurate and sophisticated measurements of human behavior. However, until such a technology is available, both research and clinical workers must depend largely upon human observers trained in objective observation techniques and in the use of manual methods of recording observational data. In this section, these methods will be described, including time intervals of observation, observation forms, and coding or symbol systems applicable to various behavioral categories.

There are three common ways in which observational data on language behavior and training can be collected in a clinical setting:

1. Records may be kept by the therapist during sessions.
2. A tape recorder can be used to record all or part of the session, and the data transcribed later.
3. An observer, trained in observation and recording methods, can record data on each session.

Each method requires explicit definition of the behavior to be observed and a systematic means of recording. Defining verbal behaviors accurately requires careful criteria for each class of behavior under study. The exact topography of correct responses must be decided upon in advance by the therapist and the observer. These definitions may frequently require modification to remain realistic as the subject's behavior changes. However, modifications should be made explicitly, and recorded with the data.

Records Made by the Therapist during Training Sessions. The least satisfactory method of observing and recording in a language training program is for the therapist to record data during sessions. It requires extra work for the busy therapist, forcing him to divide attention between the subject and the records, and it is usually difficult for the person working directly with the subject to be objective about what takes place in the session. However, if no other alternative is available, this method can be used to record a gross index of the child's responses to training cues and directions.

Before the session, the therapist should have a list of the proposed words or sounds that are planned for the session, arranged in the form of a chart or record sheet that permits him to check off correct and incorrect responses and indicates the relevant criteria. A stop watch can be used to time latencies, response durations, or the number of responses in a given period of time. An example of such a chart is given below.

Training Record Sheet

WORDS

Bob *ʋ ʋ c x ʋ c x*

Bobby *ʋ c x ʋ c x ʋ ʋ c ʋ c x*

Jan *ʋ c x ʋ ʋ c x*

Jackie *ʋ c x ʋ x ʋ ʋ ʋ # ʋ c x*

teacher *ʋ u ʋ u ʋ # ʋ c x*

help me *ʋ a x ʋ a x ʋ c x c c c x*

clean hands

zip

Cindy

Kelly

building

CODE

v: verbal cue from teacher

O: no response

u: incorrect response

a: approximate response

c: correct response

x: reinforcement

#: time out

LATENCY DATA

Immediate response	⊬⊬⊬ ⊬⊬⊬ ⊬⊬⊬
Thirty-second interval	⊬⊬⊬ IIII
One-minute interval	III
Two-minute interval	II
Three-minute interval	I

While this type of record can be of value to the therapist in determining the performance of the child, it has the disadvantage of failing to furnish data on the nonverbal behavior of the child, on spontaneous verbalizations, or on the behavior of the therapist. Although the therapist's behavior is prescribed by the procedures planned for the sessions, deviations from this plan may occur, or mistakes may be made by the therapist. Observational records that show what the therapist actually did can be very useful in identifying and correcting problems arising in the treatment program, as well as in evaluation.

Using a Tape Recording. Using a tape recorder is a practical and convenient way to record the language behavior of both the therapist and the subject. Preserved on tape, the session can be monitored at any time by the therapist or by others interested in the procedures being used. The tape also serves as an unbiased record of the speech behavior emitted during the sessions, providing evidence of progress being made. This method is especially valuable in recording verbal behavior that is difficult to measure in other ways, particularly changes in articulation or intonation, and in measuring total verbal output. It is also adaptable for use in field settings to record the generalization of verbal behavior from speech sessions to the home or classroom.

The permanency of the data collected on tape makes it readily available for different types of analysis that may become pertinent to the treatment program as it progresses. Even when a "live" observer is being used, a tape recorder can supplement the observer's work. Having other observers code the tape is one way to check the reliability of observational records.

Observing by tape has the disadvantage of failing to provide information about nonverbal behavior of the child (for example, his attending behavior during the session). It is possible to record this information manually if it is desired. Another disadvantage is that, in order to provide a useful record of what took place during the session, the tape must eventually be transcribed and the information on it put into quantitative written form. This transcription process requires the use of a coding system similar to that used by "live" observation and is equally time-consuming. Coding a tape often appears to be more tedious than "live" observation. For these reasons it is often not practical to rely solely on a tape recorder for observation, and tape recording may have more value as a supplement to direct observation.

Using Trained Observers, Systematized Observation Forms, and Coded Symbols to Record Language Behavior. Using a trained observer to record behavior in both laboratory and field settings has proved to be the most satisfactory method of obtaining accurate and reliable data. Trained observers achieve a high degree of accuracy in a relatively short time. Methods of quantitatively assessing observer reliability are discussed later in this chapter. There are a number of different ways in which observational data can be recorded. The specific procedure used by the observer will necessarily depend upon the nature of the language deficit or problem being treated.

The number of trials or length of the time intervals to be recorded, the coding system used to designate behaviors, and the form on which the notations are made should be determined before observation begins. As treatment progresses, changes in any or all of these components of the observation can be made to make the system more practical or manageable. It is desirable that such changes be instituted during the initial phase of the study, when the subject's verbal repertoire is first being studied, so that measures taken before, during, and after treatment are comparable.

Available facilities often determine the way in which an observer can be used. A therapy room with a one-way screen and microphone, with an adjoining booth for the observer, provides optimal observation conditions. An observation play room similarly arranged, where the child may be observed with other children, with a therapist, or with his parents, is another desirable facility that allows for convenient observation of behavior in a free situation. However, when such facilities are not available, or when necessary, the observer may sit in the therapy room, either behind a screen or in view of the subject. Responses of a child to an observer present in the room usually extinguish rapidly if the observer does not react in any way to the child. The absence of ideal conditions for observation is not an insurmountable obstacle.

Recording by Tabulation, Number of Trials, and Time Intervals

The actual procedure for obtaining a quantitative measure of the frequency or accuracy of verbal behaviors may vary. The number of times that a specified behavior occurs in a given time period can be tabulated. In a training or laboratory session, where the subject must respond to cues presented by the teacher or experimenter, the number of trials and the manner of response to each trial may be recorded. When the goal is to obtain a record of the frequency of occurrence of ongoing verbal behaviors, it is usually most useful to record the presence or absence of different behaviors in successive time intervals. Such data indicate the frequency of "free" speech in a laboratory or field setting.

Recording the number of times that a behavior occurs in a designated time gives a raw count of its frequency and may be especially applicable to the initial assessment of a problem behavior. If the duration of behavior is relevant to the observation, occurrences may also be timed and tabulated on a chart or check list. If information about the consequent events of the behavior is desired, notations indicating the nature of these events can also be made.

When the purpose of the observation is to record discrete stimulus presentations and responses in a training session, recording each presentation as a trial may be the most useful way to collect data. The information recorded for each trial would vary according to the procedures and goals of the training program. Typically such records would include the number of times each S^D was presented, whether additional cues were given, the correctness of the child's responses and, sometimes, the latency of the response. When response latency is being studied provision must be made for measuring and recording the time that elapses before the response. The consequences of the response, i.e., how and when it was reinforced, may also be an important part of this observational record.

When a continuous measure of the frequency of specific behaviors is desired, recording the presence or absence of such behaviors in discrete time intervals is usually most practical. The observation period is broken up into brief 10, 20, or 30-second intervals. For each interval, the presence or absence of each specific behavior being studied is recorded. As this procedure merely records whether or not a particular behavior occurred in an interval, and ignores the number of times it occurred in the interval, it is important that the time intervals be short enough that variations in the behavior will be indicated. The typical frequency of the behavior should determine the size of the intervals, with higher-rate behaviors recorded in shorter time intervals. It would be inefficient to record something that happened only once or twice in a 3-hour period in 10-second intervals. If total verbal rate was being recorded, and averaged around 15 words per minute, much information would be lost by recording presence or absence of speech in 60-second intervals. In general, with manual recording, it is impractical to use intervals shorter than 10 seconds. If an observer is recording several different classes of behavior concurrently, a 10-second observation interval may be followed by a 5-second "writing" interval, each time interval thus sampling 10 seconds of a 15-second period. This makes the observer's task easier and increases reliability, with little loss in the information obtained.

Time-sampling techniques, in which observations are recorded for selected portions of the total observation period only, are often combined with recording by discrete time intervals. Time sampling can be used to allow one observer to record the behavior of several children. Time sampling can be done by recording a particular part of each minute, part of each 5- or 10-minute interval, or specified arbitrary periods of a session or free situation.

Coding or Symbol Systems

The use of coding systems or symbols to designate specific behaviors is a form of shorthand that enables the observer to record accurately even if the behavior occurs at a high rate. This system must often be designed individually for each subject. Two kinds of coding systems are needed, one for use in recording free behaviors and another to designate cues and responses in the training sessions. In recording the broader aspects of verbal behavior, as in initial assessment periods, a more complex code may be required that permits the study of a greater variety of behaviors than are usually observed in the training sessions.

The two classes of variables most commonly relevant to training sessions relate to the cues or directions given by the therapist and to the subject's response. A list of the training material to be presented can be prepared on a chart on which correct and incorrect responses are recorded and the time elapsed between the cue and the response is noted. Other classes of verbal behavior, such as spontaneous verbalizations, and non-verbal behaviors, such as attending, sitting in the chair, or crying, may be recorded also, perhaps separately, using successive intervals. Letters, check marks, crosses, and circles are convenient shorthand symbols to designate different behaviors.

Developing an appropriate code is a process that involves much more than the design of a symbol system. The criteria for determining whether or not each specific behavior to be recorded has occurred, and thus whether the associated symbol is recorded for an interval, must be specified unambiguously. Such specification should be entirely descriptive; definition of behaviors in terms of subjective considerations such as "intent" or judgmental or valuative considerations are known to reduce reliability.

Suggested steps for developing a workable set of behaviors to be recorded, definitions of these behaviors, and a symbol set for coding them are outlined below.

1. The problems are identified broadly on the basis of statements from parents or referral agency.
2. An initial assessment of the child's speech repertoire is made by observing the child both in a free situation and in response to a therapist's cues and directions. These data are usually recorded in longhand, providing a written record of the child's verbal behavior, with emphasis on the classes of behavior related to the problem as it was initially identified.
3. Data from the assessment observations are analyzed, behaviors are tentatively grouped or classified, and a trial code is devised to designate these classes of behaviors according to specific definitions.
4. This code is tried experimentally, preferably by an experienced observer, who can note problems in the definitions of behavior, omissions of significant aspects of the behavior under study, and difficulties in using the symbol system in actual practice. Trial observations are continued, with changes being made as necessary, until a workable system, based on clear and explicit definitions, is evolved. During this step it may be found necessary

to discriminate smaller components of behavior and assign them a symbol, or to combine various symbols.

5. A reliability check is made to determine if inter-observer agreement can be achieved using the system.

6. If reliability is low, the system is reevaluated and revisions are made until reliable and accurate observational records are obtained.

Observation Forms

Any type of form or chart that serves the purpose of the observation and that permits the data to be readily interpreted and tabulated can be used in combination with a coding system to record observational data. Usually some experimentation, similar to that required in the development of a code, is necessary in order to develop the most useful form for recording for each subject.

Forms for recording language training sessions are often devised as charts, which are planned by consultation between the therapist and observer. Such charts should provide space for listing the training cues to be presented, the child's responses, and other information that may be pertinent to the remedial program.

Recording behavior in a free situation or field setting requires a more complex form, since more than one behavior is usually observed at the same time. A convenient form for this purpose codes each time interval in a different column, with several rows of spaces for each interval of time being recorded. Each row is assigned to a different class of behavior.

Sample forms, with examples of the symbols used and the classes of behavior coded, are shown below.

At the end of the Fall Quarter, the following code is used:

X — "Uh uh" vocal sound, used to ask for help, indicate wants, or get attention.

X — Any vocal sound used to substitute for "uh uh" to ask for help, indicate wants, or get attention.

V — Verbal sounds emitted in response to environmental stimuli, other children or adults.

R — (on top line) indicates T. responded to X.

O — (on top line) indicates T. did not respond to X.

W — Whines.

C — Cries

BEHAVIOR   CHILD'S NAME _____

CLASS _____   DATE _____

                             OBSERVER _____

DATE:_____ CHILDREN:_____

OBSERVER:_____

TIME BEGUN:

TIME STOP:

WHERE:
WHEN:

CHILD_____

DATE_____

OBSERVER_____

BEHAVIOR CLASS_____ CHILD'S NAME_____

DATE_____

OBSERVER_____

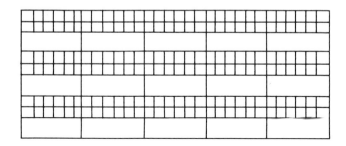

SHORTHAND SYMBOLS

For Use in Running Records

$V(o)$ = said something didn't get

V   = verbal

V+   = positive verbalization (agree)

V−   = negative verbalization (disagree)

$\overline{V}$ = no verbalization

V?   = asks questions

V^W = whines

R   = response ($\overline{R}$ = no response)

P   = physical

P^S = smile   → towards

                        ← away from

P^F = frown   ⟶ glances

P^H = hit

P^N = nod

C   = child (C^g = girl; C^b = boy)

C_s = children

w/   = with

w/o   = without

MM   = repeat 4 times

M   = mother

T_1 = head teacher

T_2 = Dmitriev

T_3 = Henke, Stoddard

Reliability Checking

Reliability checking is usually done by assigning a second observer to observe and record simultaneously with the regular observer. The reliability observer is instructed in the coding system being used and should have practice periods before actual reliability observations are begun.

Various methods of measuring reliability, or of computing some quantitative index of reliability, can be used. When several different verbal behaviors are being coded, it is usually most meaningful and most simple to compute reliability separately for each symbol, although "overall" measures of reliability can be used. However, when such global measures are low, further analysis must be done to determine which aspects of the coding account for the poor agreement.

When the observation is being recorded by trials, observer agreement in recording the subject's response as correct or incorrect determines the degree of reliability achieved. A simple quantitative measure of reliability is the percentage of trials for which both observers agree as to the correctness or incorrectness of the response.

When the reliability of time-interval observations is being checked, provision must be made to insure that the observers are in fact observing the same behavior at the same time. If watches are being used to time the observation intervals, these should be synchronized at the start of the period and both observers should start at the same interval. Other methods can also be used to insure that one observer does not get ahead of or behind the other, such as numbering the intervals in advance and having a third person call out the number of each new interval, or raising a card with the interval number on it. Another procedure is for one observer to signal the other each time a new time interval starts. Aside from such signals, observers should not communicate or compare records in any way during periods when they are making reliability checks. This includes prohibiting one observer from being able to note whether or not the other observer makes any marks during an interval. This problem is often obviated by having observers make a specified mark if nothing occurs during the interval. In general, it is not wise to have blank intervals, as observers tend to lose track of the intervals when several blanks follow each other.

When the presence or absence of particular behaviors has been recorded in successive time intervals, several methods can be used to compute reliability. The most straightforward computes for each symbol the percentage of intervals in which both observers agree. The two records are compared interval by interval, and agreement is scored if both observers agree as to the presence or absence of the symbol under consideration. The total score is then divided by the total number of intervals to give the percentage agreement. When two observers have both recorded over a fairly long period (perhaps over several days), the degree to which their observations correlate for each symbol can be computed. A convenient method is to sum the number of intervals coded for the symbol under consideration for each observer over 10- or 15-minute periods, and then compute the correlation coefficient between these two sets of numbers.

As mentioned, a separate measure of reliability is usually obtained for each coded symbol. However, several symbols may sometimes be used to record the frequency of certain behaviors, which are then classed together. Thus "giggles," "noises," and "grunts" may all be called "vocalizations" for a certain child, but each may be coded with a separate symbol. In computing reliability, all three may be treated as equivalent, or agreement may be scored only if the specific symbols agree, although only one measure of the reliability of coding "vocalizations" may be computed.

The percentage of observer agreement that is achieved may be expected to vary, depending on the complexity of the behavior under observation and the reliability measure being used. A reliability figure for percentage agreement of around 85% or more indicates an acceptable level for most observations if the behavior is neither very infrequent nor so frequent that it is occurring in nearly every interval.

Training of Observers

Personnel usually have to be trained through individual orientation and on-the-job teaching and experience. In a clinical setting, where students may not be available to fill these jobs, other personnel associated with the clinic, or volunteers, may be trained as observers. It has been found that when explicit objective observational methods are used, non-professional personnel can be used as observers. Another practical solution may be to have therapists serve as observers for each other.

Orientation and training are needed before useful observation can be carried out. Usually this can be accomplished in no more than five to ten sessions of training and observation, depending upon the degree of complexity of the observer's assignment. During the orientation phase of observer training, the goal should be to teach observers to record only observable behavior (i.e., not to make inferences) and to keep their observations free from subjective judgments. In order to maintain an objective viewpoint, observers should not interact with the subjects at any time. This is particularly important if the observer must be in the same room with the subject; it also insures that the observer's presence does not affect treatment. Experience has shown that observers can, under these conditions, succeed in becoming so unobtrusive that they become "part of the furniture" and are not noticed by children. In order to achieve this detachment, observers should be taught to maintain a neutral facial expression, to avoid eye contact with the subject, and to react to any overtures made to them as neutrally as possible, preferably by not responding at all. The observer should be seated no closer than necessary to see and hear what is happening, and move around as little as possible. These basic rules should apply to all observers and are an important part of observer orientation.

A program that progresses in small steps, starting with the observation of gross behavioral patterns and moving towards the observation of specific and carefully defined components of behavior, has been found to be the most effective method for observer training. As a first step, observers may write down in longhand informal descriptions of the behaviors under study, including the events preceding the behavior, the behavior under consideration itself, and the consequences of its occurrence. Such a record helps the observer to focus on behavior from the viewpoint of functional analysis. Following this introductory step, actual recording of specific behaviors may begin, starting with the recording of one or two classes of behavior and gradually increasing the scope of the observation, according to the requirements of the training or field situation.

During this step in training, it has been found helpful to have the observer develop a practice code as a technique for learning to define behaviors objectively and specifically. Practice with different coding systems and observation forms can also be introduced at this time. In order to teach a variety of skills related to observational methods, and also as part of this practice, a new observer may be assigned to observe and record along with an experienced observer in a situation that provides opportunity to compare their records and discuss problems as they work. Throughout the training program, the person in charge of training and other members of the staff should reinforce all progress made by new observers towards achieving appropriate levels of performance. Social reinforcement, in the form of approval and praise, has proved to be very effective in teaching observational skills, either in the training situation or in conferences following the session. Inappropriate attitudes or performance can often be modified by making only minimal responses to subjectively oriented comments or observations, and by demonstrations of the unreliability of such data. The rate at which new observers gain these skills will of course vary with the history and aptitude of the individual. The most successful observers are those who can adapt to the methodical and detailed nature of the observer's role and who are capable of maintaining an objective and detached attitude.

Scheduling Observations of Remedial Training Sessions

The duration and frequency of observations of language-training sessions can vary to provide either complete or partial records of the sessions. Partial records can be planned to record a stated segment of each session, complete sessions at regular intervals, or a combination of the two schedules. Partial observation based on time intervals (referred to as time sampling) has been discussed.

Continuous recording of all of each training session is the only method of obtaining a complete record of a subject's behavior. Such records are particularly helpful during the early phases of a remedial program when initial language behavior is being studied and therapy is beginning. During periods when modifications in training procedures are being considered or instituted, complete records again form the best basis for planning. In treating subjects with severe language deficits, whose progress may be slow, continuous observation also provides the best measurement of small changes in language behavior, which may be crucial to the therapy program.

However, in some cases sampling techniques may furnish adequate information for planning changes in training procedures, particularly when the treatment program is well established and progressing well. Observations of every third or fourth session may then provide a sufficient basis for evaluation. Sampling may also be used to determine the effectiveness of a specific technique and as a method of evaluating progress over a period of time during a long-range therapy program.

The techniques of systematic observation and recording of language behavior outlined in this chapter have been presented to suggest the many different ways in which they can be applied to the planning and guidance of a remedial language training program. The adaptability of these techniques to various settings, and the flexibility with which they can be used to observe a wide range of behaviors relevant to language therapy make this method particularly useful and practical for clinicians and therapists. The application of operant procedures to the treatment of language disabilities depends upon objective and accurate information about the subject's language behavior. Some form of systematic observation and recording, adapted to the requirements of each subject, is the principle method for obtaining this information. The further development and refinement of operant language training procedures as therapeutic techniques will require that recording also be perfected. Clinicians and therapists using these procedures in clinical programs can contribute significantly to the development of a systematic methodology of observation and recording to be used as an adjunct to remedial language training.

4

Robert F. Peterson

Imitation: A Basic Behavioral Mechanism

It has long been recognized that the growing boy or girl learns a variety of new behaviors during infancy and childhood and soon develops much of the vast behavioral repertoire of the adult. These new behaviors may range from simple mannerisms or vocalizations to the performance of extremely complex social roles involving numerous chains of verbal and motor responses, such as playing "Daddy," "storekeeper," or "doctor." Often these behaviors closely resemble those of other individuals in the child's environment.

The concept of imitation has been used frequently to describe and explain the child's acquisition of behaviors exhibited by his parents, siblings, and peers. Children have been observed to imitate a variety of responses in a host of different situations. Consequently, authorities have concluded that imitation is a basic behavioral mechanism that may account for much of the remarkable similarity and conformity in human conduct.

The observation of a model is, of course, basic to the performance of an imitative response. Some observations, however, do not lead to imitative behaviors. On certain occasions the observing organism may perform a response quite different from that of the model, with perhaps greater success. Thus, imitation should be differentiated from the more general area of observational learning. This can be done by viewing similarity of behavior between subject and model as the central feature of imitation. Nevertheless, it should be noted that not all examples of behavioral similarity are termed "imitation." The responses of a group of children simultaneously reciting the pledge of allegiance are definitely alike, yet they are not necessarily examples of imitation. This particular correspondence of behavior is probably due to the identical type of training received by each child. Furthermore, in some situations the nature of the task may be such that only a particular type of response will be successful. Thus, during mealtimes, children are observed to drink from a glass in much the same way. Again, however, this similarity of behavior should not be termed imitative. In this case, only a certain kind of response enables the child to get liquid from the glass. In both of the preceding examples, the response of one child did not produce a similar behavior in another child. Only when this occurs should the latter's behavior be termed imitative. Hence, we call a response imitative when one individual behaves to match the response of a model, and in that instance only.

The Usefulness of an Imitative Repertoire

Imitation (as well as other kinds of observational learning) may act as a teaching technique that reduces the time needed to acquire new behaviors. The model's behavior becomes equivalent to a set of instructions that programs the behavior of the observer. For this reason, the presence of an imitative repertoire may enable a child to short-circuit the long process of trial-and-error learning and quickly acquire a host of new responses. In many instances, observation of a model has been shown to be superior to other methods of learning. For example, Rosenblith (1959) found that having a child observe a model was more effective than giving him additional trials to learn a Porteus maze. A similar result was obtained by Adler (1955), who discovered that cats who had 15 observations of a model solving a ribbon-pulling problem learned more quickly than animals who did not observe. McDavid (1962) studied the relationships between imitation and the learning of other cues, and found that groups that observed a model were superior to a control group that had no model.

The Development of an Imitative Repertoire

Just how a child comes to imitate has been a matter of conjecture for some time. Imitation has been thought to be the result of certain instinctive factors or classically conditioned reflexes or neurological mechanisms. It is currently believed that imitation, like most other behavior, is learned. Exactly how this learning takes place in the normal child is not known. However, recent studies by Baer and Sherman (1964), Baer, Peterson, and Sherman (1965), Peterson (1965), and Metz (1965) suggest that individuals who imitate a number of responses may be responding to the similarity between their own behavior and the behavior of a model. Baer and Sherman (1964) demonstrated that this similarity may be functional in producing imitative behaviors. Using a talking puppet, which served both as model and source of reinforcement, these investigators found that, when three different imitative responses were reinforced, a fourth imitative response was also emitted even though it was never reinforced. The rate of this last imitative response varied as reinforcement for the original three imitative responses was withdrawn and re-presented.

Carrying this approach a bit further, Baer et al. (1965) attempted to develop imitative repertoires in completely nonimitative children. Because of its implications, this study will be presented in some detail. The subjects were three severely retarded children. They were ambulatory, had a few simple motor skills, and ranged in age from 9 to 12 years. These children were chosen for study because they lacked both imitative and verbal behaviors. The experiments were conducted at mealtimes, and food was used as a reinforcer.

Imitation was taught by the experimenter, who, after demonstrating a simple response such as tapping the table, then took the child's hand, tapped it on the table, said, "Good," and gave the child a spoonful of food. After a few repetitions of this procedure, the experimenter began to fade out his participation in the child's response. For example, instead of placing the child's hand on the table, he now would merely push it toward the table. This fading continued until the child performed the behavior without assistance immediately following its demonstration. In this manner the subjects were taught a number of simple imitative behaviors.

As the training progressed, the children began to demonstrate their learning by imitating new responses perfectly, following an initial demonstration. This tendency increased until the subjects were able to imitate, as soon as it was modeled, almost any simple motor response, such as putting on a hat, standing up from a sitting position, or ringing a bell. In addition, the children continued to imitate some responses even though they were never reinforced. These nonreinforced behaviors were termed "generalized imitations." Investigation showed that these generalized imitations were indirectly under the control of reinforcement, in that they continued to be performed as long as other imitative behaviors were reinforced; when the reinforcement was made noncontingent (given to the child regardless of performance), all imitative responses, including the generalized imitations, declined in strength. When reinforcement for some imitations was again made contingent, both generalized and reinforced imitations returned to their former high rate of performance. Thus, by making similarity of behavior between subject and model discriminative for reinforcement, a useful, comprehensive set of imitative behaviors was established in previously nonimitative children. The importance of this study to verbal behavior in general, and to remedial speech techniques in particular, will be discussed in subsequent sections of this chapter.

The Role of Imitation in the Development of Language

The development of an imitative repertoire is apparently a necessary condition for language acquisition. The child who is unable to repeat or echo the sounds made by other persons does not develop adequate speech. It is of interest to note that deaf children go through the early stages of speech development. They emit both undifferentiated and differentiated cries, begin to babble, and repeat their own vocalizations, but they do not reach the stage where they repeat the utterances of others. Although they may learn to imitate motor responses, their hearing loss prevents them from imitating verbal responses. This is because the deaf child cannot match his own response to that of a model except in extremely rough terms; i.e., he may match lip movements or other articulations of the vocal apparatus but is unable to receive other relevant cues from the model's behavior. In addition, the child gets only limited feedback in terms of proprioceptive and other stimuli from his own behavior.

In contrast, the verbally imitative child need only attend to the behavior of those around him to expand his verbal repertoire. The nonimitative child must "try out" many different vocal responses until a particular response produces a reinforcing event. The ability to imitate, then, enables the child to "stand on the shoulders (or behaviors) of others" and vastly increase his interaction with and control over the environment.

It would be difficult indeed if all verbal behaviors had to be emitted by the child and then shaped by their effects on the physical or social environment. This is not to say that all verbal responses can be acquired through imitation alone. A certain amount of shaping of basic response elements is probably necessary even when the child is fully imitative. Thus imitation may allow the child to combine or recombine basic behavioral units into new response chains. This cannot take place unless the child has acquired the fractional elements of the behavior in question. Evidence from the Baer *et al.* (1965) study supports this statement. After children developed extensive imitative motor repertoires, they were taught to imitate vocal responses. It was discovered that these nonverbal children were unable to imitate a complex set of sounds such as those found in a word unless the word was first broken into basic units. Thus before a child could be taught to say, "Hi," she had to learn, through shaping procedures, to make an "h" sound. The "i" sound, being a bit more complex, had to be broken into the sounds "ah" and "ee." This procedure was applied to other words as well. Of course, once the child had acquired some of the basic vowel and consonant phonemes, she could more easily chain them together to form new words that could be learned by imitation.

It is also possible that a child may be able to use imitation to shape new responses — responses that did not previously exist in his behavioral repertoire. Mowrer (1960) has put forth what has been called the "autism" theory of language learning. According to this view, the mother's verbal behavior develops secondary reinforcing properties as a result of being paired with her many caretaking activities, several of which involve the dispensing of primary reinforcers. The reinforcing properties of her verbal responses cause the child to reproduce them. Hence the child can reinforce himself by behaving like mother, especially in her absence. This theory implies an automatic shaping and reinforcing mechanism, since the more closely the child's behavior resembles that of the mother, the greater the reinforcement. Although some animal studies do not support Mowrer's theory (*Yerkes and Learned, 1925; Zimmerman, 1958*), Risley (1966) reports a study by Michel (1964) that suggests that the "autism" theory may have merit. In this investigation, adults were given social reinforcement for striking (randomly) the keys of a piano. The reinforcement was contingent on the rate of strikes and not on any pattern or melody. After a short time, the subjects began to approximate familiar melodies and the rate of random notes decreased. Since only rate of playing was reinforced, the melodious sequences were possibly being maintained by conditioned or secondary reinforcers involved in producing them, due to their matching familiar melodies.

A second example of the operation of possible secondary reinforcers in producing imitative responses was recently noted by the author. This occurred during the filming of the imitative behaviors of the subjects involved in Peterson (1965) and Baer, et al. (1965). In one sequence, where the child was to walk across a room, pick up and put on a fireman's hat and return, all in imitation of the experimenter, the subject attempted to pick up the hat in exactly the same manner as the experimenter, by grasping it over the top. After several failures to grasp it in this way (due to the small size of her hand), she grabbed the hat by the bill, placed it on her head and returned to her seat. This is of interest because at no time was the subject reinforced for such a precise match. Reinforcement was given as long as the hat was placed, in any fashion, on the head. Thus matching the behavior of a model may become, in itself, reinforcing and may be shown in the subject's imitations of never reinforced responses (generalized imitations) or in extremely precise matches where only rough approximations have been reinforced.

Other, more direct reinforcing operations may also be involved in the development of verbal behaviors. These reinforcers may involve attention, affection, and approval dispensed by the parent. Some investigators have confused this type of parental reinforcer with imitation on the part of the child. For example, Valentine (1946) reports imitation during the first month. He observed his own child "crooning" at an average rate of 6.5 per minute during operant level. When the child's mother crooned in return, the rate rose to 10.5 per minute. After the mother stopped, the rate fell to 1.0 per minute. Lewis (1936) observed a two-and-one-half-month-old child. This investigator found a rate of 2.0 sounds per minute when the experimenter said nothing, and a rate of 6.0 sounds per minute when the experimenter said, "Hello" in return.

Whether these results should be considered examples of early infant imitation is highly questionable. The criterion used for imitative behavior is an extremely broad one; nearly any vocal response is admissible. Employment of a more rigorous criterion would probably increase the age level at which true vocal imitation occurs. Secondly, it would appear that the experimenters were not presenting verbal stimuli as antecedents of the infant's response, but were applying them as consequents. Thus, instead of the child's imitating the parent, the parent may have been imitating and reinforcing the child. Weisberg (1963) and Rheingold, Gewirtz, and Ross (1959) have demonstrated that consequent social stimulation can affect the infant's rate of vocalization. Weisberg also investigated the possibility that the experimenter's stimuli were functioning as social releasers rather than as reinforcers. He was unable to elicit vocalizations, imitative or otherwise, by randomly presenting an aspirated "yeah" sound to three-month-old orphan infants. When presented as a consequence of the child's response, this same stimulus did influence the rate of vocalization.

Risley (1966) has pointed out that social reinforcement and the "autistic" paradigm may operate together to produce verbal behavior in the child. This could come about if social stimuli function to maintain a rate of vocalization in the child while allowing other, perhaps weaker, secondary reinforcers to modify the topography of the behavior. Thus almost any type of verbal behavior might result in social reinforcement from the parent. However, certain vocal responses that resemble those of the parent may bring additional (secondary) reinforcement because of the resemblance, and as a result may come to predominate over vocalizations in general. It should be noted that this explanation could apply not only to the development of verbal repertoires but also to the development of imitative motor repertoires.

Imitation and Language Structure

Children who have acquired an extensive repertoire of generalized imitation behave as though they have learned and internalized a rule for responding. In this case the rule could be verbalized as, "Do as I do." However, this does not mean that such a rule functioned to produce the generalized imitative repertoire. In fact, there is no need to explain the development or existence of imitative behavior by appealing to such a rule. The behavior can be accounted for in a more parsimonious manner by referring to the procedures and contingencies that produced it. Granted, one could instruct a child who was skilled at imitating to "do as I do" and observe a host of imitative behaviors. However, as Skinner (1966) has noted, behaviors that are the result of reinforcement contingencies, even though they may resemble behaviors that result from the application of a rule, are in fact different because their controlling circumstances are different.

The previous argument can easily be applied to the learning of grammar. Although differential reinforcement no doubt plays a role, the structural aspects of language could be acquired largely through a generalized imitative repertoire. Thus a child may behave verbally as if he has also learned a rule or rules concerning the form and sequence of sounds in verbal chains or sentences, while the behavior may really be the product of contingencies of reinforcement. If this is true, then one need not, as Chomsky (1959) suggests, refer to a "self-constructed, internalized grammar" or to certain "fundamental processes at work independently of 'feedback' from the environment" (p. 42) to account for what is considered grammatically correct verbal behavior. The discovery or discrimination of a rule out of a set of behaviors does not make the rule functional in producing that set of behavior, although it may function to produce the same or other behavior in the absence of the original controlling stimuli.

Imitation and Remedial Speech Training

In order to use imitation effectively in speech training, the therapist must first assess the extent of the child's imitative repertoire. The teacher should instruct the child to "Do this," and perform a variety of motor and verbal responses. A list of such responses may be found in Peterson (1965). If the child is not imitative, the therapist may consider building a class of imitative behaviors. This might be done using procedures similar to those employed by Metz (1965) or Baer et al. (1965), where the child is taught a number of simple motor behaviors, performed in imitation of the experimenter. Such training must be continued until the child responds to the similarity between his behavior and the model's, and produces generalized imitations. That is, the child should be able to imitate a number of responses perfectly following their initial demonstration. Once the child is imitating behaviors on which he received no special training, the repertoire can be utilized as a remedial technique.

Sherman (1965) used the following procedures to establish imitative verbal behavior in a mute schizophrenic patient. (The reader is also referred to Hewett (1965) and Risley (1966).) First, this investigator took responses that were under his verbal control (e.g., the patient would rise when told to "Stand up"), and then he paired the verbal command with a demonstration of the behavior. Thus the experimenter would say, "Do this, stand up," as he himself rose from his chair. Next, the procedure was changed to include only the command, "Do this," and a demonstration of the behavior by the experimenter. The patient was reinforced with food for a correct response. Subsequently, a series of responses was modeled that progressed from behaviors involving the entire body to those involving only the head, mouth, lips, and throat. These behaviors were reliably imitated. At this point a vocalization ("ah") was demonstrated, but the patient did not perform the response. As a result Sherman went back to demonstrating responses such as blowing, hissing, an aspirated "h" sound, and a "ppph" sound, and then presented the vocalization "ah," which was previously missed. This time the response was imitated.

The transition from motor to verbal imitation may not always be a smooth one. With the schizophrenic patient in the previous example, the entire imitative repertoire was disrupted when vocal responses were modeled. Similar problems were found in the Baer et al. (1965) study. One of their subjects, a nine-year-old boy, emitted no verbal imitations after motor responses were established. In this case the technique employed was similar to that previously discussed in Sherman (1965).

A somewhat different technique was used with a second subject, a 12-year-old girl. This subject also did not imitate a vocal response after developing extensive motor imitations. Here, the verbal response was paired with an imitative motor response. Thus the experimenter walked to the center of the room (which was usually imitated) and said "ah." The child approximated this response. The verbal-motor coupling was continued, with a gradual reduction in the amount of motor imitation, i.e., fewer and fewer steps, until the verbal response was imitated while both the subject and experimenter were seated. Once this behavior was established, further pairing was unnecessary. From this point, modeling (training by imitation) and differential reinforcement were used to expand the vocal repertoire.

The previous discussion dealt with individuals with limited or nonexistent imitative repertoires. Many people with speech problems will, of course, be quite skilled at matching behaviors demonstrated to them. The therapist may use this skill not only to match sounds, but also to make the necessary motor responses to produce the sound. Thus the teacher may model the lip, tongue, and mouth responses needed for proper speech.

Conditions Influencing Imitative Behavior

The fact that the therapist will be dealing with many individuals who are already imitative makes it of interest to know not only what is learned when a model is observed, but also how the model and other environmental events influence the performance of an imitative response. It has been established that individuals may learn, in addition to the model's response, other incidental cues. Wilson (1958) studied the behavior of three- and four-year-old children in a two-choice discrimination problem. Candy was placed in one of two boxes, each of a distinctive size and shape. The candy was always placed in the same box, and the subjects were to pick the correct one. One group of children observed and copied the response of a model in choosing the correct box, while another group learned a similar problem that did not involve a model. Wilson found that those subjects who had observed the model learned, in the absence of the model, to pick the correct box on the basis of its stimulus properties faster and with fewer errors than the children who had learned the analogous problem directly. In the animal laboratory, Church (1957) demonstrated that rats who learned to follow a leader also learned the stimuli to which the leader was responding. When the leader was withdrawn, the followers made the correct response using the incidental cue. Such learning can facilitate performance of the correct response in the absence of the model.

In the previous examples, observation of a model exposed the subject to stimuli which led to reinforcement. This is not always the case. Miller and Dollard (1941) investigated the effects of directing the observer's attention away from such cues and found that when imitation (observation) helped the subject to attend to relevant stimuli, learning was facilitated; when observation of a model caused the subject to miss important cues, learning was retarded.

The studies discussed in this section suggest that the therapist, when modeling a behavior, must look carefully at the cues he presents. He should not engage in behaviors that may distract the patient, such as excessive verbal or motor instructions, and should present only those cues that are relevant to the desired response or, if additional cues are needed, those that will support the patient's behavior in the therapist's absence. For example, the therapist might instruct a child how to use his own fingers to "mold" a particular facial conformation that is necessary for certain sound production.

The extent of imitation observed in a given individual may also depend upon a number of other factors relating to the model. The model's age, dress, sex, or other characteristics can determine whether his behavior will be imitated. For example, Miller and Dollard (1941) demonstrated that children trained to imitate a child model would imitate a new child but would not imitate an adult. These subjects had histories in which characteristics of the child model had been associated with reinforcement, while qualities of the adult had not. Hence, the effect of a model may depend upon the degree to which its distinctive attributes have been paired with reinforcement in the subject's history.

A second factor that can influence the emission of an imitative response is the consequence that follows the model's behavior. Bandura (1962) found that children who observed a model punished performed significantly fewer imitative responses than children who saw the model rewarded or who observed a model who had neither consequence follow his behavior. Bandura, Ross, and Ross (1963) also found differences in imitation among subjects who viewed a model punished for aggressive behavior, one rewarded for aggressive behavior, and a nonaggressive model. Not only is the type of consequence important, but the way in which it is presented or the number of presentations may also be relevant. Both Rosenbaum and Tucker (1962) and Kanareff and Lanzetta (1958) have found that the schedule of reinforcement for the model also influences the rate of imitation.

Under some conditions the observation of a model, without reinforcement to either model or observer, may not be effective, especially with severely disturbed individuals. Wilson and Walters

(*1966*) found no difference in terms of increased verbalizations between those near-mute schizophrenic patients exposed to a model and a control group that had none. Patients who, in addition to observing the model's behavior, were reinforced for vocalizations did show an increase in the rate of verbal behavior.

In summary, it would appear that one can increase the rate of imitative responses by manipulating a number of conditions that involve the model. First, one might pair a particular model with a number of reinforcers. Thus the child might be directly reinforced by the model or be given extra attention or privileges correlated with the model's presence. Second, the child should observe the model being reinforced for specific responses, perhaps by events that are likely to serve as reinforcers for the child. Hence the youngster might see the model engaging in verbal behaviors, such as "Bring me candy," which are followed by appropriate reinforcement. Finally, when exposure to a model has little effect, observation should be combined with direct reinforcement for the child's correct response. This is perhaps the most powerful technique; it can be extremely effective in developing imitative and other observational skills.

Summary

Imitative behaviors appear to develop through a learning process. Recently, investigators have established extensive imitative repertoires in nonimitative children by providing a history of reinforcement for matching the behavior of a model. This work suggests that similarity of behavior between subject and model may become a functional stimulus in producing new imitative responses. Although never reinforced, some of these imitative responses may be performed as long as other imitations are reinforced. This "generalized imitation" may provide the basis for the acquisition of other complex motor and verbal responses.

The development of verbal behaviors may also depend upon the direct shaping of basic response elements as well as "automatic" shaping due to the secondary reinforcing properties of the individual's response. Thus complex verbal behaviors are seen as the product of reinforcement contingencies rather than the result of internalized rules.

This view suggests that imitative responses may be used in the remediation of speech problems. However, a number of factors that influence the performance of the imitative behavior should be considered first, including the characteristics of the model, direct reinforcement, and the consequences of the model's behavior.

REFERENCES

Adler, E. A., "Some Factors of Observational Learning in Cats," *J. genet. Psychol.*, 1955, 86, 159–177.

Baer, D. M., R. F. Peterson, and J. A. Sherman, "Building an Imitative Repertoire by Programming Similarity between Child and Model as Discriminative for Reinforcement." Paper read at biennial meeting of Society for Research in Child Development, Minneapolis, 1965.

Baer, D. M., and J. A. Sherman, "Reinforcement Control of Generalized Imitation in Young Children," *J. exp. Child Psychol.*, 1964, 1, 37–49.

Bandura, A., "The Influence of Rewarding and Punishing Consequences to the Model on the Acquisition and Performance of Imitative Responses." Unpublished manuscript, Stanford University, 1962. Cited in A. Bandura, and R. H. Walters, *Social Learning and Personality Development*. New York: Holt, Rinehart and Winston, 1963.

Bandura, A., Dorothea Ross, and Sheila A. Ross, "Vicarious Reinforcement and Imitation," *J. abnorm. soc. Psychol.*, 1963, 67, 601–607.

Chomsky, N., "Review of B. F. Skinner, *Verbal Behavior*," *Language*, 1959, 35, 26–58.

Church, R. M., "Two Procedures for the Establishment of 'Imitative Behavior,'" *J. comp. physiol. Psychol.*, 1957, 50, 315–318.

Hewett, F. M., "Teaching Speech to an Autistic Child through Operant Conditioning," *Amer. J. Orthopsychiat.*, 1965, 35(5), 927–936.

Kanareff, Vera T., and J. T. Lanzetta, "The Acquisition of Imitative and Opposition Responses under Two Conditions of Instruction-Induced Set," *J. exp. Psychol.*, 1958, 56, 516–538.

Lewis, M. M., *Infant Speech: A Study of the Beginnings of Language*. New York: Harcourt, Brace, 1963.

McDavid, J. W., "Effects of Ambiguous Cue Relationships upon Imitation and Observational Learning." Paper read at American Psychological Association, St. Louis, 1962.

Metz, J. R., "Conditioning Generalized Imitation in Autistic Children," *J. exp. Child Psychol.*, 1965, 2, 389–399.

Miller, N. E., and J. Dollard, *Social Learning and Imitation*. New Haven: Yale University Press, 1941.

Mowrer, O. H., *Learning Theory and the Symbolic Processes*. New York: Wiley, 1960.

Peterson, R. F., "The Organization of Experimentally Generated Imitative Behaviors in the Retardate." Unpublished doctoral dissertation, University of Washington, 1965.

Rheingold, H. L., J. L. Gewirtz, and H. W. Ross, "Social Conditioning of Vocalizations in the Infant," *J. comp. physiol. Psychol.*, 1959, 52, 68–73.

Risley, T., "The Establishment of Verbal Behavior in Deviant Children." Unpublished doctoral dissertation, University of Washington, 1966.

Rosenbaum, M. E., and I. F. Tucker, "The Competence of the Model and the Learning of Imitation and Non-Imitation," *J. exp. Psychol.*, 1962, 63, 183–190.

Rosenblith, Judy F., "Learning by Imitation in Kindergarten Children," *Child Develpm.*, 1959, 30, 69–80.

Sherman, J. A., "Use of Reinforcement and Imitation to Reinstate Verbal Behavior in Mute Psychotics," *J. abnorm. soc. Psychol.*, 1965, 70, 155–164.

Skinner, B. F., "Operant Behavior." In W. K. Honig (Ed.), *Operant Behavior: Areas of Research and Application*. New York: Appleton-Century-Crofts, 1966.

Valentine, C. W., *The Psychology of Early Childhood* (3rd ed.). London: Methuen, 1946.

Weisberg, P., "Social and Nonsocial Conditioning of Infant Vocalizations," *Child Develpm.*, 1963, 34, 377–388.

Wilson, W. C., "Imitation and the Learning of Incidental Cues by Preschool Children," *Child Develpm.*, 1958, 29, 393–397.

Wilson, F. S., and R. H. Walters, "Modification of Speech Output of Near-Mute Schizophrenics through Social Learning Procedures," *Behav. Res. Ther.*, 1966, 4, 59–67.

Yerkes, R. M., and Blanche Learned, *Chimpanzee Intelligence and Its Vocal Expression*. Baltimore: Williams and Williams, 1925. P. 54.

Zimmerman, D. W., "An Unsuccessful Attempt, Based on the Autism Theory of Language Learning, To Teach Dogs To Bark Instrumentally." Unpublished manuscript, 1958. Cited by O. H. Mowrer, *Learning Theory and the Symbolic Processes*. New York: Wiley, 1960.

Instituting Speech in Severely
Impaired Children

The child who has diffuse speech impairment or who lacks speech completely always presents a challenge. If a child is not only speech-free but also nonvocal, the challenge is even greater. It is a truism that the individual with "no behavior" is harder to work with than the individual who has some behavioral repertoire, however inadequate it is. Working with the severely impaired or speech-free individual is usually further complicated by the fact that (except in some young preschool children) such problems rarely occur alone, but are usually part of a picture that includes other behavioral deficits or undesirable repertoires. Hearing defects, motor defects, temper tantrums taught the retarded child by adult reactions to his retardation ("the poor child doesn't know any better"), lack of attending behavior, and general patterns of isolate behavior are all common.

In Chapter 5, procedures that have been used for instituting speech in young children who are seriously speech-impaired, speech-free, or nonvocal are described in detail. This includes developing speech sound repertoires in such children, teaching the child to chain sounds together into words, to name objects, and to use new speech functionally, and teaching the child to chain words together. In Chapter 6 related procedures that have been used successfully with a wide range of older retardates, including many with known organic damage, are described. The methods used in Chapter 6 were developed with a population that included many hearing-impaired individuals, and the program depends heavily upon visual rather than auditory discriminative stimuli, through the use of an alphabet that is a compromise between the vagaries of the English alphabet and the more common synthetic alphabets. A significant value of this program for many persons relates to the way in which speech training blends directly into beginning reading, as a result of the emphasis upon visual stimuli.

Lovaas' work with autistic children is becoming generally known, and in Chapter 7 he describes in detail the procedures he and his colleagues have been using with these children to develop speech and language. The autistic child is characterized by the fact that few social stimuli develop conditioned reinforcer functions. The implication of this "deficit" for speech and language development and for remedial intervention is a major theme of Lovaas. Another problem with such children is the existence of behavioral repertoires that may interfere with training, or compete with desired behavior; Lovaas also addresses himself to the handling of these problems.

Speech is behavior. It is not a magical manifestation of something called "thought," which exists in a mentalistic world, although the complexity of language behavior certainly may make it appear to be such. As behavior, speech is learned, and can be taught by explicit procedures that focus upon speech itself. Part II presents some procedures for working with seriously speech-impaired children.

5

Howard N. Sloane, Jr.
Margaret K. Johnston
Florence R. Harris

Remedial Procedures for Teaching Verbal Behavior to Speech Deficient or Defective Young Children

With a limited number of young children with delayed, absent, or very poorly articulated speech, we have been exploring the possibilities of devising fairly standard remedial procedures. Many of these were originally developed by Risley (*1966*). The general approach has been to try to develop verbal behavior by providing immediate and concrete environmental consequences contingent upon the emission of specific verbal or vocal productions, and to program this development of a more adequate behavioral repertoire in a careful progression of small steps (*Bijou and Sloane, 1966*).

The values of this approach appear to be threefold: (1) the procedures seem successful; (2) the procedures seem applicable to a wide range of different speech problems; (3) the procedures are objective and specify definite behaviors on the part of the teacher-trainer. This final point has allowed us to train mothers of speech defective children to do remedial work in their own homes.

In this paper, emphasis is upon a description of the procedures

These studies were partially supported by USPHS Research Grant MH 12067–01 and OED Grant 32–23–1020–6002 to Professor Sidney W. Bijou.

we have used, with some brief illustrative data[1] presented to suggest the effectiveness of these procedures.

Setting

Some children were seen for speech training by members of the laboratory staff in the Developmental Psychology Laboratory as part of a remedial pre-school program (*Johnston*). Rooms were furnished with child-height chairs and tables or with a high chair and an adult chair. One wall in each room was fitted with a one-way mirror for observation. An intercom permitted monitoring of conversations in the speech room and allowed instructions to be given to the person with the child from the observation room. The rooms were sparsely furnished to minimize distractions.

Mothers who were trained to do remedial speech work conducted sessions initially in the laboratory rooms. Most later sessions were conducted at home with occasional laboratory sessions. Each mother wore a brightly colored apron for sessions, both in the laboratory and at home, and did not wear this apron at other times, to provide a constant "setting" for speech sessions. The rooms used for the home sessions varied. If the child used a high chair in the laboratory, a high chair was used at home; if a table was used in the laboratory, a table was used at home.

For all children, sessions were conducted daily, five times a week for children seen in the laboratory and approximately seven times a week when mothers worked at home. Session times were kept relatively invariant.

Procedures

Progression of Materials

Training started with the behavior already in the child's repertoire, and by a progression of small steps moved towards a more competent set of verbal behaviors. Formal diagnostic tests were not used as a guide in determining the initial skills of the child. Instead, samples of the verbal behavior of the child were obtained by ob-

[1] The authors would like to thank Val Dmitriev, Lydia Henke, Joan Beavers, Marion Ault, and Sophia Brown, who collected much of the data.

servers, who recorded the actual verbalizations or vocalizations of the child, the conditions under which these behaviors were emitted, and, sometimes, the consequences of these responses. The records were obtained in "free" play situations and in individual sessions in which the child was encouraged to emit speech or vocalizations. Teacher observations and reports from parents or others who had had opportunity to observe the child were also used.

The progression of training steps described below is "idealized" in the sense that not every child followed the complete progression, nor did all children start at the same place. The order, except for the final steps, was relatively constant.

1. Simple Nonverbal Motor Imitation. If a child did not initially produce many speech sounds, or did not readily imitate speech sounds, initial training consisted of the imitation of simple motor responses such as clapping, tapping, head-shaking, and arm-lifting. The teacher said, "Do this," and proceeded to make the simple response. If the child made any approximation to the correct response, a reinforcement was delivered. If the child did not imitate these simple responses, the teacher moved the child's arms, hand, etc., "through" the response and then delivered a reinforcement. This "guidance" was slowly "faded" until the child produced the response alone. By and large there was no trouble in developing simple imitation. After the responses were established under imitative control, a precise imitation, i.e., the correct hand, the correct number of taps, etc., was required before moving on. This precision was developed by reinforcing successively "better" approximations. More and more imitative responses were trained until the child immediately imitated new responses when they were first introduced (see Chapter 4).

2. Simple Imitation of Placement of the Vocal Musculature and Associated Structures. In this second step, the child was taught to imitate simple movements of the vocal musculature and associated structures. The only difference between this and the previous step is in the responses selected for imitation. Responses included such things as opening and shutting the mouth, placing the teeth on the lower lip, and different tongue placements. These responses were taught in more "exaggerated" form than occurs in the usual adult speech topography. If necessary, "guidance" of the child's lips, tongue, and mouth was provided when new responses were first introduced. "Added stimuli" to aid in response differentiation were also used at times. Thus, a teacher touched a child's lips when requesting one placement, his chin when requesting another, or held her (the teacher's) thumb and forefinger before the child in a certain way when requesting the child to open his mouth. Eventually, these "props" were dropped. The responses were still produced under imitative control; that is, when the teacher said, "Do this," and then made the desired response, her behavior was discriminative for the child's emitting a similar response.

3. *Placement with Sound.* When the behaviors in the previous step were well established, a sound was required along with the non-vocal response. Thus the teacher said, "Do this," and produced one of the mouth-teeth-tongue-lips placements and the speech sound that is produced with that placement. At this stage, reinforcement was delivered to the child if *any* sound was produced along with the correct placement.

4. *Shaping Specific Speech Sounds under Imitative Control.* The procedure described in the previous section was continued, but specific speech sounds were developed by successive approximations. Depending upon the child, the added stimuli or "props" mentioned previously were continued at this stage. Added nonverbal motor components that were not required for reinforcement, such as head-shaking and arm gestures, which the child learned along with the required response, often appeared to mediate the desired responses, and were occasionally included in the imitative S^D presented by the teacher. The instruction, "Say," was used often instead of "Do this" when appropriate, or the instruction was dropped completely.

5. *Sound Chains.* In this step, chaining two sounds together was taught. Training "blends" such as the "pl" in "play" and chains such as "ma-ma" were taught by the same procedure. Each member of the chain was separately strengthened by a series of reinforced repetitions, and then a direct attempt to obtain the entire chain was made. An example of this for teaching "baby" might be as follows. "Say bā" . . . "say bē" . . . "say bā" . . . "say bē" . . . (several more

repetitions) . . . "say bā-bē." Other auxiliary techniques were used if necessary. If the child already had a history of intermittent reinforcement in the speech sessions, material reinforcers were delivered only after the "bē" response in the entire "baby" sequence illustrated. Thus, a chain utilizing imitative control was initially established, with the teacher giving all the sounds in a single initial S^D. Procedures for developing longer chains were analogous.

6. *Tacting Objects and Pictures of Objects with Added Imitative Auditory S^D's.* After learning to produce sounds corresponding to simple words, the child was taught to "name" simple objects and pictures by imitating the teacher. The teacher presented a picture or object (e.g., a ball) and said, "Say ball," or, "Ball," reinforcing an acceptable imitative response by the child.[2]

7. *Fading Imitative Auditory S^D in Simple Tacting.* After the training described so far, a child might have responded correctly by merely imitating the verbal production of the teacher, "ignoring" the visual stimulus (object or picture). To transfer control from the teacher's verbalization to the picture or object, the auditory imitative S^D was "faded." With picture or object presentation the teacher said, "What is this?" alone. The picture or object then controlled the choice of response. Extensive training to a wide range of pictures and objects was given. The rapidity with which the imitative S^D's were faded varied. Often "What is this?" was also omitted, the child then responding spontaneously when shown the stimulus object.

8. *Single Word Mands.* Mands were taught in two ways. The most direct procedure was probably the least frequent. In speech sessions the "name" of a reinforcer was taught, the reinforcement for

---

[2] Strictly speaking, these responses are not pure tacts, as the responses characteristically (in the speech lessons) were followed by a specific reinforcer or reinforcers, usually including something edible. Thus these responses are intermediate between tacts and mands, and have functional characteristics of both: a specific environmental object is discriminative for each response, and response strength is probably related to the motivating operations relevant to the particular reinforcers used. It should also be noted that although the behaviors called "tacting" and "naming" are not necessarily synonymous, a naming response can be a tact.

saying this name being obtaining that reinforcer. Thus a glass of water was held up and presented after the response, "water." This was done when there was independent evidence suggesting that the item in question was currently a strong reinforcer; for example, the child might have been reaching for the water, or pointing at it and grunting. The methods of shaping the response were similar to those described for developing tacts. More commonly, mands were taught indirectly. The child was initially taught to *tact* an object, that is, merely to "name" it. Thus the response "door" might have been taught as was any other "naming" response, with social and candy reinforcers.

After a child had learned to name an object, the use of this name was required in appropriate situations, and nonverbal equivalents were not reinforced. If a child had learned to name doors, and was seen trying to open a door, adult help would not be given unless the correct verbal response was emitted. The adult might "cue" this by telling the child to "say door." When this was well established, the mand would be extended. The word "open" would be taught, using imitative procedures; then the required response to solicit adult help in door-opening would be the verbalization "open-door."

If the child was enrolled in the laboratory's pre-school, all teachers would be informed as to the behavior required at any stage of training.

Parental counseling was given to insure that family members did not continue to reinforce nonverbal functional equivalents of verbal mands that were already well established in the laboratory pre-school. At times counseling had to take the opposite course— parents sometimes tended to require new words before they were well established.

9. *Development of Word Chains.* The procedures to develop word chains were essentially the same as, or extensions of, the procedures used for developing sound chains. The individual words in a chain were taught first, and given a series of reinforced trials to develop them in strength. At this point, some children produced simple chains on command without trouble ("Say 'Big red car'"). If this did not succeed, procedures designed to teach chaining directly were used. The terminal word of the chain received further reinforced trials, utilizing auditory imitative cues. In addition, a "last

word of the chain" stimulus was presented at the same time that the teacher said the word to be imitated, and this stimulus was present until the child responded. A correct imitation in the presence of this stimulus was always followed by reinforcement.

After several trials of this sort, the teacher would say the penultimate word in the chain, and at the same time present the "next-to-last word in the chain" stimulus. A correct imitation in the presence of this stimulus was always followed by the stimulus for a "last word in the chain" and, until a chain was moderately established, by the teacher's saying the final word. Saying the final word was again followed by reinforcement. When this was well established, the teacher would present the stimulus for the "next-to-the last word," and then say *both* words in the chain; when the child said the first word of the two, the teacher removed the "next-to-last word" stimulus and presented the "last word" stimulus, but she did *not* cue the final word again, reinforcing the child after he produced both words.

In teaching three-word chains, when the two-word chain was well established, a "next-to-next-to-last word" stimulus was presented, and the teacher would cue the first word of the three to be said. When it was produced properly, she would present the "next-to-last word" stimulus and cue the remaining two words together, changing the chain position stimulus after the child said the first of the two, and reinforcing after completion of the final word. In the next step all three words would be cued initially, the teacher changing the chain position stimuli as the child responded. It was occasionally necessary to back-track in training, and this was done when performance degenerated. All "extra" stimuli were dropped when the chain was well established.

In one variation of the procedure, the teacher held a token out of sight as the "next-to-next-to-last word" stimulus, held it over the child's head as the "next-to-last word" stimulus, moved it to eye level as the "last word in the chain" stimulus, and delivered it as the reinforcer when the chain was completed. Another variation utilized a felt board divided into three sections by vertical strips of tape. The placement of a picture in the right, middle, or left position of the board corresponded to the chain position stimuli, the right section being used for the "last word in the chain" stimulus. As the pictures corresponded to the words comprising the chains, one benefit of using the pictures was the added discriminative control they may have exerted.

10. *Multiple S^D Control.* "Knowing the meaning" of a word usually refers to the appropriate use of the word under a variety of differing stimulus conditions and its appropriate use in many different chains. When a child had a moderate verbal repertoire, attempts were made to develop "flexible" control. The teacher varied the S^D presented to the child—no longer using only "Say this" or "What is this?" A wide range of materials, such as books, pictures, objects and so forth, were used, and the teacher presented a varying and flexible range of stimuli, in the form of questions and other leading remarks about the materials, to make them all discriminative for responses in the child's repertoire. Social reinforcement and intermittent delivery of concrete reinforcers were continued. In the classroom situation, appropriate verbalizations were also reinforced with praise, attention, and tokens or candy. Mothers were encouraged to do the same at home.

Reinforcement Variables

Explicit reinforcement for acceptable responses was programmed at all times in training. At any stage of training, reinforcement was delivered for the desired responses (or the currently accepted approximation), while unacceptable responses were not reinforced.

A great variety of reinforcers were used, based upon what "worked." When a reinforcer no longer "worked," new ones were tried until something was found that seemed to exert control. Some children received one of their regular meals as a reinforcer; that is, the ordinary meal was delivered in small spoonfuls contingent upon appropriate responding. Other edible reinforcers used were candies (M & M's Pez, Neccos), spoonfuls of sherbet or ice cream, small marshmallows, bits of graham cracker, milk, soda pop, water, pieces of dry cereals (especially sugar-coated cereals), and raisins. Many nonedible tangible reinforcers were used, for example, small trinkets such as are found in "gum ball" machines, other small toys, and balloons. The performance of some preferred activity (*Homme et al., 1963; Premack, 1959*) (usually some kind of play) was sometimes made contingent upon the desired response and used as a reinforcer. Thus one child was allowed to play with an automated puppet and another to play with small pictures and toys after correct responses.

With some children a token reinforcement system was used (*Birnbrauer et al., 1965*) (see Chapter 2). The tokens were small beads. Tokens were originally established as conditioned reinforcers by giving them to the child and then allowing him to trade them for established reinforcers, usually candy. Verbal instructions sometimes accompanied this training.

The delivery of a tangible reinforcer was always accompanied by a generalized social reinforcer — a smile or brief verbal statement such as "That's good" from a teacher. With all the children, social reinforcement seemed effective; with some it exerted more control than other reinforcers. This pairing of social and material reinforcers probably strengthened the control that verbal reinforcers had over the child's behavior (*Kelleher and Gollub, 1962*). Temporary conditions of satiation for particular foods, toys, or activities were unlikely to destroy the control exerted by such generalized reinforcers (*Skinner, 1953*).

When tokens were used, children selected items from a tray containing an array of candies and other small objects in exchange for the tokens, although with some children there was sometimes no choice—only one particular item could be traded for beads. "Trading" was often done several times during a speech session, to avoid requiring the child to save all token until the end of a session for exchange.

Schedules of Reinforcement

In initial training, and when new responses were first being learned at any stage of training, continuous reinforcement was used; that is, every satisfactory approximation was reinforced. At later stages, reinforcement was sometimes intermittent; every fifth or every tenth acceptable response was reinforced. Usually, the rate of exchange of tokens was also on a ratio; thus 10 tokens were traded for a single drink of soda or an M & M. *Every* satisfactory response received social reinforcement, even though material reinforcers were delivered on an intermittent schedule.

Time Out from Positive Reinforcement

Incorrect responding was often "punished" with a "Time Out" (TO) from positive reinforcement, a brief period during which no reinforcers were available to the child. The details of the TO procedures and the criteria for administering a TO varied slightly from child to child and from time to time. A typical procedure required the teacher to remain mute with no facial expression, head dropped upon the chest and eyes averted for 60 seconds, if the child failed twice consecutively to emit an acceptable response or a currently satisfactory approximation. A third consecutive failure required the teacher to leave the room for one to two minutes. Crying, tantrums, or other emotional behavior extended the TO period, in that a TO was always maintained for 15 to 20 seconds after the termination of such behavior. No verbal reprimands or instructions were utilized.

Thus, positive reinforcement of various sorts was explicitly contingent upon correct responding, and a TO from positive reinforcement was contingent upon incorrect responding. Failure to respond for 30 seconds was considered equivalent to responding incorrectly. TO's were infrequent after the initial few sessions.

Effect of Reinforcement

In Figure 1, the effect of reinforcement on the accuracy with which a four-and-a-half-year-old mongoloid boy could imitate speech sounds is shown. In the first six sessions plotted (which are not his first six speech sessions), reinforcement (tokens and sips of cola) was contingent upon correct echoic responses, and accuracy was between 81% and 87%. In the next three and one-half sessions, tokens and cola were delivered after arbitrary time intervals, rather than being contingent upon correct responses. The time intervals were chosen so that the number of tokens and the amount of cola received was the same as during equivalent reinforcement periods. During these sessions accuracy dropped to 30%. Half way through session 10 the reinforcement contingency was reinstated, and the accuracy with which the child imitated speech sounds quickly returned to the previous level.

In Figure 2, the accuracy with which a four-year old retarded boy "named" pictures is shown. Again, the first session plotted is not the actual first speech session. From the 10 to 15 pictures then

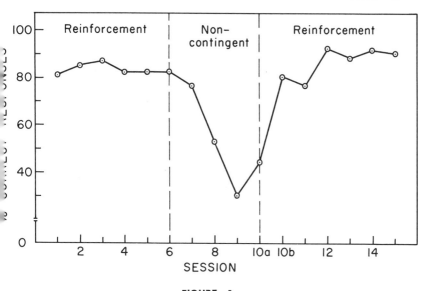

FIGURE 1

Effect of reinforcement on accuracy of sound production.

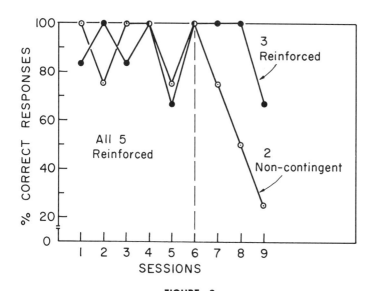

FIGURE 2

Effect of reinforcement on accuracy of tacting.

being used in training, five were selected to evaluate the role of the reinforcement contingency. These five pictures were presented in a set order a given number of times at the beginning of each of the nine sessions in the evaluation period. For six sessions, reinforcement (delivery of ice cream) was contingent upon accurate responses to the question "What is this?" when shown the picture. The child had learned specific one-word names for the pictures. For the next three sessions response-contingent reinforcement was programmed for responses to three of the pictures, and ice cream was given on a noncontingent basis in the presence of the remaining two pictures. In the first six sessions the child's responses were accurate over 85% of the time for both the group of three pictures and the group of two pictures. In the experimental period, accuracy for the group of pictures for which ice cream was not contingent upon accurate responses fell to 25%, averaging 50% for all three of the sessions. The accuracy for responses to the pictures with which reinforcement was maintained did not change from its previous level, and averaged 89%.

These results indicate that accurate responding in these two situations was a function of the reinforcement contingency. Accuracy was *not* a function of merely receiving ice cream, cola, or tokens from the teacher. That is, good "rapport" or indications of "love," along with "stimulation," did not maintain accurate productions; differential reinforcement for correct and incorrect responses did.

Motivation

Motivation was maintained in many ways. If a meal was used as the reinforcer, the session was scheduled several hours after the previous meal, or as the first meal in the morning. When other edibles were used, family cooperation was obtained to insure that the child was otherwise deprived of that edible, or of "sweets" in general. If certain activities were used as the reinforcer, these activities were not permitted at other times. With the one child for whom it appeared that social approval and attention exerted the most control, the speech session was preceded by five minutes of isolation in a high chair in the speech session room.

Attending Behavior

The development of good attending behavior was very important. Most children first starting upon our training regime were quite restless and distractible. Initially, it was difficult to get them to remain seated for any length of time, or to attend to the teacher, the materials, or the verbal stimuli presented by the teacher. In initial sessions, successive approximations to satisfactory sitting and attending were often reinforced, and a TO was programmed after the first two or three sessions if the child did not attend or left his seat. Early sessions were usually short, averaging 15 minutes. Although minimal verbal instructions were given, the *consequences* of good attending behavior appeared to exert more control than did the instructions. As the child came under better control, the length of the sessions was increased to 30 or 40 minutes. If a child was restless and did not perform well, suggesting that session termination might be reinforcing, we "held tough" until two or three performances were obtained, and then terminated, rather than terminating earlier and possibly strengthening the undesired behavior.

At all times, the child was allowed to perform and thus to obtain reinforcement only when attending well. A TO was nearly always contingent upon getting up, acting "silly," or similar behavior. However, such undesirable behaviors were frequent only in initial sessions, and a high frequency of positive reinforcement characterized most sessions.

Recording and Observers

In speech work with children done by members of the laboratory staff, trained observers were utilized. The data presented in this paper, and many of the details of the procedures were provided by the records kept by the observers. The method of observation has been presented elsewhere (*Allen et al., 1964*). A code for recording specific behaviors was developed for each child. Particular verbalizations or vocalizations, the discriminative and reinforcing stimuli presented by the teacher, as well as more extensive behavioral categories (e.g., "uncued verbalizations") were recorded in speech sessions and in the pre-school classroom. The code for each child changed frequently, as the child's verbal repertoire and the speech procedures changed. At times it was found useful for the teacher and observer to develop a code for specific sounds or words before each session. Observers also recorded certain non-speech behaviors that were under study. (See Chapter 3.)

Periodic tape recordings were obtained; tapes recorded at different stages of training can be coded "blind" at one time by an observer unfamiliar with the child.

Instruction of Mothers and Consultations with Teachers

Mothers were given only brief verbal instructions before starting actual speech work. The instructions described the setting, the use of immediate reinforcement, and the first four or five steps in the procedure. This last was at a very general level; e.g., mothers were told that the first step involved "teaching the child to imitate simple things you do, such as clapping hands and tapping."

In the first session (excluding initial meetings that preceded any actual speech training) the mother was given a card listing four simple responses and containing brief instructions, such as "for correct response, give lavish praise and candy. If incorrect, or no response after 30 seconds, repeat; if incorrect again, drop head and remain silent for 30 seconds; if incorrect a third time leave the room." These instructions were often in condensed form, and were discussed verbally in more detail. Staff members observed and listened to the session from an observation booth, and spoke to the child's mother over the intercom. The mother was told to start, cued when to reinforce and when not to, praised when she did well, and corrected for errors. Some mothers had difficulty accepting and reinforcing early approximations; others had trouble maintaining the time-out contingency. However, in our limited sample, the mothers learned rapidly. Mother and child came to the laboratory daily for seven to ten sessions. Before each session any changes in procedure were described. The sessions were briefly discussed afterwards with the mother. However, major training was done by having the mother perform in the session, with immediate feedback provided for her performance, and by prompting her less with each successive session. Everything was kept at a very concrete and descriptive level; generalities were avoided. When the mother seemed to be working well, she was told to work at home for several days, and to phone if difficulty arose. She was given a list of particular sounds or responses to work with and brief written instructions (as in the initial session). After several days of home sessions she came into the laboratory and conducted a session as she had been doing at home, and described what had been happening. She was then given a new list, and if staff observation indicated that a procedural change should occur, new instructions. This was repeated several times, the interval between laboratory visits increasing, until visits were two weeks or more apart. Mothers were encouraged to phone frequently, and sometimes given a specific time and day for a phone appointment.

Speech sessions conducted by teachers were observed periodically, particularly when progress seemed slow or to have reached an impasse. A trained observer, who, unlike the teacher, had only one task (observing), was often able to suggest beneficial changes. Just as the behavior of the adult became discriminative and reinforcing to the child, aspects of the child's behavior at times gained control over the behavior of the adult, which sometimes impeded progress by interfering with the maintenance of desired contingencies. A third person was often in the best position to note this and to intervene.

In addition, all teachers conducting speech sessions had weekly meetings with other staff members. During this time the current progress, problems, and data for the week were discussed, and decisions as to whether to change procedures or recording of data were made.

Illustrative Results

In this section, several children with whom we have used these procedures are described, along with some results. No attempt is made to present data that evaluate the procedures in any formal sense. The information presented is not complete, but is selected for illustrative purposes.

Candy

Candy was admitted to the remedial guidance nursery at age three years, seven months. At age 17 months she had been diagnosed as "developmental retardation of unknown etiology"; at three years, four months, she had obtained a Cattell IQ score of 45, and the agency that tested her reported her ". . . speech . . . at the one year level." They also noted that she had ". . . no expressive speech . . . but . . . inflective vocalizations." When she entered our nursery group she was assigned to a staff member for individual speech sessions. At that time it was noted that her only speech consisted of the sound "eh-eh" emitted in a loud grunt. This vocalization was regularly reinforced by the family (its termination reinforcing them) and was emitted under any condition of deprivation or aversive stimulation. In training, the entire program, starting with non-motor imitation and stopping short of word-chain formation, was used.

In Figure 3, data was presented showing the frequency of different classes of verbal behavior as recorded in the classroom (not speech session) throughout the year. Candy's use of the generalized mand "eh-eh" remained about constant and is not graphed. The frequency of vocalizations (speech sounds) increased quite quickly with the onset of speech training, reaching a peak at about the time Candy first started using "words" that could be reliably recorded as approximations to English. The number and frequency of words used was still increasing when summer terminated training. Nearly all the words emitted in the classroom were specifically taught in speech sessions. The total frequency represents the use of over 40 different "words" at the end of training.

Bobby

Bobby was admitted to our remedial guidance nursery group at age four years, seven months. A speech and hearing evaluation at age three reported ". . . no sound which could be considered a speech sound . . . vocalization pre-babbling in content . . . vowels, usually (a) and (i) with no consonants of any kind heard at any time. . . ." Bobby then received six months of "stimulation" speech therapy at a clinic. A university hospital did a complete evaluation of Bobby at the termination of this treatment, six months before we saw him, when Bobby was four. They noted ". . . 10 to 15 words . . ." They reported a Cattell IQ of 51, hearing normal, and stated that Bobby was severely retarded and that his communicative skills were at the 14-month level on the language development scale. Our initial assessment of Bobby indicated a low verbal and vocal repertoire, limited to naming of objects and animals, the use of the word "Mom" for all adults or demands of adults, very poor articulation with frequent sound reversals in the few words in his vocabulary, and some sentence-form babbling units with intonation that matched

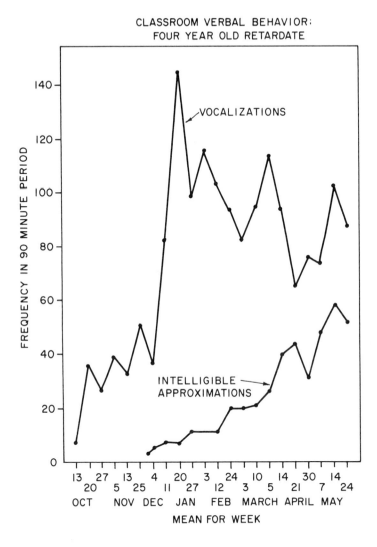

FIGURE 3

Frequency of intelligible approximations and unintelligible vocalizations emitted in classroom.

normal speech. No two-word units were reported, and it was not possible to get Bobby to chain two words together by so instructing him. He did emit a few "compressed" units, such as "c'mon." Bobby was assigned to a staff member for individual speech sessions.

Our first efforts with Bobby consisted of training him to tact to objects and pictures (procedures 6 and 7), and improving sound differentiation as needed (procedures 3, 4, and 5). This was followed by explicit training in forming word chains (procedure 9). In Figure 4, data is presented on the number of single-word, two-word and three-word tacts learned by Bobby in the speech sessions. A word or phrase was considered learned when Bobby responded correctly approximately two out of three times on several consecutive sessions. The numerals interrupting the graph indicate week-long "breaks" in training, due to vacations, illness, or other periods when Bobby did not attend school. The plateau around week five in learning two-word phrases occurred when a new teacher took over Bobby's speech sessions. Occasionally words considered already learned were checked, and when Bobby failed to produce them correctly they were added again to the training regime; this accounts for those places where the graph moves downward. The reason for the apparent loss of three-word phrases in the final three weeks before summer terminated training is that new training procedures were being tried, and training on several older phrases was reinstated at this period.

Tommy

When admitted to our remedial group, Tommy was seven years, five months, old. At age six months he was considered "abnormal" and was briefly hospitalized for observation and testing. At age one year he was diagnosed CP. He had been seen by many agencies. At age three, the diagnosis of "severe infantile emotional disturbance," and, later, "autistic, retarded, with a Cattell MA between 11 and 18 months" were made. At five he was diagnosed as mentally retarded "on an organic basis" with "emotional overlay." An EEG examination at age five revealed a slow spike focus in the posterior temporal region; a later EEG the same year was within normal limits. At age six, the diagnosis was severe mental retardation with autistic features. For a little less than three years prior to our seeing

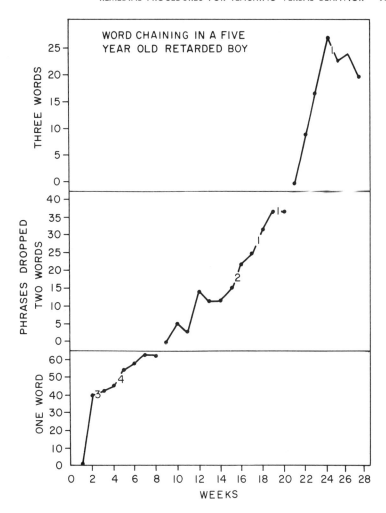

FIGURE 4

Number of single words, two-word chains, and three-word chains learned in speech sessions.

him, he was in a special school (living at home). At age four he was reported by this school to have said "mama," "hi," and "school." When he was six they reported some single words, a few sentences and echolalia; and a short time later they reported that he used the word "no" and sang school songs, that he had poor intonation and articulation, and that his speech was bizarre and infantile. In his final six months at this school, he was seen by a graduate student from our laboratory for speech work (*Risley, 1966*). At the termination of this, when first admitted to our remedial group, Tommy would name about 24 items and pictures on command, would touch these items on command or hand them to the experimenter, had about a dozen simple mands such as "out the door," could make six stereotyped social responses (e.g., "what's my name," "hello"), and could identify pictures of his family and used their names at home. He did little mimicking in speech sessions, but much at other times. His intonation was either bizarre or monotonal. His non-speech behavior contained many mannerisms, some tantrums, and other atypical features. He was assigned to a staff member for individual speech lessons. Emphasis was on procedures 6, 7, 8, and 10.

A record was kept of the number of appropriate verbalizations produced by Tommy in the classroom situation; this data is presented in Figure 5. "Appropriate" verbalizations were speech sounds that were recognizable as words, and excluded vocalizations and imitative words or sounds. It is interesting to note that although the graph shows a consistent increase in useful speech in the classroom situation, a substantial loss occurred after each of the brief vacations between school quarters.

Jan

Jan was first seen when she was three years, three months, old. At that time she made a variety of speech sounds. The only words she said were "dada," "mama," "me," and "no." It is not clear if these sounds were actually under any discriminative control.

Jan's mother was trained to conduct speech sessions with her. Objective data was not recorded from those children who were seen by their mothers; information is based upon reports of the mothers, our informal observations, and our recorded notes on the particular items the mothers were working on at different stages of training. Jan had speech sessions with her mother for a total of about three to four months (procedures 1 through 8). Sessions were quite irregular in the last month due to fatigue and illness of the mother associated with the last trimester of pregnancy. At the beginning of the sessions Jan had a vocabulary of 0–4 words, according to her mother. After four months Jan's mother reported that Jan learned the name of "nearly anything" she tried to teach her, and her mother did not feel that speech progress *per se* was any longer a

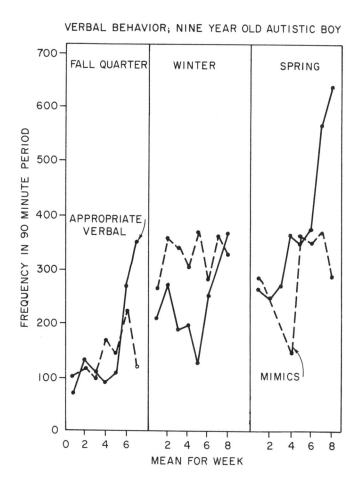

FIGURE 5

Frequency of appropriate verbal statements and of mimics in classroom.

problem, although she felt Jan was still far "behind." Jan and her mother were not seen in the laboratory after the first two and a half months, as her mother was unable to travel the distance to the laboratory; only phone consultations were continued.

Wendy

Wendy was first seen by us at age four years, eight months. She had a high verbal rate with large vocabulary, but articulation was so poor that she was difficult to understand. Her parents had been told, following a medical work-up, that she was "retarded." On a Stanford-Binet, she obtained an IQ of 63, at age four years, eight months. The examiner noted that distractibility, concern over her mother's absence, and the inability of the examiner to comprehend all of her speech contributed to her below-normal score. Observation of her play and social behavior by our staff suggested an active, normal child.

Wendy's mother was trained to conduct speech sessions with her, using procedures 2, 3, and 4. In initial speech sessions it was impossible to get Wendy to produce correctly the five sounds that she articulated most poorly. After about 10 weeks of speech sessions with her mother, Wendy would produce four of these properly in speech sessions, but in ordinary conversation only one or two of these were produced accurately with any reliability. We did not consider our work with Wendy successful.

Molly

Molly was seen by a kindergarten teacher for four months for speech training prior to our first contact with her. During the course of this treatment, the records kept indicated that she would make all speech sounds on command, but no words under appropriate discriminative control. However, this teacher and the mother both reported that for unknown reasons the child stopped producing the sounds, and that her vocal repertoire reverted to a whining, high pitched, semi-whispered babble of restricted sound content.

When first seen by us, Molly was four years old. Her mother reported that after a complete evaluation at a university clinic, she had been told that Molly was "brain-damaged" and that she should "give up." Molly's spontaneous vocal repertoire consisted of the whining babble mentioned. She also appeared to emit the words "bye" and "no" under appropriate conditions. The mother was trained to conduct speech sessions with Molly, which she did for one month, using procedures 1 through 8. At the end of this month, under imitative control Molly produced all but about three speech sounds well, and she had a vocabulary of about 10 words that she used both in speech sessions and at home. These words were not all well articulated, but were recognizable by most people.

Discussion

The importance of maintaining precise and consistent contingencies for responses cannot be overstressed. This has been the most important aspect in our training people to do speech work. "Rewarding" desirable behavior is not a new concept, but maintaining a precise, consistent and immediate relation between a specific verbal response and its consequence leads to entirely different results from the general idea of "using rewards." An occasional failure to maintain the criteria for a *time out* from reinforcement was frequently sufficient to develop some "superstitious" behavior of the type often called "controlling." Thus, if a whine, cry, whimper, smile, or some other response in a child's repertoire avoided a *time out,* when one should have been programmed, whines, cries, smiles, whimpers, and "irrelevant" responses became more frequent after failures. It is nearly impossible to maintain precise contingencies when working with a group of children. There are many well known pressures towards working with groups, such as limited time. We believe that short individual sessions are of more value than a long group session.

If mothers or other individuals without extensive training can be trained to conduct remedial speech work with young children much of the pressure towards doing group work disappears. Although training a mother initially required a large time investment per child, this rapidly declined to about one hour per week. We feel that mothers can usually conduct successful treatment themselves, and a much higher yield is returned when an hour of professional time is spent training several mothers than when it is spent seeing one child.

There are, of course, many benefits in having a child's mother conduct speech training. The mother who does such work is likely to maintain moment-to-moment contingencies in the home that will develop and maintain good speech; i.e., she is likely to reinforce appropriate speech throughout the day. It is even possible that this "generalization" may go beyond the speech realm; several mothers reported adapting aspects of procedures or principles learned in speech sessions to the modification of non-speech behavior of their children. These advantages must be balanced against the fact that the mothers do not, of course, do as skilled a job as professionally trained teachers. However, it appears that they *can* do an *effective* job.

What functions did traditional diagnostic evaluation play in planning treatment? Classification in terms of supposed etiology or "type" of disorder (e.g., psychosis vs. brain damage vs. familial mental retardation) or in terms of severity of behavioral deficit (e.g., IQ scores, classification as severely retarded) were not found to have implications for treatment. Such labels did not help in deciding where to start treatment or in making other decisions concerning treatment. Actual specification of the current repertoire did prove useful. Evaluations of "psychological functioning" or "personality" were also not of much help. Determining the particular ways in which the family characteristically reacted to particular behaviors of the child, and the effect of these consequences on the future frequency of the behavior, did help. Determining specific things that parents reported the child liked and that could be used as reinforcers in treatment was very helpful; evaluation of needs or drives in a psychodynamic framework was not.

Looking towards the future, it appears that great strides can be made in developing methods for the remedial training of speech and language skills when the professional skills and knowledge already developed in the speech and language area are reinterpreted from the point of view of a functional analysis of behavior.

REFERENCES

Allen, K. Eileen, Betty Hart, Joan S. Buell, Florence R. Harris, and M. M. Wolf, "Effects of Social Reinforcement on Isolate Behavior of a Nursery School Child," *Child Develpm.*, 1964, 35, 511–518.

Bijou, S. W., and H. N. Sloane, "Therapeutic Techniques with Children." In I. A. Berg, and L. A. Pennington (Eds.), *An Introduction to Clinical Psychology* (3rd Edition). New York: Ronald Press, 1966.

Birnbrauer, J. S., M. M. Wolf, J. D. Kidder, and Cecilia Tague, "Classroom Behavior of Retarded Pupils with Token Reinforcement," *J. exp. Child Psychol.*, 1965, 2, 219–235 (Chapter 2 in this book).

Homme, L. E., P. C. DeBaca, J. V. Devine, R. Steinhorst, and E. J. Richert, "Use of the Premack Principle in Controlling the Behavior of Nursery School Children," *J. exp. anal. Behav.*, 1963, 6, 544.

Johnston, Margaret K., "A Remedial Group for Young Retarded and Disturbed Children Based on Reinforcement Principles." Unpublished manuscript, University of Washington.

Kelleher, R. T., and L. R. Gollub, "A Review of Positive Conditioned Reinforcement," *J. exp. anal. Behav.*, 1962, 4, 543–597.

Premack, D., "Toward Empirical Behavior Laws: I. Positive Reinforcement," *Psychol. Rev.*, 1959, 66, 219–233.

Risley, T., "The Establishment of Verbal Behavior in Deviant Children." Unpublished doctoral dissertation, University of Washington, 1966.

Skinner, B. F., *Science and Human Behavior.* New York: MacMillan, 1953.

6

Barbara Dana MacAulay

A Program for Teaching Speech and Beginning Reading to Nonverbal Retardates

This paper describes a pilot project that utilized explicit reinforcement contingencies, programming, and color-coding as an approach to teaching speech and beginning reading to retardates.[1] Eleven case studies were done at an institution for retardates using various modifications of the basic technique. The program consisted of teaching individual sounds, blending sounds into words, teaching a naming vocabulary, and, in some cases, teaching word phrases. Black alphabet letters were used as visual cues for specific consonant sounds, while vowel sounds were color-coded. Initially, small colored rectangles were used to cue vowel sounds; later, the usual spelling of a sound in a word was used, but the letters comprising the sound were colored to match the original sound rectangles. A token system was used for reinforcement purposes. The pilot study inicated that the rate of sound acquisition and reading skills seemed to be rapid using the specific procedures.

Purpose

The purpose of this study was to apply operant conditioning procedures to a program for teaching speech and language to 11 non-

[1] Partial support for this study was obtained from grant number MH 12067–01 awarded to Dr. Sidney W. Bijou from the NIH, and from the White River School District #416, Buckley, Washington.

verbal retardates. An analysis of initial verbal behavior was made through observation of the children. Then a program was developed in order to teach the behaviors that were lacking.

In dealing with retarded children, the author believes that one of the strengths of operant conditioning procedures is that this approach forces the therapist to deal with specific behaviors in small, precise steps. For example, a vocal response to a visual S^D (i.e., saying [b] upon seeing the letter "b") is an entirely different response behaviorally from making a motor response to an auditory S^D (i.e., hearing the sound [b] and pointing to the letter "b"), and is also a different response from matching a written word to an object. Once the complex behavior is broken down into specific responses, reinforcement can be applied contingently and small units of behavior can be taught separately and step-wise so that the terminal behavior will be the complex behaviors involved in speaking and reading.

Sample

Eleven children ranging in age from nine to fifteen, with IQ scores from 27 to 92, were selected from 1,700 residents of the Rainier School, a state school for retarded children in Buckley, Washington. Initially, for purposes of program development and to explore procedures involving reinforcement techniques, imitation, and eye-hand coordination, five children were seen in a group situation four times a week for two months. The children were selected on the basis of known language deficiencies. After program development, six additional children were added in the succeeding 10 weeks. All children were then seen individually, 10 children twice a week, one child four times a week. Sessions varied in length from 20 minutes to a little under an hour. A college sophomore, unfamiliar with speech work or working with retarded children, was obtained as a part-time assistant at this point, and conducted the speech sessions with a few of the children.

Method

General Procedures. First, the production of 31 phonemes was taught. This was combined with repetition and varying of sequences. After the sounds were produced correctly most of the time, the blending of sounds was taught, also involving repetition and varying of sequences. Next, and in some cases along with blending, a core-naming vocabulary was devised and taught gradually, thus adding meanings or concepts. All the children were observed to perform adequately in visual recognition tasks, so visual discriminative stimuli (S^D's) were used. An additional S^D was added, as it was obvious that the children had not learned to speak or to speak clearly through traditional or incidental means. The alphabet letters were used as visual S^D's for the consonant sounds, and color S^D's were used for vowels. Initially, vowel sounds were represented by small colored rectangles. Later, the actual letters representing the vowel sound, printed in the appropriate color, were introduced. Thus the color orange indicated the [i] sound regardless of actual spelling. Therefore the children learned to speak and read simultaneously.

In the present study it was decided to use a specific color for each vowel to maintain consistency (needed in programming) within the English spelling system. The vowels taught were:

Vowels	Key Word	Color Key
[i]	beat	orange
[I]	bit	yellow
[e]	bait	red
[ɛ]	bet	brown
[æ]	bat	black
[ʌ]	but	purple
[ɑ]	hot	blue
[o]	boat	chartreuse
[U]	book	pink
[u]	boot	green

The consonants taught were [p], [b], [t], [d], [k], [g], [θ] (*thin*), [dʒ] (jud*ge*),[tʃ] (*church*), [f], [v], [s], [z], [ʃ] (*shoe*), [h], [l], [m], [n], [w], [r], and [y]. [M] (*when*), [ʒ] (vision), and [ð] (*the*) were not taught. They were added later when required to teach specific words. Phonetic placement procedures used to teach the individual sounds were similar to those mentioned in Van Riper (*1954*).

Reinforcement consisted of the immediate presentation of a token for correct or corrected responses. The tokens were placed in a dish on the table. Tokens were exchanged for a variety of candies after all the tokens (90) were given out. Tokens were exchanged two to three times a session, depending upon how many the child earned. If the tokens were not completely used during the last part of the session, they were still exchanged. Every session ended in an exchange. In the pilot study "M & M" candies were originally used instead of tokens. Later, tokens were given in small amounts and immediately exchanged for "M & M's"; later yet, tokens were exchanged only twice per session. The switch to tokens occurred after the beginning of the individual sessions. Other candies besides "M & M's" were also introduced, as it was found that a choice seemed to be more reinforcing.

A desk model amplifier was available for the children's use. Five of the children used the auditory training unit most of the time.

Procedure 1: Teaching New Sounds. The first procedure was used to train production of new sounds. The desired terminal behavior was the correct production of each new sound under the discriminative control of a letter symbol or color symbol. In starting training, the teacher pointed to a letter or color symbol on an easel in front of the child, and said the sound with his mouth hidden (an auditory S^D). If the child produced a crude approximation of the sound, the teacher instantly placed a token in a dish in front of the child and verbally praised him. The giving of tokens was always paired with verbal, social approval. After successful attempts, better approximations were required for reinforcement. In other words, the criteria for reinforcement were made more strict. This procedure was continued until a close-to-perfect approximation was produced. If no acceptable approximation was made after 10 trials, a visual S^D was added (mouth observation). If no acceptable approximation was made after 10 additional trials, a hand cue was added.

A hand on the throat indicated a voiced sound, and a hand in front of the mouth indicated a voiceless, plosive, or fricative sound. One of the child's thumbs was placed in front of the teacher's mouth with the other four fingers on the teacher's throat. The child's other hand was placed in a similar fashion in front of his own mouth and against his throat.

Usually no further cues were needed; however, in some cases additional phonetic placement methods were used. After obtaining a correct or reasonable approximation, while continually pairing the sound production with the observation of the letter symbol or color symbol, the child repeated the accepted approximation 10 times. For each response the child was given a token. If the response was incorrect, cues or prompts were given until the correct response was made and reinforced.

Procedure 2: Teaching 31 Sounds. Procedure 2 was used to train differentiation of 31 sounds under correct discriminative control of the appropriate symbol. The desired terminal behavior was the correct production of all 31 sounds under discriminative control of the letter or color symbols. The sounds [m] and [b] were taught first. After each sound had been produced correctly or with an acceptable approximation 10 times in response to the symbols (Procedure 1), the child was drilled on the two sounds. The two symbols were on an easel in front of the child. The teacher pointed to one symbol and the child responded with the accepted production. He then was reinforced with a token paired with social approval. If the sound was incorrect, he was given an auditory S^D. If the response was still unacceptable, a visual S^D (mouth observation) was given. If the first two prompts did not work, a hand cue was added. For the first two sounds about 60 to 70 presentations were made.

Seven sounds were taught initially, adding one new sound at a time. For the pilot group of five, the sounds were taught in the group; and four of the five children could produce the seven sounds under the discriminative control of the symbols by the end of the two-month group situation. Some could produce more than seven sounds under discriminative control.

Each of the seven sounds was taught according to Procedure 1, then added to the general drill described above concerning [m] and [b]. The first seven sounds taught were [m], [b], [i], [f], [a], [l], and [u], in that order. After the child's responses were under discriminative control of the seven symbols, he was given Lesson 1. From Lesson 1 on, all teaching was done in individual sessions. All of the six children added after the pilot group were also taught the first seven sounds individually.

Lesson 1 began by placing a chart listing the current number of learned sounds in front of the child. The instructor pointed to each symbol; the child responded and was reinforced for his correct or corrected responses. Next, the instructor presented flash cards. The flash cards largely contained actual words in consonant-vowel-consonant combinations. Each card was placed on a table in front of the child, the instructor pointed to the first sound symbol, and the child responded and was reinforced for his correct or corrected response. Then the instructor pointed to the next sound, etc. About 50 flash cards were presented in Lesson 1. If the child was successful most of the time, he moved on to the next lesson. The error rate varied for each child (see individual case studies). Vowel sounds were associated with blocks of color until flash cards were used, at which time actual colored letters were used.

After the first lesson was completed, sounds were added three at a time, making a total of nine lessons before all 31 sounds were taught. The number of responses ranged from 150 to 350 for each lesson, as the number of reviewed sounds and flash cards varied. The sounds taught in Lesson 2 were [θ], [w], and [æ]. The only vowel taught that was spelled out rather than associated with a block of color was [æ], because [æ] is generally spelled with the letter "a" and therefore remains consistent when the other vowel sounds and letters are color coded. In Lesson 3 the sounds added were [h], [ʃ] and [t]. In Lesson 4 the sounds taught were [s], [k], and [n]. In Lesson 5 the sounds were [p], [r], and [I]. In Lesson 6 the sounds were [d], [g], and [ʌ]. Lesson 7 consisted of the sounds [v], [z], and [o]. Lesson 8 contained the sounds [tʃ], [y], and [e]. Lesson 9 included the sounds [dʒ], [ɛ], and [U]. Procedure 1 was used for teaching each new sound. When each of the three sounds was learned (i.e., each done correctly 10 times in response to the consonant symbol or vowel color), the previously learned sounds were reviewed on the review chart for that lesson. Then the flash cards for the particular lesson were presented, with the vowel letters printed in the appropriate colors. Records were kept of correct and incorrect responses. It should be noted that the children sounded out the flash card words but were not taught the meanings for them. The teaching of meaning for particular words occurred later in the program.

Procedure 3: Reviewing the Sounds. This drill procedure was used to reduce the error rate on the entire 31 sounds. After the 31 sounds had been taught, the teacher and child sat before the full review chart and the teacher pointed to each letter symbol or color square representing vowel sounds. The child responded with the correct or accepted sound and was reinforced with a token. If the response was incorrect, the previously mentioned additional S^D's were added until his response was corrected and reinforced. The teacher started with the sounds at the upper left hand corner of the chart and went down by two's; for example, first [p] then [b], [t] and [d], thus adding some information as to whether or not the sound was voiced. The differentiation and discrimination of voiced and voiceless sounds was not explicitly taught; however, if, for instance, a child said [b] for [p], the teacher pointed to the [b] and then back to the [p]. Usually the first change made by the child involved the voiced-voiceless aspect. The percentage of sounds given correctly without additional S^D's was recorded. If the child responded correctly 100% of the time for five consecutive reviews, the review was done only once a week.

Procedure 4: Blending Sounds. This procedure was used to progress from the initial behavior of saying each sound separately in a word on the flash card to the desired terminal behavior of blending the sounds together. The teacher and child said the sounds simultaneously while the teacher held the card under his mouth and slowly moved his finger along under the sounds as they were produced. The teacher and child slowly mouthed the sound combinations together. The hand cue of moving the open palm slowly indicated blending. Most of the children needed very little prompting on blending, and it was not found necessary to teach blending more directly.

After the 31 phonemes could be produced in an acceptable fashion with reliability, and could be blended, the program moved to teaching whole words and word drill.

Procedure 5: Teaching New Words. This procedure was used to place the words produced under the discriminative control of the corresponding picture or object. The teacher and child said the word simultaneously as the teacher held the printed word card under his mouth and moved his hand along with the sounds being produced. The vowel sounds were still color-coded. The teacher and child slowly mouthed the word together. If the response was poor the child was still reinforced for the attempt. The instructor moved his hand more rapidly as the approximations improved, and the improved approximations were reinforced with tokens paired with social approval. After several acceptable approximations were obtained speaking simultaneously, the instructor said the word and the child imitated him. If the approximation was acceptable, the child was next required to respond to the printed word alone. When the child successfully read the word in a blended fashion, the instructor pointed to the picture or object and asked the child to name it. The printed word was then covered. When the child named the picture or object successfully 10 times, the word was included in the word list. If the child had difficulty in naming, the procedure was started again from the beginning.

Words selected included words for objects already discriminative for much nonverbal behavior of the child. For example, if the child often played ball, the word "ball" might be included. Second, words were chosen that were easy to say, preferably consonant-vowel-consonant combinations, single syllable words, or words that had two identical syllables, such as the word "mama." Third, words for objects that the children showed an interest in using or playing which were selected, along with words that would be useful in everyday life in their particular environment. In some cases, words needed to begin the Sullivan Programmed Reading Series (*Buchanan, 1963*) were used.

Procedure 6: Word Drill. This procedure consisted of six tests used to determine retention and comprehension. The number of words taught per session varied with the child. Usually one word was taught per session.

The first test consisted of having the child name the pictures or objects correctly. Usually this task was done twice for each word. If the child was correct, he was reinforced. If the child did not name correctly, techniques in Procedure 5 were used until an acceptable approximation was obtained and he responded to the object or picture with the correct name ten times. A token was given for the corrected response. If the child was successful each time the naming was requested for each of the several objects or pictures representing the word, the word was considered learned. The number of learned naming words was recorded.

In the second test, the child read the printed word and matched the word with the correct picture or object. Usually this was done twice for each word. If the child did not match correctly, he was shown the correct response. If the child did not read the word correctly, techniques used in Procedure 5 were used to correct the response.

In the third test, for the hard-of-hearing children, a speech-reading test was given. The teacher said the word as the child watched. The child pointed to the correct picture or object and was reinforced. The teacher spoke very softly. If the child was incorrect, the response was corrected and reinforced.

The fourth test was for auditory discrimination. The instructor covered his mouth and said the word out loud, and the child pointed to a picture or object. The child was reinforced if correct, or reinforced for the corrected response.

Test five was the same as test four, only the child wore an auditory training unit. This was used with the hard-of-hearing children.

Test six consisted of having the child read the word aloud before matching it with an object or picture.

To a great extent, the individual behaviors required by these six tests, in which a particular word is permuted through various response and stimulus modalities, corresponds to much of what is usually meant by having the "concept" for that word.

Procedure 7: Intelligibility Rating. On occasion, tests three, four, and five were used to record good, fair, and poor intelligibility of spoken words. Each word was rated by the following criteria: "good" pronunciation consisted of a normal, acceptable, understandable spoken word, all sounds correctly articulated and blended; "fair" pronunciation was characterized by an acceptable, understandable approximation in which all the sounds were included and correctly articulated, but not blended; and "poor" pronunciation included the reversal of sounds, substitution of sounds, or the omission of sounds. In summarizing the data, a word was considered to have good pronunciation if all responses were "good" according to the above criteria. A word was considered to have fair pronunciation if responses were rated both "good" and "fair." A word was considered poor if it had even one response rated as "poor."

Results

Five of the children were initially mute and had not learned to speak through regular delayed-speech therapy procedures, or in any other situations, such as the classroom or home. At the end of the study these children could produce sounds and, in some cases, words. Six of the children were initially highly unintelligible and had not improved through standard procedures or incidental learning. At the end of the study the six could produce sounds correctly and could speak understandable words. In addition five of the children were reading by the end of the program.

Each of the children will be briefly reviewed and representative data will be presented.

Case #1: Doug. Doug was a 12-year-old boy with IQ scores between 50 and 53. Before training he had a few highly vowelized words. Doug had a bilateral atresia resulting in a moderate to severe bilateral conductive hearing loss. He used an auditory training unit during the session. When data were first recorded, he had 13 sounds under discriminative control, and by the 12th session he had all 31 sounds under discriminative control about 60% of the time.

Case #2: Dickey. Dickey was a 10-year-old boy with IQ scores ranging from 40 to 50. Before training Dickey had very choppy, erratic speech consisting of highly unintelligible single words and many echoic responses. He was very hyperactive. His birth was reported as normal, but after measles at age three, his rate of development decreased. Dickey entered the program in April and was taught one sound at a time even after the initial seven sounds. Figure 1 shows that after 27 half-hour sessions, he could produce 14 sounds (vertical bars) in response to the visual stimuli of consonant letters and color-coded vowel letters. Notice that after learning the first five sounds, Dickey's percentage of correct responses increased even though new sounds were added. This phenomenon was noted in several cases.

Dickey was taught to pair the motor response of holding a closed

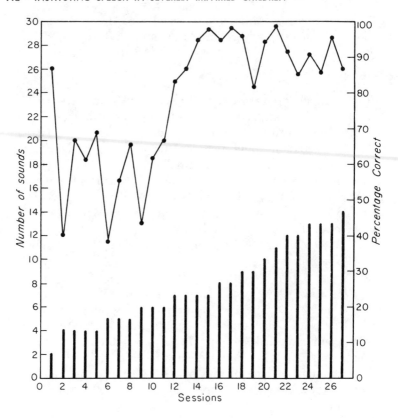

FIGURE 1

Percentage of sounds under discriminative control.

fist at the side of his face and opening it quickly while producing the [t] sound. In this manner the correct [t] sound was produced; and the motor response then dropped out of its own accord as the frequency of correct production increased. Also, because of perseveration, additional reinforcement was given if he responded correctly the first time; he was told when he was correct the first time, and given two tokens, (instead of one) and strong social praise. Dickey then put the tokens into the dish.

Case #3: Ted. Ted was an 11-year-old mongoloid boy with an IQ score of 56. Prior to training his speech was highly vowelized and unintelligible, though quite fluent. After 14 individual sessions, he had 31 sounds under discriminative control 90% of the time (see Figure 2). In auditory discrimination training, each sound was

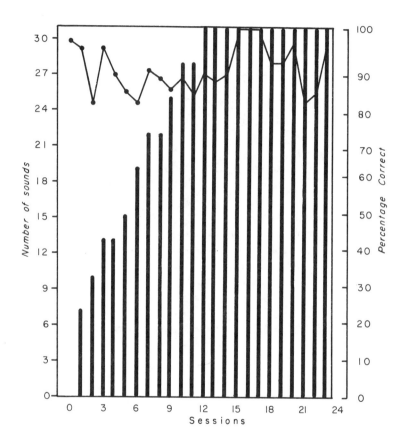

FIGURE 2

Percentage of sounds under discriminative control.

presented in isolation while the teacher's mouth was screened from view, and Ted pointed to the appropriate symbol or color. After 10 sessions of this training, Ted was able to point correctly 90% of the time. Ted learned nine words, most of which were needed to start in Book I of the Sullivan Programmed Reading Program

(*Buchanan, 1963*). Ted named the nine objects or pictures correctly with good or fair pronunciation, and matched the nine words to the pictures or objects. Ted started to read Book I in the Sullivan Program by the end of the study.

Case #4: Timmy. Timmy was an 11-year-old boy with an IQ score of 43. The psychological report described the boy as "autistic.'" He rarely spoke, but occasionally did respond with a high-pitched "uh-huh" or fairly understandable but echoic speech. After 24 individual sessions he produced the 31 sounds correctly in response to the visual stimuli 80% of the time. He was then taught three words that he could name clearly and that he could match to the correct objects or pictures.

Case #5: Mike. Mike was a 12-year-old boy who had obtained an IQ score of 52. Initially, Mike had no speech and made no response to speech or noise. He made no attempt to communicate with others and did not maintain eye contact with people outside of the therapy situation. After one month of group lessons, he had 19 sounds under discriminative control; after four more individual sessions he could produce all 31 sounds; and after 10 more individual sessions, all 31 sounds were under discriminative control over 90% of the time. Figure 3 shows that Mike matched 17 words to pictures or objects and read the 17 words; however, he named only nine of the objects or pictures. Some of the words Mike learned were for Book I in the Sullivan Program. At the end of the study he attempted to communicate through drawings and pictures, had a group of friends, and was generally more animated and responsive. He was retested toward the end of the study and received IQ scores of 83, 84 and 92.

Case #6: Harry. Harry was a 14-year-old boy with an IQ score of 28. Initially, he used two to three words and usually hummed or clicked his tongue. Audiometric testing indicated a moderate bilateral sensori-neutral hearing loss. Having started the program in the group, when individual sessions started he had 19 sounds under discriminative control. In eight more sessions the entire 31 sounds were under control about 80% of the time. He was taught seven words, six of which he matched correctly to the appropriate picture or object. He could name three of the pictures or objects on command. Of the seven words he was taught, he pronounced six

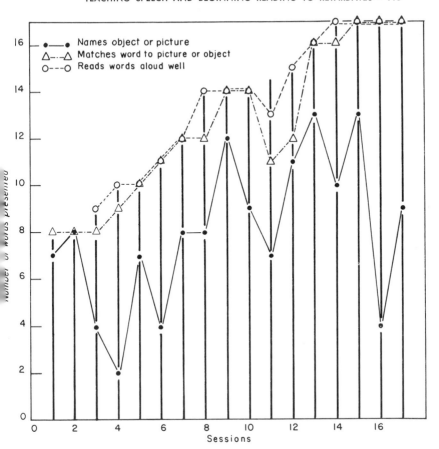

FIGURE 3

Naming, matching, and reading aloud words.

well. When retested after speech training he obtained an IQ score of 45.

Case #7: Jim. Jim was a nine-year-old boy with an IQ score of 30. Initially, he had no speech and made few noises, with an occasional echoic response that was highly unintelligible. After 12 individual sessions he could produce five good approximations in response to five visual stimuli about 80% of the time.

Case #8: Denny. Denny was a nine-year-old mongoloid with an obtained IQ score of 31. He had been given a complete transfusion at birth because of an RH incompatibility. Initially, his speech was fluent but highly unintelligible. He had some understandable words such as "bye-bye" and "O.K." In 29 individual sessions he produced 28 sounds correctly under the discriminative control of the visual stimuli (see Figure 4). Note that the percentage of correct responses decreased and then increased again as new sounds were added. This was quite common in many of the cases.

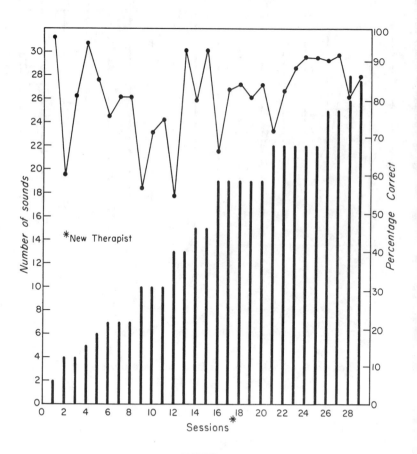

FIGURE 4

Percentage of sounds under discriminative control.

Case #9: George. George was a 15-year-old boy with an IQ of 80. His speech, though fluent, was highly unintelligible. He made use of gestures and the drawing of pictures to communicate. The medical diagnosis included ". . . mixed, major and possible psychomotor

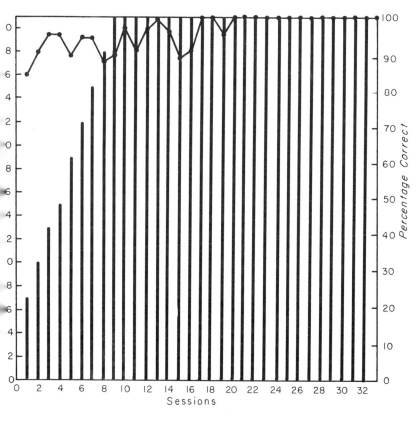

FIGURE 5

Percentage of sounds under discriminative control.

seizures, aphasia and dysarthria." After nine individual sessions George could produce correctly all 31 sounds in response to the visual stimuli about 90% of the time (see Figure 5). Audiometric testing ruled out a hearing loss. George was then taught 49 words.

Figure 6 shows that at the end of the study George could match the 49 words to pictures or objects, could name the 49 objects or pictures, and 47 of the words were rated as having good pronunciation. The words were selected by George as words he would like to say clearly and words he could use on his living hall. Note that the number of words rated as having good pronunciation increased even as the number of words increased. George also began to work on producing understandable phrases; four such phrases were in use by the end of the study.

In the auditory discrimination program, the initial procedure required George to point to the consonant letters and vowel colors on the full review charts in response to consonant-vowel-consonant

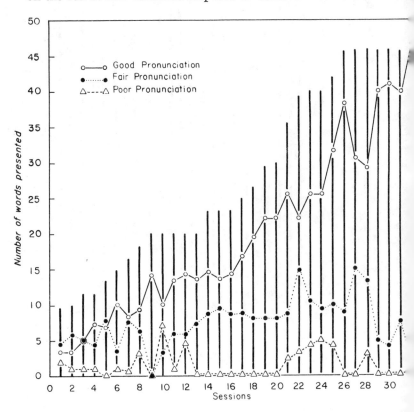

FIGURE 6

Good, fair, and poor pronunciation of words.

nonsense words produced by the therapist while her mouth was screened from view. George listened, repeated the nonsense word, and pointed to the three symbols. After his performance increased, the procedure was changed so that he was no longer allowed to imitate the nonsense syllable before pointing. His performance dropped but eventually increased to his former level of about 90% right (Figure 7).

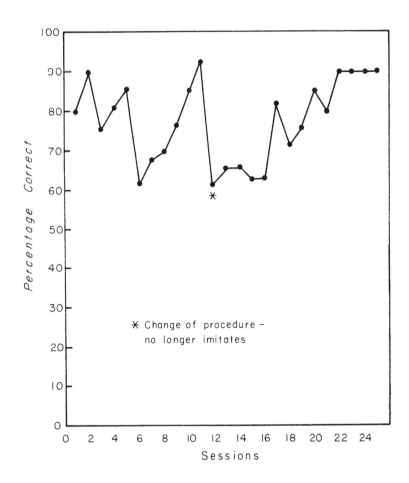

FIGURE 7

Percentage of correct auditory discriminations.

George also had difficulty blending sounds, especially voiceless-voiced combinations, such as the [p] in the word "please." Figure 8

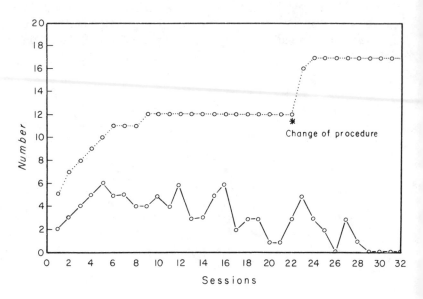

FIGURE 8

Errors in blending voiceless-voiced combinations.

shows the number of voiceless-voiced combinations in the initial position in words he was learning to pronounce intelligibly, as well as the number of "fair" and "poor" pronunciations decreased, while the number of such combinations increased, after the change of procedure was instituted. George dropped the motor response after the frequency of blending increased.

George lived on a hall that was on a point-reinforcement system; so points, (instead of tokens) were given for each correct response. Points were traded in for money and for a trip to town to purchase items. He was also given points for using the words in appropriate situations on the hall.

Case #10: Linda. Linda was a 14-year-old girl with an IQ score of 33. Initially, she had no speech, and made only a few whining noises. Linda had normal hearing, but the psychologist reported an expressive aphasia. By the time data were recorded, she had 13 sounds under correct discriminative control. After four more sessions she could produce 22 sounds under discriminative control of the visual stimuli about 80% of the time. During the remainder of therapy, time was spent working on the production of particular sounds that were difficult for Linda to produce.

Case #11: Polly. Polly was a 12-year-old girl with an IQ score of 50, and with hearing loss. She used an auditory training unit during the sessions. She initially had no speech, but made noises to get attention. Polly started the program in the group; and by the time data were recorded and individual sessions started, she could produce seven sounds. She learned to produce the entire 31 sounds, but the discriminative control exerted by the consonant letters and colors was very poor (about 35% of the time correct). She was also taught four words, she could name two pictures or objects, and could match three of the words to pictures or objects.

Discussion

The rate of sound acquisition seemed to be rapid using these procedures. Most children acquired a full repertoire of speech sounds within four to six months while being seen only twice a week. It also appears that consistently pairing the sounds with another prompt (i.e., letters, colors, and in some cases motor responses), facilitated sound acquisition. Case #5 acquired 31 sounds under good discriminative control after about four months, the first two of which involved group sessions.

Also, it seemed that reading skills were acquired rather quickly using the program. Children who previously recognized only their names and had not shown any progress in reading in their regular classes, began to read new words. For example, Case #3 initially could recognize only his name; but at the end of the study he could reliably match nine words with objects or pictures.

In addition, the procedures provided an effective means of consistently administering reinforcement. No desired response was unreinforced. In many procedures, there are few explicit criteria to aid the therapist in applying reinforcement contingently and consistently. When the therapist is required to deliver some reinforcer after each correct response, he is forced to define what response is considered correct, what kind of a reinforcer he will use, and how much of the reinforcer will be supplied. However, probably the most important part of any behavior modification program is the use of specific reinforcement contingencies. Each correct response and (usually) each corrected response in this program was immediately reinforced with a token. Immediate feedback was provided for right or wrong responses, and errors were corrected immediately; thus error responses were never allowed to continue or to be maintained.

Because the procedures were specific and detailed, the author found no difficulty in training others to follow them. The assistant, a college sophomore, was trained and using the procedures in three days. In Cases #6, #8, and #11, no difference in performance was noted when therapists were changed. Two cases, #1, and #4, did show some changes in performance. Another teacher was trained in eight sessions to continue the program with one of the subjects.

Regardless of extraneous stimuli and frequent observers, the children attended to the lesson. This is at variance with the idea that it is necessary to reduce environmental stimuli (Strauss and Lehtinen, 1947) for such children to learn effectively. The children maintained good attending behavior as attending was required to respond correctly, and thus to be reinforced. Despite institutional records describing the children as being distractible and hyperactive, the children always remained in their seats, even during the first sessions of the pilot group.

Two of the children were given new psychological evaluations, at the author's request, because they exhibited behavior that did not seem consistent with their low IQ scores. Case #5 initially received an IQ score of 52; upon retesting a year later he received IQ scores of 83 and 92. Case #6 was also retested, and his score increased from an IQ of 27 to an IQ of 45. These results confirm some of the work of Bayley (1949), Lowell (1941), and Bradway (1944). (Robinson and Robinson, 1965), suggesting that IQ is not "constant." The above findings imply that there are some changes in IQ scores as a result of this program and probably indicate the degree to which IQ scores are dependent upon language skills. Case #6's performance improved on the Peabody Picture Vocabulary Test, perhaps as a function of his auditory discrimination improving. Case #5 improved his scores on various performance tests, suggesting that the training in visual discrimination had been beneficial. Though the other subjects were not retested, there may have been changes in their test performances.

It was also noted that each child varied as to the kind and number of prompts or additional S^D's needed for each sound and each word. For example, Cases #3 and #9 required prompts in addition to the visual S^D's of the flash cards containing the consonant symbols and color-coded vowel symbols for some of the words; and the prompts needed varied (i.e., either simultaneous mouthing or imitation). The same kind of variation in amount and kinds of prompts needed was found in the learning of specific sounds.

Another interesting finding was that after some children learned four or five sounds, the rate of acquisition of further sounds increased rapidly.

Some of the children retained behaviors used as cues in teaching certain sounds and words. For example, Case #5 still used a hand cue for a long time for voicing when saying [m]. No records were kept as to the maintenance and frequency of this kind of behavior, but it was noted anecdotally that eventually the additional cues were dropped as the frequency of the correct response increased. No attempts were made in therapy to extinguish or to maintain these behaviors.

Conclusions and Implications

The results of the 11 case studies, and of other recent studies in this area, demonstrate that operant procedures applied to speech and language training can be quite successful. The particular program described in this paper is useful in teaching sounds and words, and, in one case (#9), phrases. A general program for teaching speech, language, and beginning reading to retardates could be developed by combining this program with procedures that develop word chaining and more complex stimulus control of speech, and that fade out the color-coding of vowel sounds. With children who progress beyond sight vocabulary, the previous phonetic training should facilitate more advanced reading skills. As spoken language and auditory discrimination improved, children using phonetic techniques could discriminate their own productions when reading, and would no longer have to rely upon a sight vocabulary alone.

None of the case studies included control procedures, and no formal baseline data were collected, although performance was assessed at the start of the program. However, five of the children (Cases #5, 6, 9, 10, and 11) were initially mute and had not learned to speak through regular delayed speech therapy procedures, or in any other situations such as the classroom or home. At the end of the study these children could produce sounds and, in some cases, words. Six of the children were initially highly unintelligible and had not improved through standard procedures or incidental learning. At the end of the study the six could produce sounds correctly and could say understandable words. Some of the children were reading by the end of the program.

REFERENCES

Bayley, N., "Consistency and Variability in the Growth of Intelligence from Birth to Eighteen Years," *J. genet. Psychol.*, 1949, 75, 165–196.

Bradway, K. P., "IQ Constancy on the Revised Stanford-Binet from the Preschool to the Junior High School Level," *J. genet. Psychol.*, 1944, 65, 197–217.

Buchanan, D., and Sullivan Associates, *Programmed Reading Book I.* New York: Webster Division, McGraw-Hill Book Co., 1963.

Lowell, F. E., "A Study of the Variability of IQ's in Retest," *J. appl. Psychol.*, 1941, 25, 341–356.

Robinson, H. B., and N. M. Robinson, *The Mentally Retarded Child.* New York: McGraw-Hill, 1965.

Strauss, A. A., and L. E. Lehtinen, *Psychopathology and Education of the Brain-injured Child.* New York: Grune and Stratton, 1947.

Van Riper, C., *Speech Correction: Principles and Methods.* Englewood Cliffs, N.J.: Prentice-Hall, 1954.

O. Ivar Lovaas

A Program for the Establishment of Speech in Psychotic Children[1]

During the last few years several investigators, using learning theory paradigms, have been successful in altering the behavior of patients usually resistant to change when traditional treatment techniques were employed. This general area of application of learning theory principles to treatment has been labeled behavior therapy. The program which is outlined in this paper has attempted to use learning theory principles to establish and modify speech behavior of severely psychotic, autistic and schizophrenic children. The investigations were derived from that part of learning theory known as reinforcement theory (operant conditioning, instrumental, and trial and error learning are roughly synonymous terms). Therapeutic interventions designed from reinforcement theory probably are based on the most comprehensive body of experimental data in Psychology today. Experimental-laboratory research on reinforce-

[1] The preparation of this manuscript was facilitated by grant No. 6–1188 from the Office of Education. The paper is based on a research project on childhood schizophrenia in its fourth year of operation, with the collaboration of James Q. Simmons, M.D., Chief, the Children's Inpatient Services, the Neuropsychiatric Institute, UCLA. The author expresses his appreciation for the help of the Staff at the Institute, and of the large number of students from the Department of Psychology who assist on the project.

From John K. Wing (Ed.), *Childhood Autism*. Oxford: Pergamon Press, 1966. Reprinted with permission.

ment theory dates as far back as 1898 with Professor E. L. Thorndike's work. Although much is known about the basic constructs of this theory, the application of the theory to treatment and education is sufficiently new to warrant considerable additional research to clarify its usefulness and limits.

The first large scale investigation on the applicability of reinforcement theory principles in modifying psychopathological behaviors and establishing adjustive behaviors was initiated by Ayllon (1), who worked with chronic schizophrenics. Since then, researchers have investigated the usefulness of the theory for the modification of pathological behaviors in childhood schizophrenia (e.g., *Wolf et al.* (24)), juvenile delinquency (e.g., *Schwitzgebel and Kolb* (20)), and a number of other problems. Of particular interest might be the studies carried out on mentally retarded children, where this research is becoming extensive. Bensberg *et al.* (2), Parsley and Hamilton (17), and the Violet project (23), provide examples of how reinforcement theory principles can be applied to profoundly retarded children and help in the establishment of basic self-help behaviors (such as dressing, eating, elimination). The work of Birnbrauer *et al.* (3) demonstrates how these principles may be employed to establish intellectual behaviors (beginnings in reading, writing, and arithmetic) in retarded children. The research mentioned above serves only as an introduction to the large amount of work presently being done in this area.

Considerable interest has been focused on the application of reinforcement theory principles to modification of language behaviors. Goldiamond (7) has applied these principles to the modification of stuttering. Isaacs *et al.* (10) and Sherman (21) have employed these procedures in reinstating speech in adult schizophrenics. The studies of Risley (19) and Hewett (9) are examples of how these principles can be applied in modifying or establishing language behaviors in schizophrenic and autistic children. The present paper will outline certain procedures for the application of reinforcement theory principles to the acquisition and modification of speech in autistic and schizophrenic children.

Introduction to Reinforcement Theory

The reader who may want to obtain a more thorough introduction to reinforcement theory is well advised to read Keller's text (11)

A short introduction to the theory will be provided here. In everyday terms, certain behaviors are a function of their consequences, and as a result of their consequences can be either strengthened or weakened. A certain behavior is strengthened when it results in obtaining gratifications (technically, these are called positive reinforcers; popularly, they are called rewards), or the removal of discomfort and pain (technically, negative reinforcers). These same behaviors will be weakened when positive reinforcers are withheld, or when the behavior results in pain and punishment (technically, aversive stimuli). Positive and negative reinforcers can be grouped in two classes, primary and secondary. Certain stimuli in the environment are called primary reinforcers since they appear to have reinforcing properties from birth on. They seem to be related to the biological structure of the organism, and include such stimuli as food and physical pain. Other aspects of the environment, while seemingly neutral at birth, come to acquire reinforcing properties as the child develops. These are called secondary (learned, acquired, conditioned) reinforcers. In everyday language these have been called symbolic rewards, or punishments. For example, social stimuli such as the parent's smile, his voice, physical closeness, and so on, while neutral at birth, acquire reinforcing properties as the child develops. In general, it is argued that previously neutral stimuli take on reinforcing properties as a function of their association with already powerful reinforcers. Although primary reinforcers can be few in number, there might develop in the child's particular interaction with his environment an enormous variety of secondary reinforcers.

It is important to make the interaction between the reinforcers and behavioral development more explicit. While the child's behavior during the first few months of life might be regulated by primary reinforcers, secondary reinforcers take over an essential controlling function rather soon. That is, when a child talks or does well in school, or plays with his peers, the consequences of such behavior do not involve the presentation of biological rewards, or the alleviation of biological pain. Rather, the immediate consequences of such behavior are symbolic. The child smiles because he has an effect upon his social environment. The child's first communicative behaviors, such as his cry, are probably regulated by the mother attending to his physiological needs. When the child first starts to talk, however, he is not rewarded by food, but probably by the similarity between his own speech and that of the attending adults. When he does well in school, he is not fed, but rather is rewarded by correctness, novelty, achievement, etc. What we are confronted with, then, is an enormous variety of behaviors which are regulated by a prodigious number of social, interpersonal, or intellectual consequences which we would argue have acquired the property of rewarding or punishing a particular expression. It is difficult at first to appreciate the great complexity of this interaction between behavior and environment, and reinforcement theory illuminates, rather than attenuates, this complexity. It promises no easy solution to this problem. It is particularly true that what we call secondary reinforcers are vast in quantity, and vary from one child to another, and for the same child as he develops. Because the acquisition of secondary reinforcers would be a function of deviations both in organic structure and prior environment, there is ample opportunity for development to go astray.

If we do examine deviant development from reinforcement theory, emphasis can be placed on deviations of behavior. For example, one might define a certain deviation, or abnormality, in terms of the failure in the acquisition of speech behaviors, or the acquisition of excessive aggressive behavior. Similarly, one might approach deviations in terms of distortions in the acquisition of secondary reinforcers. For example, a child may develop for whom a smile has no reinforcement function or has a function different from that which society initially intended it to have. Since secondary reinforcers regulate behavior, it would be difficult to observe a deviation in the acquisition of such reinforcers without simultaneously observing deviation in behavior.

It is assumed, then, that normal behavioral development presupposes the acquisition of a large variety of secondary reinforcers. It follows that the child who has failed in the acquisition of such reinforcers, should demonstrate a deficiency in the behaviors which typically terminate in such stimuli. In the extreme case of complete failure in the acquisition of such secondary reinforcers, the child should evidence little, if any, social behaviors. That is, the child should fail to attend to people, fail to smile, fail to seek your company, to talk, etc., because his environment did not provide him with the rewarding consequences for such behaviors. Ferster (6) and Rimland (18), (for different reasons) have argued that such is the case in autism, and probably, in varying degrees, in childhood schizophrenia. It is apparent that such failure in the acquisition of secondary reinforcers need not be complete, but may be partial. For example, some children may be reinforced by correctness, and intellectual achievement, while interpersonal events *per se* are inoperative. To that extent, such a child' should excel in intellectual behaviors, while being deficient in interpersonal behaviors.

If one approaches treatment from a reinforcement theory framework, one could concentrate one's effort either on building behaviors directly, or on the establishment of secondary reinforcers and stimulus functions in general. In the long run, one might be more therapeutic by addressing treatment efforts to the establishment or rearrangement of stimulus functions. This kind of intervention would give to the child's environment (his peers, parents and teachers) the tools with which to help the child acquire the myriad behaviors necessary for adequate function. On the other hand, it is apparent that we have to address ourselves to the direct manipulation of behaviors when these are so complex that they can only be acquired in specific environments designed to create them. This seems to be the case with certain intellectual and speech behaviors in children who have fallen behind in their development.

Introduction of the Speech Training Program and Definition of Terms

With the great majority of children, the problem of teaching speech never arises. Speech develops within each child's particular environment without parents and teachers having to know a great deal about how it occurs. Yet, for some children, because of deviations in organic structure or prior experience, speech fails to develop. Children with the diagnosis of childhood schizophrenia, and especially autistic children, often show little in the way of speech development (18). The literature on autism suggests two conclusions regarding speech in such children: first, that the usual treatment setting (psychotherapy) in which these children are placed might not be conducive to speech development (4); and secondly, that a child failing to develop speech by the age of five years remains withdrawn and does not improve clinically (4). That is, the presence or absence of speech is an important prognostic indicator. It is perhaps obvious that a child who can speak can engage in a much more therapeutic interchange with his environment than the child who has no speech.

The failure of some children to develop speech as a "natural" consequence of growing up poses the need for an increased knowledge of how language is acquired. A procedure for the development of speech in previously mute children would not only be of practical importance, but might also illuminate the development of speech in normal children. Although several theoretical attempts have been made to account for language development, the empirical basis for these theoretical formulations is probably inadequate. This paper will outline a procedure by which speech can be made to occur. Undoubtedly there are or will be other ways by which speech can be acquired. The program for the development of language will be presented in two phases: (1) the establishment of vocal behaviors in previously mute children (verbal imitation training), and (2) the establishment of an appropriate context for speech. Since the description of these procedures requires usage of a set of technical terms, these will be introduced first.

A *neutral* stimulus is a stimulus (e.g. a verbal request to "place the book on top of the table" or "point to my nose") which prior to training does not give rise to (cue) the correct response. A *training* stimulus is any neutral stimulus to which a correct response will be trained. A *prompt* is a stimulus which cues the correct response prior to training, or with minimal training. Examples of prompts would be (a) manually moving the child's hand through the correct response (e.g., manually moving the child's hand, with the book, releasing the book on top of the table), or (b) giving the child the correct answer (e.g. instructing the child: "the book is on top of the table"). *Fading* denotes the gradual removal of the prompt over trials. Examples of fading a prompt would be (a) to gradually reduce the amount of the attending adult's participation in the child's response by lessening the hold on the child's hand, to touching his arm, then his shoulder, or (b) to reduce the decibel level of the verbal prompt, or supplying the child with only components of that prompt (such as "the book is on t.. .. ..". Use of prompts proceeds along the following lines: (1) a training stimulus is paired with a prompt, and appropriate behavior is positively reinforced, and (2) the prompt is gradually faded until the training stimulus alone is sufficient to elicit the correct response. *Correct response* is defined as the child emitting the appropriate response to the previously neutral stimulus, without the aid of a prompt. It is to be noted that the *rate* of fading of the prompt has to be determined by the child himself, only the amount of prompt needed for the child's execution of the correct response should be employed. Sometimes the correct response will be emitted with sudden fading, at other times one has to rely on considerable prompting. *Positive reinforcement* is any stimulus, given contingent upon appropriate behavior, which serves to strengthen that behavior. It is crucial that the reinforcement be given immediately (within a second of the occurrence of the appropriate response). It is also crucial that strong reinforcers be used, particularly in the early stages of training. Because many psychotic children are unresponsive to secondary reinforcers (such as praise) we have frequently relied on primary reinforcers, such as small bites of the child's own meal. To maximize the likelihood that a reinforcer be effective, the child may in the beginning receive all his meals during training (while food is withheld between training sessions). Incorrect or inappropriate behaviors (such as echolalic repetition of the adult's instructions, tantrum behaviors, etc.) have been accompanied by a five-second removal of all positive reinforcers (the attending adult assumes an inattentive position, and removes the food). This operation serves to weaken such behaviors. When exceptionally strong, the inappropriate behaviors are accompanied by a more extensive positive reinforcement withdrawal (such as half-hour isolation) or a noxious stimulus, such as a slap on the child's bottom, or hand, immediately contingent upon the inappropriate behaviors.

Verbal Imitation Training

Phase one of the program, establishment of verbal imitative repertoires in previously mute children, or children with inadequate vocal repertoires, will be presented first. It is appropriate to introduce this program with some comments on our early unsuccessful efforts in building speech.

Working within the reinforcement theory paradigm, we employed a *shaping* procedure in our earlier efforts. Briefly, in direct shaping of speech, one initially reinforces (e.g., with bites of food) random vocalizations, raising the frequency of their occurrence, and then subsequently reinforces only those sounds which more and more closely approximate the desired product (the word "mama," perhaps). This procedure is similar to that employed by Hayes (8) in establishing a three word vocabulary in a chimpanzee, and to Isaacs' (10) and Sherman's (21) procedures in *reinstating* verbal behavior in adult schizophrenics. Although our patients learned a few words in this manner, it became apparent that despite extensive efforts we would produce only a very restricted vocabulary.

Casual observation would suggest that in normal children speech is not acquired because the environment shapes each word, but that children acquire words by hearing speech; that is, children learn to speak by imitation. The mute schizophrenic children with whom we have worked evidenced no imitation. Thus, the establishment of imitation in these children appeared to be the most beneficial and practical starting point for building speech. The first step in creating speech, then, became one of establishing conditions in which imitation of verbal responses would be learned.

The method that we eventually found most feasible for establishing verbal imitation has been reported elsewhere (14). The method involves a discrimination training procedure. Early in training the child was rewarded only if he emitted a sound within a certain time after an adult had emitted a sound. In this manner the adult's speech became the cue for the child's speech. In the middle of training the child was rewarded only if the sound he emitted within the prescribed interval resembled the adult's speech. Towards the end of training he was only rewarded if his vocalization very closely matched the adult's vocalization, and was, in effect, imitative. Thus verbal imitation was taught through the development of a series of increasingly fine verbal discriminations.

Method

In our program, training has been conducted several days a week, several hours a day. The actual number of hours has varied from one child to another, from two to seven hours daily. During the training sessions the child and adult sat facing each other, their heads about one foot apart. If necessary, the adult physically prevented the child from leaving the situation by holding the child's legs between his own legs. Reinforcement, in the form of single spoonfuls of the child's meal was delivered immediately following (contingent upon) correct responses. Inattentive, self-destructive and tantrum behaviors which interfered with training were accompanied by a five-second removal of all positive reinforcers, or when particularly resistant to extinction, by punishment (a loud, stern "no", or a slap on the hand). Interfering behaviors were suppressed within a week. Punishment was never delivered contingent upon incorrect verbal behavior.

It is important to point out that the children frequently respond to our demands by a temporary increase in tantrums or self-destructive behavior. In our early efforts (13) to cope with such behavior we would deliver sympathetic comments contingent upon such behavior (for example, by reassuring the child he was not bad) only to observe an increase in self-destruction. Removal of positive reinforcement, sometimes coupled with punishment, has served to effectively suppress or extinguish such behaviors. It is possible that the tantrums and self-destructive behavior served to remove demands in the child's past, thereby strengthening that behavior.

Four distinct steps were required to establish verbal imitation. In step (1) the child was reinforced for all vocalizations. We frequently would fondle the children, and avoid aversive stimulation. This was done in order to increase the frequency of vocal responses. During this stage in training the child was also rewarded for visually fixating on the adult's mouth. When the child reached a level of about one verbal response every five seconds, and was visually fixating on the adult's mouth more than 50 per cent of the time, step (2) of training was introduced.

Step (2) marked our initial attempt to bring the child's verbal behavior under our verbal control in a manner such that our speech would ultimately stimulate speech from the child. Mastery of this second step involved acquisition of a temporal discrimination by the child. The adult emitted a vocal response, e.g., "baby," about once on the average of every 10th second. The child was reinforced only if he vocalized within six seconds after the adult's vocalization. However, *any* vocal response of the child would be reinforced in that time interval. Step (3) was introduced when the frequency of the child's vocal responses within the six second interval had tripled its initial level.

Step (3) was structurally similar to the preceding step but included the additional requirement that the child actually match the adult's verbalization before receiving reinforcement. In this and in following steps, the adult selected the verbalizations for imitative training from a pool of possible verbalizations that had met one or more of the following criteria. First, we selected vocal behaviors that could be prompted, that is, vocal behaviors that could be elicited by a cue prior to any experimental training such as manually moving the child through the behavior. An example of training with the use of a prompt is afforded in teaching the sound "B". The training would proceed in three stages: (a) the adult would emit "B" and simultaneously prompt the child to emit "B" by holding the child's lips closed with his fingers and quickly removing them when the child exhaled; (b) the prompt would be gradually faded, by the adult moving his fingers away from the child's mouth, to his cheek, to finally gently touching the child's jaw; (c) the adult would emit the vocalization "B" only, withholding all prompts. The rate of fading would be determined by the child; the sooner the child's verbal behavior came under the control of the adult's, without the use of the prompt, the better. The second criterion for selection of words or sounds in the early stages of training centered on their concomitant visual components (which we exaggerated when we pronounced them), such as the labial consonant "m" and open-mouthed vowels like "a." We selected such sounds after having previously found that the children could discriminate words with visual components more easily than those with only auditory components (the guttural consonants, "k" and "g," proved extremely difficult to train, and, like "l" and "s," were mastered later than other sounds). Thirdly, we selected for training sounds which the child emitted most frequently in step (1).

Step (4) was a recycling of step (3) but with a new sound that had not been presented before. To make the discrimination between the new and the old sounds as easy as possible, we selected a very different sound from that which had already been presented in step (3). To make certain that the child was in fact imitating, we randomly interspersed the sounds of step (3) with the sound of step (4), in a randomized ratio of about 1:3. This random presentation "forced" (or enabled) the child to discriminate the particular sounds involved, in order to be rewarded. There was no requirement placed upon the child in step (3) to discriminate out specific aspects of the adult's speech — a child might master step (3) without attending to the specific properties of the adult's speech. In fact, the child would emit his vocal response to any vocal response of the adult. Each new introduction of sounds and words required increasingly fine discriminations by the child, hence provided evidence that the child was in fact matching the adult's speech. The inattention of psychotic children has proven to be a major problem in all teaching efforts. Discrimination training (selective delivery and withdrawal of reinforcement, rotation of stimuli, etc.) is the primary tool whereby we enable or force the child to attend to the relevant stimulus dimensions.

All steps beyond (4) consisted of replications of step (3), using new sounds, words and phrases. In each new step the previously mastered words and sounds were rehearsed on a randomized ratio of 1:3. The next step was introduced when the child had mastered the previous steps, that is had made a total of 10 consecutive correct replications of the adult utterances.

Results

The children vary enormously in their rate of acquisition of imitative vocal behavior. In general, if a child has some imitative vocal behavior at the onset of training, the acquisition is very rapid. In such children we have established rather elaborate imitative behaviors within one or two weeks of training with one or two hour training sessions per day. In those children who evidence no imitative behavior of any form, and consequently seem more unresponsive to social stimuli, only extensive training efforts have brought about imitative speech. Billy was one of the most profoundly disturbed children to whom we taught imitative speech. Billy's first 26 days of imitation training have been plotted in Figure 1. The abscissa denotes training days.

The words and sounds are printed in lower case letters on the days they were introduced and trained, and in capital letters on the days they were mastered. It can be seen that the rate of mastery increased as the training progressed. While it took several days to train a single word during the first two weeks of the program, only a single day of training was necessary to master several words during the last two weeks. The positive acceleration of the curve indicates the acquisition of imitation.

After a certain point in training, the children can imitate new words with such ease and rapidity that merely adding verbal responses to their imitative repertoire seems pointless. At this stage

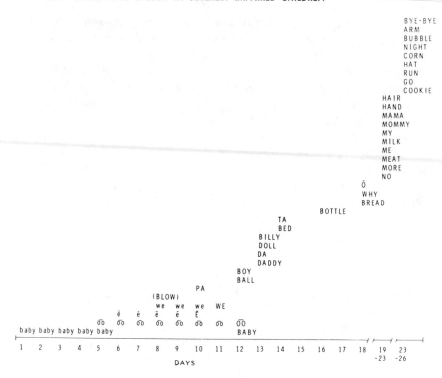

FIGURE 1

The first 26 days of imitation training on Billy. The abscissa denotes training days. The words and sounds are printed in lower case letters on the days they were introduced and trained, and in capital letters on the days they were mastered.

the children are introduced to the second part of the language training program, wherein the children are taught to use language appropriately. We have labeled this program the Establishment of an Appropriate Context for Speech.

The Establishment of an Appropriate Context for Speech

The training program for appropriate use of speech has proceeded through three stages which can be characterized as involving increasing complexity. In the first stage, the child is taught to correctly verbalize and identify common objects and behaviors of himself and others. In the second stage, the child is trained to appropriately use, and respond to, increasingly abstract terms, such as prepositions, pronouns, and time. In stage three, the child is trained to use his language for spontaneous and conversational speech. Space does not allow for a detailed examination of all the procedures associated with this training; they have been presented in detail elsewhere (15, 16, 5). Sufficient information about the training will be given to enable the reader to extend the program on his own, should he so desire.

Almost all the language training, subsequent to the training in verbal imitation, can be viewed as the establishment of three basic discriminations. These discriminations are summarized in Table 1, which is presented below. The Table is reasonably self-explanatory, and will be referred to for illustration.

Discrimination	Stimulus	Response	Examples
1	Nonverbal	Verbal	
	Objects		Labeling, or describing environment
	Symbols		Testing
	Behavior		Describing behavior of self or others
	Self or others		
2	Verbal	Nonverbal	
	Self or others		Instructions (Giving or receiving)
3	Verbal	Verbal	Conversation
	No experimentally manipulated stimulus	Verbal	Spontaneity

TABLE 1

Outline of the Language Training Program

Training a Labeling Vocabulary

In this training, the child is involved in both discrimination 1 and discrimination 2 as given in Table 1: to correctly label objects and behaviors of himself and others, and to correctly identify the same objects and behaviors when requested to do so. A large number of everyday objects (such as toast, bacon, chair, table, book), personal possessions and parts (shirt, shoes, eye, ear, etc.) and common behaviors (walking, laughing, pointing, etc.) are selected. The training then proceeds along the following paradigm. The attending adult presents a training stimulus, such as a piece of bacon. As soon as the child visually fixates the stimulus, the adult says the word "bacon." The child responds to the prompt and is reinforced. The training stimulus is then immediately removed and re-presented at the next trial. In the next step, the prompt is gradually faded (e.g., the adult may present "b" only) the rate of fading being such that it enables the child to emit the correct response and be reinforced. Eventually the prompt is dropped altogether, and the child responds to the presentation of the training stimulus alone (the bacon). Once this is accomplished, a new training stimulus is introduced (maximally different from the first, e.g., a glass of milk). To facilitate the child's attention to the stimuli one might want to initiate the training on food items. In order to insure that the child is in fact responding to the particular objects (training stimuli) involved, previously mastered stimuli are interspersed with new stimuli. It is impossible, then, for the child to respond correctly unless he is attending to the particular object involved. Once the child has mastered discrimination 1, on half a dozen objects, he is introduced to discrimination 2. In discrimination 2 the adult will ask the child to nonverbally identify (e.g., point to) a particular object. Since the child is unlikely to behave correctly on the first presentation of that stimulus (he will not understand the instructions) he is prompted (the adult may manually move the child's hand toward the milk). This prompt is faded in the same manner as during discrimination 1. As soon as this first nonverbal identification is mastered, the child is moved on to identification of the second object, and prompted as in previous stages. These two objects are then intermixed (displayed simultaneously) as during previous training, in order to make certain that the child is in fact attending to, or discriminating, the particular training stimulus. The stimulus might be considered mastered when the child can give a series of consecutive correct responses (e.g., five) to that stimulus when other stimuli are intermixed. Mastered stimuli might be rehearsed on a daily basis in the early stages of training, and less frequently later on.

In order to insure that the child discriminates (attends to) the particular attribute of the object involved, such as that of a table and a chair, and indeed forms concepts at this level, numerous examples of each object are introduced. One can argue that the child has mastered the particular concept involved when he has generalized, i.e., when he gives a correct label, or correctly identifies, members of classes of objects upon their first presentation.

The eleven psychotic children we have seen to date have all acquired this kind of a labeling vocabulary. The children have varied enormously in their rate of acquiring these discriminations, particularly during the early stages of training. The variation extends anywhere from three or four trials, upward to several thousand. The acquisition rates are positively accelerated for each child. It is interesting to note that all the children have generalized, that is, formed concepts, with apparent ease. Once the child can correctly label a chair, as compared to a table, he almost simultaneously can label almost all members of the class of chairs.

The echolalic children pose certain problems not characteristic of the children who have been taught an imitative vocabulary. The echolalic children persist in repeating the instructions given, for example, repeating the instructions "point to the chair." In order to extinguish such inappropriate responses, we have introduced echolalic children to a somewhat separate program during the early stages of language training. Essentially, echolalic or inappropriate repeating of the adult's speech is accompanied by removal of positive reinforcers or presentation of noxious stimuli in a manner analogous to that outlined earlier. Training to extinguish echolalia is illustrated in the following example. As part of training on discrimination 1, the adult may, in addition to presenting an object, ask the child "what is this?" The echolalic child will invariably repeat the question, which the adult accompanies by reinforcement withdrawal. After five seconds of reinforcement withdrawal, the adult will prompt the child by correctly labeling the object, e.g., "chair" and reinforce the child for responding to ("echoing") this prompt. Over successive trials, the echolalic child will inhibit his restatement of the adult's question, while he will respond to the prompt. Once this has been accomplished, the adult may then start to fade the prompt. While presenting the chair, the adult may ask "what is this?" (the child will not respond), and the adult will lead or prompt the response "ch" (and the child will emit "chair"). During the last stage of this training, the adult merely points to the chair and asks the question, at which point the child will give the correct response. Discrimination 3 provides a rather ideal setting for extinguishing echolalia. Here the adult may ask the child "what is your name?", extinguish the echolalic response, prompt the correct response, fade the prompt, and so forth. In cases where the echolalia has been difficult to extinguish by mere withdrawal of positive reinforcers, we have resorted to a loud "no" and, on occasion, a slap on the hand. It is important to note that while this extinction is going on, the child *must* be reinforced positively for correct verbal behavior, and the adult must construct a situation where the child can respond appropriately (such as presenting a prompt). This is needed both to maintain the child's language, as well as to enable him to make the appropriate discriminations as to when he will or will not be reinforced. The extinction of echolalia generalizes; that is, once the echolalia has been extinguished in one context, it is easier to extinguish echolalia in another context. The echolalic children vary enormously in their rate of extinction of echolalic behavior. Some echolalic children will be essentially free of echolalia after one to two months of training, while others may only have extinguished echolalia after a year.

As is the case of all language training, it is crucial that the training be extended beyond the concrete training sessions into a more informal training within the child's day-to-day environment.

Our experience has been that once an adult has acquired mastery over the steps involved in teaching the child a labeling vocabulary, he can use these same principles to teach increasingly complex uses of language. As the training progresses, we have observed, in addition to great variation from one child to another, considerable variation within the child, depending upon the kind of material which forms a basis for the training. Certain kinds of training have proved surprisingly easy. For example, all the children who have been exposed to our reading program have successfully mastered correct identification of a 50 word vocabulary, including phrase reading, within a matter of weeks. Other kinds of training, such as those involved in appropriate response to and use of time concepts, have proved more difficult for the children to master.

Training of Appropriate Use of, and Response to Prepositions, Pronouns, and Other Abstract Terms

The essential paradigm for training such language has already been given above. We will illustrate this step by stating the procedure for establishing response to prepositions and pronouns. Other abstract terms are trained in the same manner. The training can be seen to involve all three discriminations.

Preposition Training. Training may be initiated on the following prepositions: *on top of, under, beside,* and *inside.* These prepositions are used in relationship to objects which the child commonly encounters in his everyday environment. A set of such objects is selected, such as book, pencil, table, shoe, cup, penny, etc. The exact number of objects needed for training the concept (i.e. until the child can respond correctly with these objects) varies from one child to another, and with the preposition involved. Prior to training, the child must correctly label, and nonverbally identify (recognize) these objects (but *not* be able to arrange, or verbally describe, the prepositional aspects involved). That is, he must have mastered the first program (establishing a labeling vocabulary).

Discrimination 1: The child verbally describes a nonverbal arrangement of objects. The adult asks the child (while the penny is inside the box) "where is the penny?" If the child fails to respond or responds incorrectly, the adult prompts the child by saying, "The penny is inside the box." The child might have to be trained to repeat this prompt. The mere repetition of this prompt is rather simple to train.) On succeeding trials of the same question the adult fades the prompt by supplying only those words that the child omits or uses incorrectly until the child's verbal response comes under the control of the nonverbal placement of the objects and the verbal question of the adult. This phase is completed when the child can reliably respond (five consecutive responses) to the question and the placement of the objects, without any prompts from the adult.

Discrimination 2: The adult gives a verbal stimulus (instruction) involving a preposition, and the child must nonverbally arrange the objects according to the instructions. The adult instructs the child, "put the penny inside the box," waits five seconds, and if an incorrect response is forthcoming, repeats the instructions while simultaneously prompting the child (i.e., moving the child's hand, with the penny, inside the box and depositing it). The prompt is gradually faded by the adult removing his hand until the child's response comes under the control of the verbal instruction alone. The phase is completed when the child can reliably respond (five successive correct responses) to the training stimulus (the previously neutral stimulus).

The training of Discrimination 1 and Discrimination 2 is done concurrently, the adult alternating the stimulus for Discrimination 2 ("put the penny inside the box") with the stimulus for Discrimination 1 (a particular arrangement and the question "where is the penny?").

The same procedure is then used in the training of the prepositions *on top of, underneath,* and *beside,* using the same two objects, the penny and the box.

When the child is responding reliably to these eight discriminations (four prepositional relations for each of Discrimination 1 and 2), training begins on generalizing the behavior with these prepositions. Discrimination 1 and 2 are repeated with each preposition using two objects, a pencil and a jar. The child is considered to have generalized, or understood, the prepositions when he can place, and verbalize the placement, of any two new objects on the first five trials without any prompts.

Pronoun Training. The following pronouns may be introduced first: *I-mine, you-yours, he-his.* These pronouns are used in relationship to common behaviors and possessions of the attending adult and the child. The child must be able to correctly label these behaviors and possessions, but be without the appropriate pronoun understanding, as described below in the training. The pronoun training involves two discriminations since there are two forms of the pronoun: (a) the personal (nominative) case, and the (b) possessive (genetive) case.

Discrimination of the personal case: This discrimination involves training in the appropriate use of and response to the personal pronouns "you" and "he" (the attending adults) and "I" (the child). They are trained in conjunction with a large sample of ordinary, day-to-day behaviors (such as standing, sitting, laughing, jumping, clapping hands, etc.). The child must, prior to training, be able to correctly label these behaviors. The discriminations involved include combinations of Discrimination 1 and 2, in the sense that the stimulus situation is a combination of verbal and nonverbal stimuli, while the response of the child is sometimes nonverbal (Discrimination 2), at other times verbal (Discrimination 1). The training proceeds along steps which are very similar to those employed in the training of prepositions.

The attending adult presents the question "what am *I* doing?" while simultaneously pointing his finger at the wall. This stimulus is followed by a five second delay. If no response, or an incorrect response is forthcoming, the teacher repeats the question and immediately gives the prompt "*you* are pointing." (To facilitate the discrimination, the teacher might initially also prompt by pointing to himself. This is facilitative on the assumption that the child more easily discriminates a visual stimulus, such as pointing, than a verbal stimulus, such as a pronoun. If necessary, the child can be pretrained to respond with "you" when the teacher points at himself, and "I" when the teacher points to the child.) The prompt is then gradually removed, until the child's response ("*you* are pointing") is under the control solely of the adult's behavior (pointing) and the question "what am *I* doing?" In the next step the stimulus situation consists of the child pointing (e.g., he is asked or prompted to point), and the adult's question "what are *you* doing?" The correct response "*I* am pointing" is then prompted and faded. The discriminations are interspersed to insure the appropriate discrimination of the pronoun. An additional step involves introduction of a second adult, and the training of appropriate response to the question "what is *he* doing." Additional training, and tests of generalization, are run on new behaviors, such as sitting, standing, etc. Generalization is assumed to exist when the child can use the correct pronoun on five consecutive trials, with behaviors not previously encountered in the discrimination training, while the appropriate pronoun varies from one trial to another.

Discrimination training on the possessive case proceeds along the same lines as those for the personal case. These discriminations are trained in conjunction with parts of the person (nose, ear, eye, hair, etc.) and his personal belongings (shirt, shoe, watch, etc.). For example, the adult touches the child's nose and asks "whose nose is this?" then prompts (*"my* nose"), fades, etc., as before. He may then shift the discrimination, and ask the child "point to *your* nose," prompt, etc., as before. The same criterion for generalization, or understanding, is employed here as held during the discrimination of the personal case.

At this point we have proceeded to train the children on combined usage of personal and possessive pronouns. This training involves all the discriminations given in the training of personal and possessive pronouns. For example, the adult may touch the child's nose and ask "what am *I* doing?" He will prompt the child as in previous trainings (*"you* are touching *my* nose"). In the same manner, the adult may instruct the child to touch his own nose and ask "what are *you* doing?" A third person may be introduced after the two person interaction is mastered. This third person adds five more combinations of personal and possessive pronouns.

During the latter stage of this training, we have combined both pronouns and prepositions. This training has involved all the discriminations mentioned above in the training of pronouns and prepositions. The training emphasizes discriminations where the child has to give a verbal response to a combination of verbal and nonverbal stimuli, but the essential stimulus for correct responding is verbal (the adult's question). Objects are placed in various relationships to other objects in the room. The child is instructed to engage in an action at the same time as the attending adult engages in a different action. Within that stimulus complex the child is asked specific questions involving pronouns and prepositions. For example, "what am *I* doing?" And the correct response may involve *"you* are placing the book *on top of* the table," combining both pronoun and the preposition.

The particular paradigm which has been outlined for establishing an appropriate context of language has been used to teach the acquisition of several abstract terms, such as are involved in color, size, form, place, etc. One of the most important aspects for future use of speech involves the establishment of appropriate use of and response to temporal cues (time). The first step in this particular program has involved the training of correct response to terms such as "after" and "before." The adult may touch object A, then touch object B, and ask the child, "what did I touch *before* I touched B?" The child would then be prompted, the prompt faded, and the stimulus presentation reversed and intermixed in order to make certain that the child was in fact attending to the temporal cues involved. This training was then extended to the child's behavior; for example, the adult would ask the child to stand up, then sit down, and ask, "what did you do *after* you stood up?" The temporal interval between behaviors would then be extended, for example, to going out for a play period, then coming back to the laboratory ("what did you do *before* we came back in?"). In this manner, we can teach the children to describe the weekend experiences, trips to the zoo, etc. The adult may initiate such conversation by asking the child to tell "what did you do this morning?" or "what did you do before you had breakfast?" Three of the psychotic children we have worked with have reached this stage of training, where they can recall, in some detail, weekend activities.

Training of Spontaneous Speech

Although several children had been in the language training program for considerable time, with one or two exceptions, they rarely volunteered to speak. They seemed over-trained since they responded only to specific cues given by the attending adults. It was this problem which prompted us to consider training spontaneous and conversational speech.

It is apparent that the establishment of spontaneous and conversational speech would be the most significant and useful training program for the children as well as the adults in their environment. Normally, through appropriate conversation, a person exchanges information with others, and thus establishes and maintains interpersonal relationships. By speaking, he can express wants and seek information, thereby controlling his environment, and he can express his feelings and verbalize other types of information, thereby enriching the environment of others.

Briefly, we have proceeded in the training of spontaneous and conversational speech in much the same manner as we have trained other behaviors; but the emphasis has been on bringing the child's verbal behavior under the control of an increasingly large array of stimuli which often can only be inferred *ad hoc*. These comprise those stimuli which the child encounters in his day to day environment, rather than in the training sessions. The training falls within two somewhat overlapping phases: the establishment of demands, and the development of comments and stories, which include recall.

The development of demands consisted simply of prompting the desired response than fading the prompt, and finally "waiting the child out." The child received no rewards unless he asked for them, although in the initial phases we helped him as much as possible in formulating the correct requests. Once the child could label an object or behavior we most often would withhold that object, or prevent the behavior, unless he verbalized his wants. For example, once he could label "milk," he would receive milk only after emitting "milk." Similarly, if he wanted to go outside, he would be able to do so only after he verbalized "out." We would extend this request by adding, in step by step fashion, additional words to form sentences (such as "want out," then "I want out," and finally "I want to go out"). While the adult may prompt this response initially, for example, state "out" as the child was standing in front of the door, he gradually would remove such prompts until the sight of the door alone was sufficient to elicit the behavior. (The adult would also prompt the building of sentences, such as prompting "want out", next giving "want . . ." for the child to give the complete "want out," and finally withholding all prompts). Similarly, should the child make a request, the adults would immediately fulfill that request. The child would be trained to give the adult orders ("clap your hands," "sit down," etc.), which invariably became very reinforcing for the child, generating considerable spontaneity. As the child acquired mastery of this kind of speech, the criterion for delivery of rewards was gradually increased, in such a manner that the rewards would either be postponed ("we go outside *after* you have finished your work") or withheld contingent upon more elaborate requests.

We used the same paradigm in teaching the child to ask questions, and information seeking behavior in general. For example, the adult would select an object and ask the child what color it was. Once the child had responded correctly, he was prompted to ask the adult the identical questions ("Say: 'What color is it?' "). Finally, prompts were faded altogether, the adult merely told the child to "ask me some questions." Eventually, these questions might pertain to what the adult was wearing, what he was feeling, and rather elaborate situations. Informal observations suggest that at this level of speech, the children received a considerable degree of reward from the use of speech, and would frequently be "insatiable" in their questions. It is also at these stages that the child begins to evidence a real "feel" for speech.

To further increase their speech, we have asked the children to tell about a broad topic, such as a picture of a social interaction (e.g., child and mother). The questions and prompts needed to establish such behavior are virtually limitless ("who is this?" — "Mommy"; "what is she doing?" — "giving the baby some food," etc.). The children who have reached this stage can give rather elaborate stories.

One of the most important aspects of spontaneous speech, or conversation, involves recalling past events. Environmental cues function as stimuli which mediate associations of past experiences, and this interaction between past and present facilitates conversation. People converse, to some extent, because they have common elements in their past experiences. The training program on the discrimination of temporal cues leads directly into conversation. For example, the adult who took the child to the zoo has something to talk about with that child. Obviously, the child must already have mastered time concepts in order to converse at this level.

At this stage of training, the program becomes very elaborate. In general, the teacher who has reached this level of proficiency in the training of speech (and extensive familiarity with the child's language strengths and weaknesses) can readily engineer rather elaborate situations which serve to further broaden the child's speech. An example of such extensions can be given in a recent commonsensical step. When the children ask questions, the attending adult may reply: "I don't know," and then prompt, and later fade: "go ask someone else." Such steps enable the child to verbally interact with as many people as possible.

The data reflect enormous differences in the rate at which the children master the more abstract language and the conversational-spontaneous use of speech. The previously mute children, even after one and one-half years of intensive training have barely mastered correct usage of pronouns and prepositions. Because of such slow development, we have been unable to initiate programs for teaching time to these children. Their spontaneous speech is very restricted, and involves primarily the use of demands (for toys, play, food, etc.). Their sentence structure rarely goes beyond five or six words. The previously echolalic children have progressed at a much faster rate. One of these children, even after a very short training (three hours a week for eight months supplemented by informal teaching by his parents), can carry out meaningful and spontaneous conversations, using language correctly, which often involves rather sophisticated use of abstract terminology.

It is apparent that we receive elaborations on the children's language which we did not place there by design. One of the best examples of this is given in Ricky's comment on growth. After about one year of intensive language training, Ricky was taught the concept of size, and in training this we talked about all kinds of small and large things, including large and small boys, and large and small plants. In describing to Ricky (a small boy) that small plants grow up to become big plants, by putting water on them, Ricky reflected for a moment, then said: "Put some water on my head." No doubt, the children contribute much of their own to the training program, and we observe distinctively human behavior. We mention this because one of the objections to a program, such as the one outlined above, is that it will generate "trained seal" or robot-like qualities. Other organisms, such as seals, would behave like seals and fail miserably in our program.

Comments

This paper provides only an outline of the language acquisition training program for psychotic children. The reader who wants additional information about this program should consult the more detailed presentations given elsewhere, i.e., establishment of a labeling vocabulary (15), preposition and pronoun training (16), and establishment of spontaneous and conversational speech (5). Smith, Kline, and French (22), has produced a film which covers part of this program, and may be helpful in further illustrating the steps. The studies of Risley (19) provide a particularly detailed presentation of a program which is similar to the one described here. Similarly, Hewett (9), provides information about a language program originating from reinforcement theory.

Obviously, this program is new and leaves much room for improvement. We made a number of decisions which might have been far from optimal. For example, we were under great pressure to investigate whether the children could, in fact, be taught imitative speech or the understanding and use of abstract language. It might be more therapeutic to proceed at a less demanding rate and in a more playful manner. It also might be beneficial to terminate the intensive training of imitative speech after the child has mastered two or three words, and allow the child to immediately experience considerable control over his environment with only a restricted vocabulary. This would be more similar to the speech development in normal children. The program has been largely worked out with severely psychotic children. For example, in our initial work we dealt with children who had experienced several years of psychodynamically oriented treatment, without improvement, or children who had been rejected from treatment because of the severity of their psychosis. In our recent work, with less psychotic children, we have been able to circumvent some of the steps outlined above. For example, in working with a child who had some imitative speech (he occasionally was overheard to clearly enunciate certain words, but never gave these words on request), the program was considerably altered. We have frequently used noxious stimuli, such as a slap on the hand, to extinguish certain behaviors which interfered with the teaching situation, and which were resistant to extinction when positive reinforcement was withdrawn. On the other hand, we have progressed with some children without the use of aversive stimuli, because such stimuli interfered with that particular child's performance. It is probably of most value to approach the children in an individual, empirical manner, while allowing the program to provide guidelines only. Our experience has been that autistic and schizophrenic children form a very heterogeneous population, and that the diagnosis is a poor discriminator.

The program differs considerably from psychodynamically oriented attempts to facilitate communication in the psychotic child. For example, we have purposefully avoided all attempts to respond to, or otherwise "understand," the child on the basis of his psychotic verbal or nonverbal communications. Preliminary data from our laboratory indicate that attempts to respond to psychotic communications strengthen such behavior, and therefore may prolong the psychotic condition, e.g., Lovaas et al. (13). The child has had to learn to cope with reality at the level where we present it to him, rather than as determined by him. We place immediate demands on the child, and we allow the child to assume control only after he has mastered the basic format for acceptable social intercourse. Our data indicate also that relationship variables, which are central to psychodynamic treatment, can work to the child's disadvantage if prescribed in orthodox form. For example, when we shift to an *ad lib* presentation of gratifications (meeting the child's needs, independent of the adequacy of his behaviors) we observe a deterioration in his behavior. No doubt, very different data would be observed if one had worked with children who were not psychotic, for example, children characterized by anxiety neurosis. In such children love *ad lib* might be the only milieu which allows for improvement. Finally, we have refrained from employing hypothetical inner determinants (such as "impermeable autistic barriers" based on early traumatic experiences). We have neglected these for *methodological* reasons, since it has proven difficult to reject statements which contain such constructs. Therefore, procedures for treatment which originate within such conceptualizations are resistant to change, and do not allow for flexibility in exploring new methods. The differences in approach outlined above are based on conceptual considerations. There is a dearth of information describing the empirical steps involved in psychodynamically oriented treatment. Furthermore, the translation of psychodynamic theory to empirical operations is very obscure. Therefore, some of the differences may appear upon closer examination to be more apparent than real.

The program has extensive similarities to teaching techniques developed by educators. For example, it is virtually identical to the principles involved in programmed learning (teaching machines), which rely on prompts, step-by-step procedures determined by the child's speed in acquisition, immediate reinforcement, and so on. The program has extensive similarities to the one described by Ann Sullivan for the education of Helen Keller (12). Most educators, however, object to the use of primary reinforcers. Without primary reinforcers, the program would not work with many psychotic children. In this connection, it is important to point out that we have been able to shift from primary to secondary reinforcers after two or three months of training. Early shifts, such as might be attempted during the first days of training, are invariably accompanied by substantial deterioration in performance, necessitating the reinstatement of primary reinforcers. A skillful educator should be able to add considerably to a program such as the one outlined above. For example, teachers have considerable familiarity with all the nuances of reinforcers which serve to motivate children.

In addition to the choice of powerful reinforcers, it is crucial that the program proceed in a step-by-step manner, starting at a level where the child can be successful. There have been occasions when professional people, after a brief visit on this or similar projects, have felt encouraged to place more demands on their patients. Consequently, the child's food, or other gratifications, have been withheld contingent upon some arbitrarily chosen verbalization, such as "food." Often this step has been accompanied by some conceptualization, such as "in order for the child to cathect other human beings, the child should become helplessly dependent upon a ministering agent." The results of such efforts might be catastrophic, where the child experiences great agony because he does not have such a response in his repertoire. Or, it might produce a stereotyped, frequently occurring response, such as "food," for the child who was fortunate enough to have such behavior available. The conceptualization ("object cathexis") illustrates well that some people choose to refer their interventions to a level beyond behavior. We would propose that central, organizing, behavior-initiating constructs, such as cathexis, may not provide an easy out for the work which the therapist or teacher will have facing him when he attempts to establish speech in psychotic children. Programs designed to establish language may require more than occasional visits to the therapist in order to work. There might even be an advantage in dealing directly with behavior, rather than concentrating on hypothetical inner determinants. If one concentrates on behavior, as a subject matter in its own right, then one is unlikely to make mistakes which involve too unrealistic demands on the patient, or unrealistic hopes for the family.

One of the disadvantages of the program, as it now stands, lies in the large amount of time which is consumed in accomplishing its ends. It is fortunate, therefore, that the procedures can be easily communicated to parents and others who are emotionally committed to the child, and have the patience needed to carry them out. In carrying the program out in the day-to-day functioning of the child, one also assures oneself of maximal transfer and learning within that environment where the child will benefit most from acquisitions in speech.

Another major weakness of the program lies in its failure to specify the contents, and not just the format or process, of the training. While this might not be a problem in the teaching of prepositions, color, and so on, it should become an important variable during the teaching of reading (to facilitate meaning), and particularly important for the facilitation of conversational speech.

Summary

This paper has provided an outline of a program developed for the establishment of speech in autistic and schizophrenic children. The program is based on a learning (reinforcement) theory paradigm. It relies heavily on a step-by-step, graduated progression of tasks, stimulus fading techniques, positive reinforcement delivery contingent upon correct behavior and positive reinforcement withdrawal contingent upon incorrect behavior. The procedures are analogous to those which form the basis of programmed learning.

The program is divided in two parts. The first part outlines a procedure for the establishment of imitative speech in mute children. The second part gives a series of operations designed to establish appropriate use of, and response to, an elementary labeling vocabulary, more abstract terms as are involved in prepositions and pronouns, and finally conversational and spontaneous speech.

The data show that previously mute, socially unresponsive, nonimitating children can be taught imitative speech and the use of such speech for the labeling of rather concrete environmental events and the expression of simple demands. The program to date has failed to establish conversational speech in such children. Previously echolalic children have mastered more elaborate speech, including conversational speech involving the use of abstract terminology.

REFERENCES

1. Ayllon, T., and N. H. Azrin, "The Measurement and Reinforcement of Behavior of Psychotics," *J. exp. anal. of Behav.*, 1965, 8, 357–383.

2. Bensberg, G. J., C. N. Colwell, and R. H. Cassel, "Teaching the Profoundly Retarded Selp-Help Activities by Shaping Techniques," *Amer. J. of Mental Deficiency*, 1965, 69, 674–679.

3. Birnbrauer, J. S., S. W. Bijou, M. M. Wolf, and J. D. Kidder, "Programmed Instruction in the Classroom." In L. Ullmann and L. Krasner (Eds.), *Case Studies in Behavior Modification*. New York: Holt, Rinehart and Winston, 1965.

4. Brown, Janet, "Prognosis from Presenting Symptoms of Pre-School Children with Atypical Development," *Amer. J. Orthopsychiat.*, 1960, 30, 382–390.

5. Dumont, Diane A., Gail Klynn, O. I. Lovaas, and Joan Meisel, "Establishment of Spontaneous and Conversational Speech in Schizophrenic Children. Working paper no. 3.

6. Ferster, C. B., "Positive Reinforcement and Behavioral Deficits of Autistic Children," *Child Developm.*, 1961, 32, 437–456.

7. Goldiamond, I., "Stuttering and Fluency as Manipulatable Operant Response Classes." In L. Krasner and L. Ullmann (Eds.), *Research in Behavior Modification*. New York: Holt, Rinehart and Winston, 1965, 106–156 (Chapter 17 in this book).

8. Hayes, C., *The Ape in Our House*. New York: Harper & Row, 1951.

9. Hewett, P. M., "Teaching Speech to an Autistic Child through Operant Conditioning," *Amer. J. Orthopsychiat.*, 1965, 35, 927–936.

10. Isaacs, W., J. Thomas, and I. Goldiamond, "Application of Operant Conditioning to Reinstate Verbal Behavior in Psychotics," *J. Speech Hearing Dis.*, 1960, 25, 8–15.

11. Keller, F. S., *Learning: Reinforcement Theory*. New York: Random House, 1954.

12. Keller, Helen, *The Story of My Life*. Garden City, N.Y.: Doubleday, 1925.

13. Lovaas, O. I., G. Freitag, Vivian J. Gold, and Irene C. Kassorla, "Experimental Studies in Childhood Schizophrenia: Analysis of Self-Destructive Behavior," *J. exp. Child Psychol.*, 1965, 2, 67–84.

14. Lovaas, O. I., J. P. Berberich, B. F., Perloff, and B. Schaeffer, "Acquisition of Imitative Speech in Schizophrenic Children," *Science*, February, 1966.

15. Lovaas, O. I., J. P. Berberich, Irene C. Kassorla, Gail A. Klynn, and Joan Meisel, "Establishment of a Texting and Labeling Vocabulary in Schizophrenic Children." Working paper no. 1.

16. Lovaas, O. I., Diane A. Dumont, Gail A. Klynn, and Joan Meisel, "Establishment of Appropriate Response to, and Use of, Certain

Prepositions and Pronouns in Schizophrenic Children." Working paper no. 2.

17. Parsley, N. B., and J. W. Hamilton, "The Development of a Comprehensive Cottage-Life Program," *Mental Retardation*, 1965, 3, 25–29.

18. Rimland, Bernard, *Infantile Autism*. New York: Appleton-Century-Crofts, 1964.

19. Risley, T. R., "The establishment of verbal behavior in deviant children." Ph.D. dissertation. University of Washington, Seattle, Washington, 1966.

20. Schwitzgebel, R., and D. A. Kolb, "Inducing Behavior Change in Adolescent Delinquents," *Behav. Res. Ther.* 1964, 1, 297–304.

21. Sherman, J. A., "Use of Reinforcement and Imitation to Reinstated Verbal Behavior in Mute Psychotics," *J. abnorm. Psychol.*, 1965, 70, 155–164.

22. Smith, Kline, and French Laboratories, Philadelphia, Pa., *Reinforcement Therapy*. Film. 1966.

23. Violet Project, Austin State School, Austin, Texas. "Personal Communication," 1965.

24. Wolf, M. M., T. Risley, and H. Mees, "Application of Operant Conditioning Procedures to the Behaviour Problems of an Autistic Child," *Behav. Res. Ther.*, 1964, 1, 305–312.

Echolalic Speech

In Part 2 overall programs for working with severely impaired children were discussed. As Lovaas pointed out, there are many reasons why it is easier to develop functional speech in an echolalic child than in a nonvocal or speech-free child. However, echolalic speech presents some specific problems that have not received wide attention in professional publications. These involve shifting the stimulus control of verbal behavior from echoic variables to non-echoic variables. Problems arise since most training procedures utilize imitative behavior, and thus tend to reinforce echolalic speech patterns. Most persons who have worked with echolalic individuals are familiar with the common occurrence in which the echolalic child or adult responds to an instruction by repeating the instruction along with the desired response. Thus echolalic children, when instructed to "say dog" say, "say dog." In the paper by Risley and Wolf, procedures for developing tacting, manding and intraverbal behavior from echolalic speech are described, as well as methods for reducing excessive echoic control. Heavy emphasis is placed upon the gradual shifting of stimulus control of speech from echoic to nonechoic variables by slowly fading out certain discriminative stimuli while others are faded in. Although there is no data other than anecdotal data to indicate how infants typically learn to tact, mand, and emit intraverbal responses, it appears that the same procedure occurs informally which Risley and Wolf are explicitly programming. Initial verbal behavior in the child is probably imitative (echoic), and echoic control is gradually faded as other forms of control develop. Although the editors believe that the point of view that states that remedial procedures should recapitulate typical ontogenetic development is without basis, it is interesting to note that in studying the atypical individual suggestions often arise about normal development. As Peterson indicates, it is by studying children who lack imitative repertoires that we learn about the variables that lead to the development of imitative behavior.

Johnston pursues some additional problems that often arise with echolalic individuals. Even when echolalic speech is greatly reduced, the verbal behavior of such individuals often appears to be under extremely restricted stimulus control — though speech is nonecholalic, it also appears to be nonspontaneous. On analysis, this often seems to be due to the fact that a limited range of specific discriminative stimuli are always followed by specific responses, as if the verbal repertoire of the individual were comprised of a certain number of particular "recordings," each of which is rotely emitted if, and only if, the correct "button" is pushed. In typical speech such "automatism" is not apparent. Control generalizes to a wide range of stimuli similar in some concrete or abstract way to the stimuli to which particular responses have been learned, and sub-units of responses appear to come under independent control and thus get chained in many different sequences. In the chapter by Johnston procedures for training this "flexibility" are discussed.

8

Todd Risley

Montrose Wolf

Establishing Functional Speech in Echolalic Children

Appropriate verbal behavior is the most important aspect of a normal child's repertoire. Verbal skills are a prerequisite for a large share of a child's social and academic education as well as being instrumental in a great deal of his day-by-day activities. Without verbal skills a child is foredoomed to "developmental retardation" no matter what other advantages may accrue to him.

This paper is a summary of research by the authors in the development of speech in echolalic children. The procedures are based on operant behavior modification techniques such as: (1) *shaping* and *imitation training* for the development of speech; (2) *fading in* of new stimuli and *fading out* of verbal prompts to transfer the speech from imitative control to control by appropriate stimulus conditions; and (3) *extinction* and *time-out from reinforcement* for the reduction of inappropriate behavior in conjunction with the *differential reinforcement* of appropriate responses which are incompatible with the inappropriate behavior.

This work was partially supported by PHS grant HD 00870–04 and OEO contract KAN CAP 670694/1 to the Bureau of Child Research, University of Kansas. We are indebted to Stephanie Stolz, Nancy Reynolds and Betty Hart for critical readings of the manuscript.

Echolalia

". . . autistic children usually do learn to talk, sometimes very well, but their speech fails to follow the normal patterns. Often prominent in their speech is a compulsive parroting of what they hear, called echolalia. They pick up a phrase, a name, a snatch of song, or even a long verse, and repeat it endlessly" (*Stone and Church, 1957*).

The sporadic and usually inappropriate imitation of words, phrases and snatches of song, is observed in many deviant children. Although this behavior pattern is generally associated with the diagnosis of emotional disturbance or autism, it is also a frequently observed behavior pattern of children diagnosed as retarded or brain-damaged. The procedures described in this paper have been developed from work with echolalic children with almost every conceivable diagnosis. Indeed, the records of each of these children usually contained diagnoses of retardation and brain damage as well as autism, each label applied to the same child by a different diagnostician. For our procedures, the diagnostic classification of the child is largely irrelevant. The presence or absence of echolalia is the important predictor of the ease of establishing more normal speech in a deviant child.

In alleviating any deficit in behavior, the most time-consuming task is the teaching of new topographies of behavior. When a child's repertoire does not include a particular behavior and the child cannot be taught by conventional means, training can be carried out by the behavior modification technique called *shaping*. This procedure involves the long and intricate process of reinforcing behaviors which resemble (although, perhaps, only remotely) the desired terminal behavior, and then, in successive steps, shifting the reinforcement to behaviors which more and more closely resemble the terminal behavior. When the terminal response is obtained, the response can then be shifted to imitative control by *imitation training*.

Imitation training involves reinforcing a response made by the child only when it immediately follows the same response made by the therapist. The child's response may already have existed in his echolalic repertoire or it may have been shaped into a high probability response. The therapist can shift the response to imitative control by reinforcing it when it occurs after the presentation of an identical modeled stimulus or *prompt*. In this manner large units of previously randomly occurring behavior can be brought under imitative control. Once a child accurately imitates most words, phrases, and sentences, then any topography of verbal behavior (i.e., any word, phrase, or sentence) can be produced when desired by presenting the child with the prompt to be imitated.

Echolalia, then, is of significance to the therapist, for, since the echolalic child already has verbal responses, the arduous task of shaping them is unnecessary. Once the child's responses are brought under imitative control, so that, for example, he says, "That's a cow" when the therapist has just said, "That's a cow," the only remaining step is to shift the control of his responses to the appropriate stimuli, so that, for example, he says "That's a cow" to a picture of a cow. This shift to naming is made by *fading out* the imitative prompt in gradual steps, as described in detail below. In this manner the responses acquire their appropriate "meanings." Thus, the procedures for establishing functional speech in echolalic children are relatively simple and produce appropriate speech rapidly, in contrast to the procedures which have been used in establishing speech in non-echolalic, speech-deficient children (e.g., Lovaas, 1966; Risley, 1966).

General Procedures

The authors developed the procedures summarized in this paper while working with children with echolalic speech. The general methodology was initially developed in the course of dealing with the behavior problems of an autistic child named Dicky (*Wolf, Risley, and Mees, 1964*). We will review his case before describing the more refined procedures which evolved from it.

Our contact with Dicky began four years ago when he was three and a half years old. He had been diagnosed as autistic and had been institutionalized previously for a three-month period. Prior to this he had been diagnosed variously as psychotic, mentally retarded, and brain-damaged. Dicky had a variety of severe problem behaviors, and lacked almost all normal social and verbal behavior. His verbal repertoire was quite bizarre though not atypical of children diagnosed as autistic. He was echolalic, occasionally exactly mimicking in form and intonation bits of conversation of the staff. He sang songs — "Chicago," for example. He emitted a variety of phrases during tantrums, such as "Want a spanking," and "Want to go bye-bye," but none of his verbal behavior was socially appropriate. He never made requests, asked questions, or made comments. Although he mimicked occasionally, he would not mimic when asked to do so.

Our training began with the attendant presenting, one at a time, five pictures approximately 3 inches by 4 inches in size, of a Santa Claus, a cat, etc. The attendant would prompt, for example, "This is a cat. Now say cat." After she had gone through all five pictures, she would mix their order and go through them again. Just as Dicky occasionally mimicked the speech of other people, he would occasionally mimic the attendant by saying "This is a cat," or "Now say cat." On those occasions the attendant would say, "Good boy" or "That's right," and give him a bite of his meal. As a result Dicky began mimicking more frequently, until after about a week he was mimicking practically every prompt, in addition to almost everything else the attendant said during the session.

However, during this time Dicky was not looking particularly closely at the pictures. Instead, he twisted and turned in his seat. So an *anticipation procedure* was introduced, where anticipating the correct response would result in a reinforcer sooner than if he waited for the prompt. The attendant would present the picture for a period of several seconds before giving the prompt. Gradually, Dicky began looking at the pictures and saying the phrases in the presence of the pictures without the prompts. In three weeks he did this in the presence of about ten pictures. We then introduced picture books and common household objects which he learned with increasing ease. At the same time temporally remote events were taught in the following manner. Dicky would be taken outside and swung or allowed to slide and then brought back inside and asked: "What did you do outside?" and then after a few seconds given a prompt. Imitations and finally the correct answers were followed by a reinforcer.

He was taught the answers to other questions such as "What is you name?" and "Where do you live?" The question would be asked and, if after a pause he had not answered, the prompt would be given and the correct response reinforced.

After several weeks of training Dicky's verbal repertoire was markedly expanded, although he still had several verbal anomalies, such as imitating the question before answering and reversing his pronouns, e.g., he would ask for a drink by saying, "You want some water." Dicky was released from the hospital seven months after our contact began. The training was continued by his parents, and after about six months he was using pronouns appropriately and was initiating many requests and comments, although he still was making frequent inappropriate imitating responses. After attending the Laboratory Preschool at the University of Washington for two years, his verbal skills had developed to the point that he was ready for special education in the public school.

Dicky's verbal behavior now resembles that of a skilled five-year-old. This means that since his operant training his rate of language development has been approximately normal. This probably has been the result of the diligent efforts of his parents and teachers to provide an environment that reinforced his verbal behavior.[1] However, now the naturally occurring rewards of verbal behavior (see *Skinner, 1957*, for a discussion of these) appear to be the most important factors in maintaining and expanding his verbal repertoire.

These procedures for developing speech were subsequently refined in the course of working with the following echolalic children:

Pat was a blind 12-year-old boy who had been recently institutionalized with the diagnosis of childhood autism. He had previously been enrolled in a school for the blind, but had been dropped from the program due to his disruptive behaviors and general lack of progress.

Billy was a 10-year-old boy who had been institutionalized for several years with the diagnosis of childhood autism.

Carey was a seven-year-old boy who lived at home although he had been diagnosed variously as autistic, retarded, and brain-damaged, and institutionalization had been recommended. He had attended a day school for special children during the previous two years, but had been dropped due to a general lack of progress.

Will was an eight-year-old boy who had been institutionalized for two years with the diagnosis of severe retardation and brain damage. He was not considered to be trainable and had been placed on a custodial ward.

The Physical Arrangement. To work most efficiently with a deviant child, particularly one with disruptive behaviors, the speech training should be carried out in a room containing as few distractions as

---

[1] The teachers who played particularly important roles in Dicky's speech development were Florence Harris, Margaret Johnston, Eileen Allen, Nancy Reynolds, and Thelma Turbitt.

possible. In our training room, we usually have only chairs for the child and teacher, a desk or table between them, and a small table or chair next to the teacher on which to place the food tray. Such an arrangement is shown in Figure 1.

In a room where the child may reach for, throw, or destroy many items, turn on and off light switches, and climb on furniture, the therapist may inadvertently train the child to engage in these behaviors, since they must be attended to by the therapist. For some

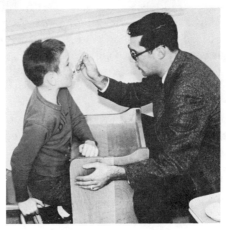

FIGURE 1

These three pictures illustrate the physical arrangement of the therapy room, and the method of presenting the food reinforcers.

children with high rates of tantrums and disruptive behavior, the rooms have been entirely cleared except for the chairs and tables that have been secured to the floor.

The Reinforcer. Certain consequences of a behavior will increase the frequency of that behavior. These consequences, which are technically termed "reinforcers," are usually events that are commonly described as important, significant, or meaningful for the particular child. With normal children, attention and praise can be used as consequences to strengthen behavior (*Harris et al., 1964*). Such sophisticated social consequences often are only weak positive reinforcers for a severely abnormal child. For this reason food must often be relied upon as a reinforcing consequence for modifying speech and other behaviors of deviant children.

The ideal food reinforcer is one that the child particularly "likes," many bites of which can be eaten, and that cannot be readily "played with." We have found that the food reinforcer that best satisfies these criteria is ice cream or sherbet. It is generally a favorite food of children, it can be eaten in quantity, and it disappears rapidly from the mouth. Many other foods have been used, such as sugar coated cereals (Captain Crunch, Fruit Loops), TV dinners, peanut butter sandwiches, and regular meals. Bites of food are given to a child on a spoon or fork. Each bite is small, which allows large numbers of responses to be reinforced before the child becomes satiated.

A small portion of the food (e.g., ¼ teaspoon of ice cream) is placed on the spoon (Figure 1a). The spoon is held directly in front of the therapist's face. As a child will tend to look at the food, this procedure insures that he will be looking toward the therapist's face. The therapist then waits until the child's glance shifts from the spoon to his face and reinforces this by quickly presenting the stimulus for the child to imitate (Figure 1b). As the sessions progress, a child will tend to look at the food less and at the therapist's face more, and the position of the spoon can then gradually be varied to suit the convenience of the therapist. The same procedure is used later in the program to train a child to attend to pictures or objects, except that in that case the spoon is held behind the items.

When the child responds appropriately, the therapist *immediately* says, "Good," or "That's right," while extending the spoon of food to the child. This verbal statement serves to bridge the time between the appropriate response and the presentation of the food, and makes the reinforcement contingencies more precise. To save time, the food on the spoon is placed directly in the child's mouth by the therapist (Figure 1c).

The effectiveness of the food reinforcer can be increased by mild food deprivation of about half a day. For example, when training sessions are held around noon, the mother or institutional staff are told to provide the child with only a very light breakfast, such as a glass of juice and a vitamin pill. Similar instructions involving lunch are given for sessions later in the day.

For the most rapid and significant changes in deviant children, the necessity of using powerful extrinsic reinforcers, made more effective by sufficient deprivation, *cannot be overemphasized.* (Examples showing the importance of the food reinforcers in the treatment of two children will be presented later.)

The Elimination of Disruptive Behaviors. Most deviant children exhibit behaviors that are incompatible with the behaviors involved in speech training. With echolalic children the most usual disruptive behaviors are repetitive chanting of songs or TV commercials, inappropriate imitation of the experimenter's comments, and, frequently, temper tantrums whenever the reinforcer is withheld. The frequency of these behaviors must be reduced before notable progress can be made in establishing functional speech. Systematic extinction procedures, in conjunction with reinforcement of appropriate responses incompatible with the disruptive behaviors, have usually been sufficient to eliminate these behaviors.

Mild disruptive behaviors in the therapy situation (such as leaving the chair, autistic mannerisms, mild temper tantrums, repetitive chanting, or inappropriate imitation) can usually be eliminated by removing all possible positive reinforcers for these behaviors. Once the child spends at least some of the session sitting quietly in the chair and has come into contact with the reinforcers, the experimenter should simply look away from the child whenever mild disruptive behaviors occur (Figure 2). When the child is again sitting silently in his chair, the experimenter reinforces this by attending to him and proceeding with the session. (This procedure is technically termed *time out from positive reinforcement.*)

The temper tantrums of a child (Carey) were eliminated as a consequence of these procedures (Figure 3). The duration of cry-

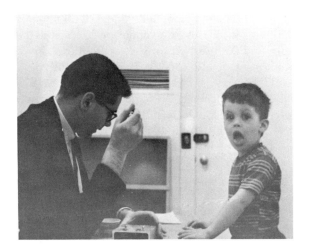

An illustration of a therapist extinguishing disruptive behavior by looking away from a child contingent upon disruptive behavior.

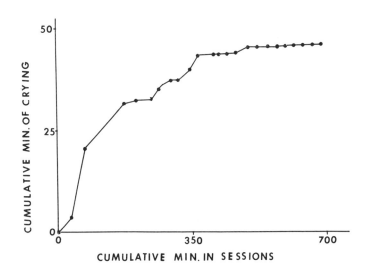

FIGURE 3

The elimination of temper tantrums (crying) of Carey. (Each dot represents the end of session).

ing systematically declined from an average of 16 minutes per hour in the first three sessions to an average of 20 seconds per hour in the 24th, 25th and 26th sessions of these conditions.

The procedures were also effective in reducing the frequency with which a child (Carey) inappropriately imitated and repeatedly chanted the verbal statement, "Very good," which accompanied the food reinforcer (Figure 4). During the four sessions in which this behavior was recorded, the rate declined from 3.4 per minute to .12 per minute. By the eighth session this behavior was almost totally absent.

Where disruptive behaviors are at high strength or experimental conditions are such that these behaviors are inadvertently reinforced, a more rigorous time-out procedure may be necessary. This involves both extinction of the undesirable behavior and the re-

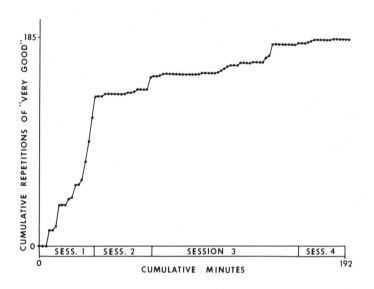

FIGURE 4

The elimination of Carey's inappropriate repetitions of the statement "very good," which accompanied the food reinforcer. Whenever the child would say, "Very good," the therapist would look away for approximately five seconds. Each dot corresponds to two minutes of session time.

moval, for a period of time, of the possibility of *any* behavior's being reinforced. Whenever an instance of disruptive behavior occurs, either the therapist leaves the room (with the food tray), or the child is removed to an adjacent room. The therapist re-enters or the child is allowed back in the therapy room only after both: (1) a set time period has elapsed (e.g., 10 minutes) and (2) the child has not engaged in the disruptive behavior for a short period of time (e.g., 30 seconds). Dicky's severe temper tantrums accompanied by self-destructive behaviors were eliminated by this procedure (Figure 5). The severity of the tantrums, which necessitated their rapid elimination, also made the tantrums difficult for observers to ignore. It appeared highly likely that the attendants who were working with the child, while attempting to simply ignore (extinguish) the tantrums, would feel compelled to "stop the child from hurting himself" whenever the self-destructive behaviors became severe. If this had occurred, they would have been, in effect, differentially reinforcing the more extreme forms of self-destructive behaviors, thereby increasing the problem.

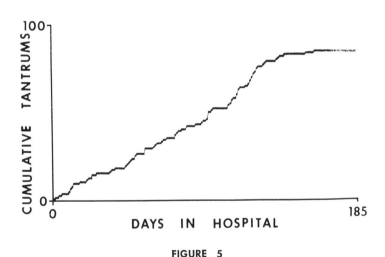

FIGURE 5

The elimination of Dicky's temper tantrums. The child was isolated in his room for 10 minutes contingent upon each tantrum, after which time he was allowed to leave the room following 30 seconds of silence. Each dot represents one day.

To avoid this, the child was isolated in a room whenever temper tantrums occurred. This *time-out* procedure resulted in a gradual decline in the severity of the tantrums (which is not reflected in Figure 5, as only the frequency of tantrums was recorded), and finally a complete cessation of tantrums.

The effectiveness of either of these procedures is dependent upon the strength of the positive reinforcer that is being withheld. This is another important reason for using the strongest reinforcers possible. When only weak positive reinforcers (such as M & M's with a non-food-deprived child) are used, not only will the progress in speech be slow, but disruptive behaviors will be persistent.

The Establishment of Control over Imitation. Although echolalic children do imitate words and phrases, usually this imitation is sporadic and cannot be consistently evoked. Imitation must reliably occur immediately after a word or phrase prompt is presented before significant advances in speech can be made.

Reliable and immediate imitation can be obtained by systematic reinforcement of imitation. The therapist presents a given word over four to five seconds. Whenever the child says this word he is reinforced. Initially the probability of imitation can be somewhat increased by varying the intonation, pitch, level and loudness of the word presented; however, this procedure should be deleted as soon as the child is reliably repeating the word.

Systematically reinforcing an imitated word will increase the frequency with which the child imitates that word, but it may also increase the frequency of nonimitative repetitions of the word. Other verbal utterances such as phrases or snatches of song may also increase and should be extinguished. The therapist should wait until the child is silent before again presenting the word to be imitated. In this manner only *imitation* is being reinforced.

When the child is frequently imitating the word (five to six times per minute), extraneous behaviors should be extinguished and attending to the therapist reinforced by presenting the word to be imitated only when the child is sitting quietly, looking at the therapist. As the probability of immediate imitation is greater when the child is looking at the therapist, this procedure, which increases the proportion of attending, increases the number of immediate imitations.

When the child is reliably and immediately imitating the first word, a new word is introduced, and the above procedure is repeated. The two words are then alternately presented. When the child is reliably imitating both words, new words are presented, interspersed with the two original words. Usually by the second or third word, a general imitative response class will have been established; the child will then reliably and immediately imitate any new word.

Figure 6 shows the establishment of control over a child's (Carey's) imitation. From the start of session 2 the word "train" was repeated

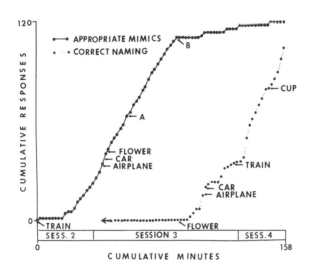

FIGURE 6

A record of the initial rate of appropriate imitations (mimics) and correct naming of objects by Carey (see text). Each dot represents two minutes of session time.

by the experimenter. The child imitated this word once early in the session, and was reinforced. Sixteen minutes later, during which time he was intermittently tantruming, he again imitated "train" and was reinforced. After this the rate of imitating the word rapidly increased. Three other words, "flower," "car," and "airplane," were then introduced, and the child imitated each of them on the *first* presentation as well as on each subsequent presentation. Thus, in approximately 30 minutes, control was established over the child's imitative speech.

The Transition from Imitation to Naming. Naming involves the emission of the appropriate verbal response in the presence of some stimulus object. After imitative responses occur with high probability and short latency following each verbal prompt, stimulus control is shifted from the verbal prompts (imitation) to appropriate objects and pictures (naming).

Once reinforcement for imitation has produced a high probability of successful imitation of the verbal prompt alone, a picture or object is presented together with the verbal prompt, and the child is reinforced for imitating the name. Then the imitative prompt is faded out, while the child continues to receive reinforcement for saying the object's name.

The therapist holds up an object (if necessary holding the spoonful of food behind it) and says, "What is this?" When the child looks at it, the therapist immediately prompts with the object's name. The child is reinforced for imitating the prompt. When the child is reliably looking at the object without the food's being held behind it, the time between the question, "What is this?" and the prompt is gradually lengthened to more than five seconds. If after several trials the child continues to wait for the presentation of the verbal prompt, a *partial prompt* is given, for example, "Trrr" for train. If the correct response does not occur within about five seconds more, the complete prompt is then presented. A correct response is followed by a social consequence such as "right" or "good," and the partial prompt is immediately repeated. A correct response to the partial prompt results in a bite of food.

When the child begins saying the name when only the partial prompt is presented, the therapist continues the above procedure but begins to say the partial prompt more softly. The loudness of the partial prompts is varied according to the child's behavior. When the child fails to respond to a partial prompt and the complete prompt is presented, the next partial prompt is given more loudly. When the child correctly responds to the partial prompt, the next partial prompt is given more softly. This continues until the therapist only "mouths" the partial prompt and then, finally, discontinues it altogether as the child responds to the object and the question "What is this?" with the name of the object.

Throughout this procedure, whenever the child inappropriately imitates the question, "What is this?", a time out is programmed; that is, the object is withdrawn and the therapist looks down at the table. After two or three seconds of silence by the child, the therapist looks up and continues the procedure.

The transition from imitation to naming with one child (Carey) is illustrated in Figure 6. From point A in Figure 6, the pictures of the four objects were held out one at time, and the child was required to look at them before the therapist said the name. The child quickly began attending to the pictures. The therapist's presentation of the words had been discriminative for the child to imitate and be reinforced. The increased proportion of attending indicated that the word presentations themselves had become reinforcers.

Just before B in Figure 6, the therapist began delaying naming the picture, requiring a longer period of attending by the child, so that he would be more likely to name the picture instead of imitating the therapist. At B the child began to tantrum during an especially long delay. The therapist merely sat quietly looking down at the table. The tantrum gradually subsided and the therapist again held up the picture (the flower). The child attended to the picture and promptly named it. After this he named the picture with increasing speed with each presentation.

The picture of the airplane was re-introduced. The child immediately said, "Car." The therapist said, "No, airplane." The child mimicked this and correctly named the picture when it was immediately re-presented. The remaining two pictures were then re-introduced, and the child correctly named each after a single prompt. After this he correctly named four pictures when each was presented. Next, a new object, a cup was presented. After imitating only two prompts, the child correctly named it and continued to name it correctly when it was presented interspersed with the original four pictures. Thus, by the end of the third session a small naming vocabulary had been established.

The following two examples demonstrate the role of food reinforcers in the maintenance of appropriate naming behavior. During the first five training sessions with Will, reliable imitation and then appropriate naming had been developed. The reinforcer involved a variety of edibles, such as ice cream, coke, and M & M's. The contribution of the food reinforcer was investigated by reversing the relationship between the naming behavior and the reinforcer. About a third of the way through the sixth session, the procedure was changed so that the child was reinforced only when he *did not* correctly name a picture for 10 seconds. This procedure is tech-

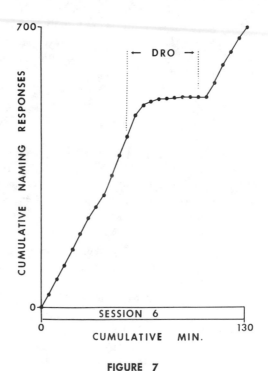

FIGURE 7

A cumulative record showing the results of changing the food reinforcement contingency on Will's rate of correct naming. During the sixth session a DRO contingency (see text) was introduced for nine minutes and Will's rate of naming decreased to zero. When the original food reinforcement contingency was reinstated the behavior increased to its pre-DRO rate.[2]

[2] This data was collected by Jacqulyn Raulerson and Thomas Dillon under the senior author's supervision.

nically termed *differential reinforcement of other behavior* (DRO) because any behavior except one particular response, in this case naming, is reinforced. As can be seen in Figure 7, the naming responses dropped from eight to zero per minute. After 45 minutes, when no naming responses were being made, the procedure was changed back so that naming responses were again the only responses being reinforced. The rate of naming quickly increased to approximately the same rate as during the first part of the session. These results show the power of the reinforcer over the occurrence and accuracy of Will's naming behavior.

Once a reliable rate of naming had been developed with Carey the procedure was changed in that ice cream was given on a non-contingent basis. Instead of being given bites of ice cream after each correct response, he was given the spoon and the bowl of ice cream and allowed to eat at his own rate. Pictures continued to be presented, he was still asked to name them, and when he named them correctly he was praised. The rate of correct naming dropped immediately from approximately eight per minute to three per minute and then stabilized at about two per minute (Figure 8). When the ice cream was again presented only after correct naming responses, the rate immediately increased to approximately 10 responses per minute.

To summarize, Carey's results show that after naming responses have been acquired, it may be possible to maintain them (although at a lower rate) with a weak reinforcer such as praise alone, but, as shown in the case of both children, the more powerful food reinforcer maintained a much higher and more steady rate of appropriate behavior.

Expansion of the Naming Vocabulary. After the child has been taught to name several pictures or objects, naming any new picture or object can be quickly established. However, the child often will not correctly name an item at the beginning of the next daily session or subsequent to learning other new items in the same session. A new response cannot be considered to be added to a child's naming vocabulary until he can name an item when it is presented again after other items have been learned, and following a lapse of time. This is accomplished by gradually changing the context in which the item is presented. Once a child is consistently naming new items

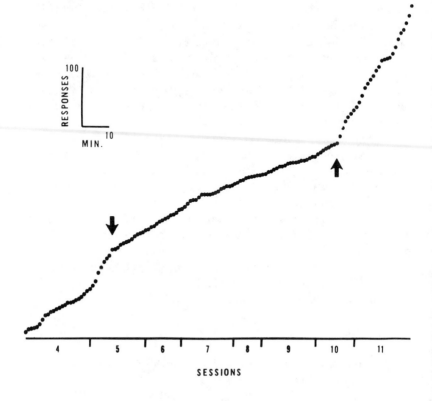

FIGURE 8

A cumulative record showing the effects of Carey's receiving bites of ice cream independent of his picture-naming responses. For the first session and a half Carey was fed a bite of ice cream after each correct response. At the first arrow Carey was allowed to feed himself ice cream independent of his naming responses. At the second arrow the food reinforcers were again made contingent upon correctly naming the pictures. Each dot represents a one-minute period.

on repeated presentations, a previously learned item is presented. When the child names the old item he is reinforced and the new item is presented again. When the child is reliably naming a new item when it follows one presentation of any of several previously taught items, two, then three, then four old items are presented between each presentation of the new item. (The well established naming of old items need be reinforced only intermittently with food to maintain accuracy and short latencies.) When the child is reliably naming a new item under these conditions, another new item is introduced. When an item is reliably named the first time it is presented in several subsequent sessions, it can be considered to be a member of the child's naming vocabulary; only occasional reviews in subsequent sessions are needed to maintain it.

Figure 9 shows the increasing naming vocabulary of Pat, a blind echolalic boy, who was taught to name common household objects that were placed in his hands. An item was considered to be "learned" when the child correctly named it on its first presentation in three successive sessions.

Carey's naming vocabulary was expanded under two reinforcement conditions. The items to be named were pictures (line drawings) of various objects. Two 10-minute sessions a day were held,

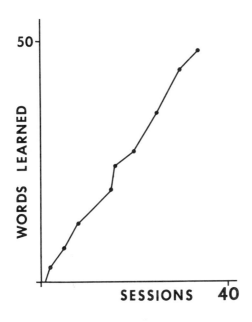

FIGURE 9

A cumulative record of Pat's learning to name objects correctly. The name of an object was recorded as "learned" when Pat named it correctly the first time it was presented in three successive sessions.

with separate pictures for each session. In one of the sessions each day, the reinforcer was praise ("that's right," "very good") and a bite of ice cream, whereas praise alone was used in the other session. Several pictures were repeatedly presented in a random order during each session. New pictures were added when the child was consistently naming all the pictures used during a session. A picture was considered to be learned when the child correctly named it the first time it was presented, three sessions in a row. It would then be retired until 10 subsequent pictures had been learned, at which time it would be presented again to test for recall.

While the child learned to name 50% more pictures when both praise and ice cream were used as reinforcers (solid line, Figure 10), his naming vocabulary was significantly expanded when praise was the only reinforcer (broken line, Figure 10). Furthermore, items were recalled equally well whether they had been reinforced with praise only or with both praise and ice cream (bar graph, Figure 10). However, following this evaluation, since only one session per day could be held, the more effective reinforcer, a combination of ice cream and praise, was used throughout the remaining sessions. Approximately one new word per session was established with this reinforcer (dotted line, Figure 10).

Just as Figure 8 demonstrates that established naming can be maintained (although at a lower rate) with praise as the only reinforcer, Figure 10 shows that when a child can readily be taught to name new items with food reinforcers his naming vocabulary can then be significantly expanded (although at a lower rate) when only social reinforcers of the type available in a "normal" environment are used.

The authors consider it necessary to use strong reinforcers such as food to establish the initial instances of appropriate mimicking and naming behaviors and to eliminate disruptive behaviors in a reasonable period of time. However, it appears that once disruptive behaviors have been eliminated and some appropriate mimicking and naming have been established, these appropriate behaviors can be maintained and expanded by the systematic use of social reinforcers. This does *not* imply that food deprivation and food reinforcers should then be discontinued. The magnitude of a child's speech deficits and the value of a therapist's and of a child's time require the utilization of those procedures that will produce the

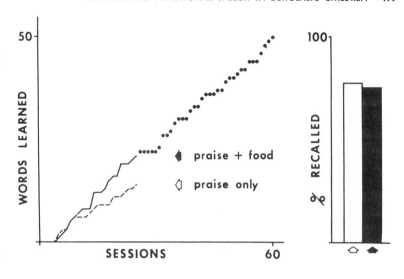

FIGURE 10

Records of the number of pictures that Carey learned to name and later recalled in daily sessions under two reinforcement conditions, praise alone ("that's right" or "very good") and both praise and food (bites of ice cream). A picture was considered to be learned when the child named it when it was first presented in three successive sessions. A picture was considered to be recalled when the child correctly named it when it was re-presented after 10 subsequent pictures had been learned.

greatest gains in the shortest time. The strongest reinforcers or combination of reinforcers available should be used in the therapy sessions as long as large behavioral deficits exist. However, social reinforcers outside the therapy sessions can generally be relied upon to maintain and expand the behaviors established in the sessions.

The Establishment of Phrases. Once naming is established, the response units can be expanded to phrases and sentences. In most cases this expansion occurs without explicit training. In those instances where multiple word units have to be taught, the procedure is the same as in teaching individual words; that is, mimics of the phrases are reinforced until the phrases are consistently imitated.

Then the control is shifted to the appropriate circumstance itself, by introducing partial prompts, which are gradually faded out. In this case, the partial prompts are the first word or words of the phrase.

At first phrases such as "That's a _____," or "I want _____," are taught, using the child's newly acquired naming vocabulary. Then more varied phrases are taught, such as answering the appropriate questions with "My name is _____," "I live at _____." "I am _____ years old," My sisters' names are _____ and _____."

Food reinforcers are used to build the initial responses, but, once established, the opportunity to obtain some natural consequence can usually maintain the behavior. For example, for Carey the comment, "Out (or in) the door," was maintained by opening the doors to and from the therapy room. The therapist would say, "Out the door," and when the child would mimic this, the door would be opened.

After several trials on succeeding days, the therapist began introducing a partial prompt, saying only, "Out _____," and the child continued to say, "Out the door." The partial prompt was then gradually faded out until the therapist put his hand on the door knob and looked at the child (see Figure 11), and the child said, "Out the door." The therapist gradually faded *in* the appropriate controlling stimulus — the question, "Where are you going?" This was presented by at first mumbling it softly as they approached the door and then increasing the volume on succeeding trials. Whenever the child inappropriately imitated the question "Where are you going?" the therapist repeated the question at a lower volume and followed it with a loud partial prompt: "Where are you going? OUT _____." On succeeding trials the partial prompt, "Out _____," was then decreased in volume until the child responded to the closed door and the question, "Where are you going?" with the response, "Out the door."

The same procedure was used to establish appropriate answers to the question, "Where are you going?" such as "Up the stairs," "Down the hall," or "In the car." In each case, the reinforcer that maintained appropriate answering was simply being allowed to proceed up the stairs, down the hall, and so on. In this manner the

FIGURE 11

An example of the therapist's maintaining appropriate verbal behavior outside the formal session. Here the door is opened contingent upon Carey's answering the question, "Where are we going?" The correct response was gradually developed as described in the text.

child came to make appropriate verbal comments about his environment. Once such simple comments have been learned, the child tends to generalize the grammatical form with appropriate substitutions. One example of such establishment and generalization, which could be termed "generative speech," resulted from a procedure used with Carey. On many occasions at home, this child would chant a word or short phrase over and over, with gradually increasing volume that terminated in piercing shrieks and crying. For example, while standing by the couch, he would repeat "Sit down, Sit down." His parents could terminate this by responding in any way, e.g., "Yes, Carey," "OK, sit down," "You can sit down if you want to," "Be quiet." The parents were requested to record these instances of stereotyped chanting, and also to send him to his

room for five minutes whenever the chanting developed into shrieking and crying. This decreased the occurrences of the shrieking
(solid line, Figure 12), but did not decrease the frequency of the
stereotyped chanting episodes (dotted line, Figure 12). The therapist decided to change the form of this behavior, rather than attempt to eliminate it, as it contained elements of appropriate social
behavior.

The parents were instructed to turn away from the child when
he chanted. One parent (e.g., the father) would then call out the
name of the other ("Mommy"), and when the child would mimic
this the mother would attend to him and say, "Yes, Carey." The
first parent would then say a complete sentence. ("I want to sit
down, please.") When the child would mimic this, the other parent
would respond accordingly ("Oh, you want to sit down. Well, you
can sit down right here."). On subsequent occasions the verbal
prompts were faded out. Finally, the parents withheld reinforcement by looking away until the child called their names, and they
would wait while looking at him until he gave the complete sentence before responding to his request. This procedure was begun
at the arrow in Figure 12. The stereotyped chanting soon decreased
to zero as the child began to initiate more appropriate requests
such as, "Mommy, I want to sit down, please," or Daddy, I want a
drink of water, please."

The grammatical structure of "(Name), I want _____, please,"
after being established with several people's names and many different requests in the home, began to generalize to new people and
new requests. One recorded instance of this occurred in the therapy
sessions. Prior to the start of each session, when Carey was seated
in the room, the therapist would spend some time setting up the
tape recorder. During this time the child would usually start chanting "Ice cream, ice cream" softly. When the therapist was ready, he
would turn to the child and say, "What do you want?" to which
the child had been taught to answer "I want some ice cream." Prior
to one session, after the grammatical form of requests mentioned
above had been established at home, the child was, as usual, chanting, "Ice cream, ice cream," while the therapist threaded the tape
recorder. He suddenly stopped and after a pause, said "Mr. (therapist's name), I want some ice cream, please." Most of the elements
of this sentence had been established in the therapy sessions, e.g.,

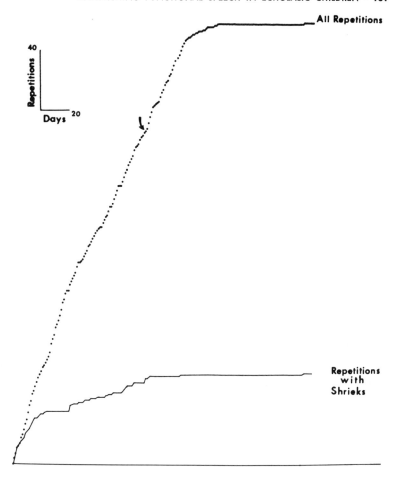

FIGURE 12

A cumulative record of episodes of repetitious chanting by Carey at home. From the onset, he was sent to his room for five minutes whenever he began shrieking during one of those episodes. At the arrow his parents began establishing appropriate speech behavior, which was incompatable with chanting. Each dot represents one day.

"Hello, Mr. (therapist's name)," and "I want some ice cream," but they had always been given as responses to specific stimuli (e.g.,

"Hello, Carey" and "What do you want?"). However, the particular grammatical structure of "(Name), I want _____, please," had only been taught in the home.

Carey's extension of his home training exemplifies our general observation that once rudimentary generative speech and grammatical structure have been established they will tend to generalize broadly, often with appropriate substitutions.

Other Considerations

The Generalization of Appropriate Speech. The term "generalization" can refer to the *phenomenon* of the occurrence of appropriate behavior under other than the original training conditions, or it can refer to the *procedure* used to establish this occurrence.

While newly acquired appropriate speech often will "spontaneously" generalize widely, the therapist need not passively rely on this phenomenon. He can, instead, set out to extend the occurrence of the behavior to other situations by systematically reinforcing appropriate speech under a variety of conditions. The child can be systematically trained to respond appropriately to a variety of individuals, including members of his family and other caretakers, and in a variety of situations, such as at home, in the family car, and in the therapist's office. Once appropriate speech has been established in the therapy sessions, the child's parents can be present during occasional sessions and the child reinforced for responding appropriately to their questions. Whenever a new word has been established in a therapy session, the therapist can continue to ask for, and reinforce, the appropriate use of this word after the formal session, for instance, while walking around the building. The therapist can also conduct therapy sessions in the child's home, teaching him to name household objects, for example.

Generalization training can be facilitated by initially selecting words and phrases to be taught that can be appropriately asked for frequently during the day (for example, "car" is better than "zebra," and that are immediately functional in the child's environment ("I want a cookie").

Perhaps the most effective means of generalizing the appropriate use of speech is to train the parents or caretakers to use the therapeutic procedures. They can then take advantage of naturally occurring events during the day to generalize appropriate speech to a wide variety of situations, as well as to establish new speech in appropriate contexts.

The Usefulness of Data in Therapy. The gathering of continuous data throughout the course of therapy can be valuable in many ways. For example, it can provide objective information about the long-term course of therapy. Behaviors followed over a long period of time, as described in this paper, often reveal an orderliness that is not clear from the day-by-day observations. Gradual changes can be discerned in spite of large daily fluctuations, as in the instance of the rate of Carey's shrieking (Figure 12). The frequency of the shrieks decreased in a manner that was orderly overall, even though some of the individual days (sometimes several consecutive days) showed considerable variability.

A second use of data is in the analysis of the functions of therapeutic procedures. An *experimental* probe is usually necessary if the therapist wants to isolate the variables responsible for a behavioral change. Isolation is accomplished by keeping all of the therapeutic conditions the same except one. If varying this condition produces a reliable change in the data, which disappears when the condition is reversed to its pre-experimental value, then the importance of the variable has been established. Sidman (1960) has discussed in detail strategies and considerations for research with individual subjects. Probe experiments of the above type were described in this paper. For example, the role of the food reinforcement contingency in Will's progress in naming was evaluated (Figure 7). Its importance was dramatically demonstrated when the DRO procedure was interjected into a session. A similar probe experiment, in a slightly different manner and over a longer period of time, demonstrated the function of the food reinforcement in Carey's rate of naming pictures (Figure 8).

The easiest of data gathering methods is to use a tape recorder to record all of the sessions. The therapist or an assistant can replay tapes from previous sessions and count the frequencies of various responses (e.g., correct imitations) or the durations of certain behaviors (e.g., temper tantrums, inappropriate chanting). Tapes of earlier sessions are particularly useful for gathering data about behaviors that were not originally thought to be of interest.

A multi-pen event recorder can be used if the therapist is certain in advance of the classes of behavior that he will want to record.

A bank of push-button switches can be wired from the therapist's table to the recorder so that durations and frequencies of responses can be recorded by the therapist and/or by an independent observer.

A pencil and paper can always be used to take simple frequencies. Duration of a specific behavior can be recorded during each session with a stop watch.

Such data and probe experiments enable the therapist to give a more complete and objective description of his procedures and their effects to others, including colleagues who are also interested in developing a more effective technology of speech modification through a systematic analysis of speech modification procedures.

A Final Word

This paper indicates that functional verbal behavior can be developed from rudimentary imitative behavior by established behavioral techniques. We have outlined procedures that were effective in establishing functional speech in echolalic children. However, the procedures as they are described here should not be taken as fixed and unchanging. The developing strength of behavioral technology lies in the continued refinement of its procedures.

REFERENCES

Harris, Florence R., M. M. Wolf, and D. M. Baer, "Effects of Adult Reinforcement on Child Behavior," *Young Child,* 1964, 20, 8–17.

Lovaas, I. O., "A Program for the Establishment of Speech in Psychotic Children." In J. K. Wing (Ed.), *Childhood Autism.* Oxford: Pergamon Press, 1966 (Chapter 7 in this book).

Risley, T. R., "The Establishment of Verbal Behavior in Deviant Children." Unpublished dissertation, University of Washington, 1966.

Sidman, M., *Tactics of Scientific Research.* New York: Basic Books, 1960.

Skinner, B. F., *Verbal Behavior.* New York: Appleton-Century-Crofts, 1957.

Stone, J. L. and J. Church, *Childhood and Adolescence.* New York: Random House, 1957.

Wolf, M. M., T. R. Risley, and H. I. Mees, "Application of Operant Conditioning Procedures to the Behavior Problems of an Autistic Child," *Behav. Res. Ther.* 1964, 1, 305–312.

9

Margaret K. Johnston

Echolalia and Automatism in Speech: A Case Report

A unique type of language disability, echolalia, or automatism in speech is frequently found in children who are considered emotionally disturbed. It is particularly common among children diagnosed as "autistic" or "schizophrenic." Some authorities consider echolalic speech to be a significant symptom of these behavioral disorders, a viewpoint well summarized by Rimland in *Infantile Autism* (*1964*), in which a detailed description of echolalic speech and its relation to autism is presented.

Children with limited language development related to general retarded development are also often echolalic, and echolalic speech frequently occurs when words and phrases are first being learned in the normal course of language growth in children. Indeed, echoic control is of primary importance in the typical acquisition of speech and language. However, persistent echoic speech presents a problem that seriously interferes with the functional use of language and impedes learning of appropriate speech and language patterns.

Echolalia or automatism in speech, as used in this chapter, are terms that encompass several classes of echoic verbal behavior, and include a child's mimicking the speech of others, mimicking his own verbalizations, and the repetitive verbalization of words and phrases. The echoic nature of this language, in which phrases are repeated

Support for this work was received from grant 32–23–1020–6002 from the U. S. Office of Education to Professor Sidney W. Bijou.

exactly as said by others, typically causes reversal of pronouns and sentence structure and the inability to respond to questions. Mands often are single words that are the echoic repetition of adult questions ("water?"). Deviations in phonation, rhythm, and articulation also are common in the speech of the echoic child. Some echoic children do enunciate speech sounds well and have fairly adequate repertoires of words and phrases, but their verbal behavior does not serve the purposes of communication.

A language training program for the treatment of echolalic children requires special procedures and techniques aimed at bringing the child's verbal behavior under appropriate rather than echoic stimulus control. Traditional speech therapy techniques have proven valuable in correcting articulation defects, but generally have been found inadequate in correcting echoic speech patterns. The emphasis in designing remedial procedures for echolalia must necessarily be on restructuring the language that the child possesses, in addition to building a repertoire of words and phrases. Since inappropriate speech patterns are often well established in the typical echoic child, designing corrective procedures presents a challenging problem to the speech therapist, requiring an experimental approach and a willingness to try a variety of techniques tailored to the requirements of each subject.

Operant language training procedures, based on principles of behavior modification, offer a new and promising method for the remediation of echoic speech in children. These procedures, based on a functional analysis of the subject's language, provide a method for establishing stimulus control of this behavior by systematic modification of the environmental contingencies that maintain verbal behavior. Several experimental treatment programs based on these principles recently have been reported (*Dameron; Hewett, 1965; Lovaas et al., 1966*). The experimental program described in this chapter is presented as an example of such a program, illustrating typical procedures and special problems that arise in a language training program for children with this particular speech disability.

The subject whose treatment is described here was a seven-year-old boy, diagnosed as both retarded and emotionally disturbed. He was enrolled in a small remedial guidance group for deviant children, designed for the dual purpose of treatment and research, which was conducted at the University of Washington.

Before the child was enrolled in this group he had had language training in a laboratory setting for a period of several months. The procedures used in this phase of his training are reported by Risley (1966), who developed the first phases of the program described in this chapter. The techniques that he used are summarized briefly to show the complete sequence of training procedures, and are more completely described in Chapter 8. Risley also worked with the child's parents, going into the home to teach them remedial techniques that they could apply in daily living with the child.

When first seen by Risley for training, the child (then age six) spoke only a few words, had a high rate of crying, shrieking, and tantrum behavior, and did not attend to or respond to adults. The program used by Risley started, therefore, by teaching attending behavior, extinguishing screaming, shrieking, and other tantrum behavior, and teaching a repertoire of verbal tacts, mands, and intraverbals. These last included picture and object naming, a limited number of mands, such as "I want ice cream," and a limited number of intraverbal responses, such as responding to "How are you?" with "I am fine."

After completing work with Risley, the child entered the remedial group. He had a fairly extensive repertoire of tacts and used some phrasal mands by this time, and could respond correctly when asked his name, greet other people appropriately and make some self-report statements. Cues still were necessary to correct frequent mimics and to stimulate appropriate responses. He usually attended well enough to participate in a 15- or 20-minute laboratory training session.

The language training program that was carried out during the child's attendance in the remedial group included procedures used both in laboratory training sessions and in the classroom. This program was in effect during the three quarters that he participated in the group. Data on his language behavior were collected for this entire period, in both the laboratory and the classroom, by an observer trained in the technique of systematic observation. These observational records served both the requirements for research and as a guide in planning the treatment program, enabling the staff to modify the procedures according to the results shown by the data records. For details on recording procedures see Chapter 3.

Three training phases can be described for the period during which the child was in the remedial group after working with Risley. The first group of procedures was designed to reduce echoic speech, both in the one-to-one tutorial laboratory session held each day for 20 to 30 minutes, and in the general classroom, and to increase the child's use of mands and intraverbal responses in the laboratory and class sessions. The second set of procedures was designed to increase the flexibility and spontaneity of speech, to reduce automatism, and to increase the degree of nonechoic control over speech exerted by the current environment. The third set of procedures involved training the parents to evoke correct speech patterns at home. Each of these will be described in greater detail. In all laboratory sessions spoonfuls of sherbet plus praise were used as reinforcers. In the classroom, social reinforcement and infrequent "M & M" candies were used.

Procedures Used to Correct Echolalic Speech

Laboratory Procedures

A. The procedures used by Risley to teach tacts, mands, and good attending behavior were continued. Picture cards and objects were both used to expand the child's vocabulary. Tacts were taught by teaching the correct responses to sets of pictures, each one depicting a discrete object. When the picture was first presented, the object was named for the child. In subsequent presentations cues were given if needed. For example, in teaching him to respond to the picture of a stove, the therapist might cue the correct response by producing the first three letters of the word. On the next trial only "st" would be used as a cue, and finally only "s." The response was considered correct when it was emitted in response to the visual stimulus of the pictures, without verbal clues. This technique of "fading cues" was applied in various phases of the program.

Mands were also taught during this period of training, and included requests such as "I want ice cream." Once the phrase had been learned, the ice cream was withheld until the child made the correct verbalization, with the aid of a cue if necessary.

B. Self-report tacts and intraverbal responses were also taught. Questions concerning the child's activities, such as "What are you doing?" or "Where did you go yesterday?" were asked, and the correct answer was then given by the teacher. The child was reinforced for imitating this answer. Cues were gradually faded, one word at a time, until the child responded to the question alone. Intraverbal responses were taught in the same manner.

C. Teaching the child to give more complete descriptions of pictures (complex tacts) was next added to the program. Simple picture books and mounted pictures were both used for this training. For example, the subject was taught to respond with a complete sentence, such as "The little boy is playing with the blocks," to a picture depicting this action. After the sentence was learned, directions to the child were varied so that sometimes the therapist asked, "What is the boy doing?" and at other times, "Tell me what you see in the picture." Response to the pictures without cues or directions was one of the goals of this procedure. Cues were used to establish this response and were faded out as they became unnecessary.

Classroom Procedures

Concurrently with the daily laboratory sessions, procedures to stimulate speech and correct echoic verbalizations were implemented in the classroom. These procedures were carefully planned to generalize language behavior learned in the laboratory sessions to the group setting. In this small class it was possible to maintain nearly a one-to-one relationship between teacher and child, so that continuous speech training could be carried on as part of the daily program. Because classroom procedures were systematically planned in frequent staff meetings, all three teachers working with the group could maintain consistent contingencies for the child's verbal behavior.

A. Procedures were developed to teach more complex mands. When the child was first enrolled in the group he used only a few one-word mands, repeated until his demands were met. The child was given models of correct phrases to imitate, and when these had been learned the teachers ceased to respond to one-word mands, turning away and ignoring them until he used a phrase or sentence. For example, the child learned to say, "I want to paint," instead of repeating "paint."

B. Appropriate responses to questions were also taught in the classroom by cuing the child to answer, and again fading out the cues. For instance, in reply to "What are you doing?" the child learned to say, "I'm climbing," or "I'm playing in the sand."

C. Repetitious intraverbal responses were extinguished. During this period of training, perseveration of some learned speech behavior became a problem. For instance the child would greet the teacher with "Hello teacher," which was then repeated over and over again until the teacher responded with "Hello" to the child, which often was a stimulus to repeat the sequence. The procedure used to modify this behavior was for the teacher to ignore the initial greeting and to respond with another statement discriminative for a different response.

At this point in the program (near the end of Winter Quarter), evaluation of the child's progress indicated that his rate of mimicking speech was no longer increasing, although appropriate verbalizations, both cued and uncued, were showing a gradual increase (see Figure 1). The child's total verbal output, in both the laboratory and the classroom, also had increased, and some improvement in his articulation was noted. However, in spite of attempts to vary the materials presented to the child and to make the cues and S^D's given to the child flexible, much of his language was sterotyped. Many of his newly learned responses became somewhat automatic and took on unchanging patterns of intonation and rhythm. At this time, too, the teacher's name inadvertently became chained to the end of many of his responses. While this had been appropriate in answering some questions, it was not desirable when added automatically to all his verbalizations. A similar difficulty arose in teaching the child to answer "yes" to questions. When this was first attempted in the laboratory session, the instruction given to the child was "say yes," rather than just cuing with "yes." "Say yes" then became the response to all questions requiring "yes" as the answer.

Responses once established in this child's speech repertoire were difficult to correct or extinguish. While his ability to mimic most speech patterns was an asset in teaching him new words and phrases, it also presented special procedural problems, which point up the importance of careful selection of specific cues to be used in speech training with echolalic children. The general rule appears to be that no model should be given to the child that is not appropriate for exact repetition.

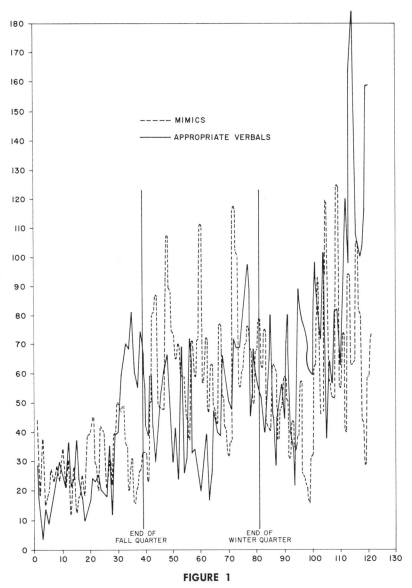

FIGURE 1

Frequency of appropriate verbal statements and of mimics in the classroom.

On the basis of the child's progress and because of the problems encountered in this phase of the program, the next procedures were planned to promote more flexibility in his language behavior.

Procedures Used To Develop Spontaneity and Flexibility

Laboratory Procedures[1]

A. A greater variety of pictures was presented, and the order in which they were used was randomized.

B. The correct use of "yes" and "no" was taught. "Say yes" was extinguished by not accepting it as an answer and by avoiding using any cue but "yes" in prompting the correct response. Pictures and questions were introduced, to which the child was asked to respond with either "yes" or "no." For example, a picture of a dog might be shown the child with the question, "Is this a cow?"

C. Practice in both following and giving directions was continued, with the emphasis on changing one part of the direction at a time. Thus, the same direction might be presented using a variety of differently worded but semantically equivalent statements. Initially, one word, or the position of a single word or phrase in the direction, might be changed. With progress, a wider range of similar directions was introduced.

D. Picture cues were varied, one aspect at a time, in order to teach more flexible responses. A series of pictures was designed that were identical except for one object. Discriminating this object required close attention to the picture as well as a novel response. One such set consisted of a series of pictures of a boy, each differing from the other only in the item the boy held in his hand.

E. Simple conversational patterns and greater spontaneity in speech were programmed by introducing a number of conversational sentences in the training sessions. For example, the child might be asked, "Who brought you to school today?" or "Who did you play with at home this morning?" Exchanges of comments about such everyday incidents became part of the training procedures.

[1] Some of the procedures described in this section were developed with the assistance of Nicholas Long.

Classroom Procedures

A. The child was asked to carry verbal messages from one teacher to another or to another child. He was also frequently cued to ask other children for a toy or a piece of candy.

B. Conversations with both adults and children were frequently stimulated, and were reinforced when obtained.

C. The correct use of "yes" and "no" was required in the classroom, and training in responding to various kinds of questions and comments from others was continued.

Training the Child's Parents To Stimulate and Cue Correct Speech Patterns in the Home

Training of the child's parents to stimulate, reinforce, and correct the child's speech at home was carried on throughout the period of treatment. The mother observed the laboratory sessions regularly and also visited in the classroom. She was taught to use the same cues and directions that were being used at school. Both parents were encouraged to maintain contingencies for the child's speech behavior at home that were consistent with those enforced in the remedial setting. They were reinforced by the staff when they were successful in implementing their part of the program. Frequent parent conferences were held to inform the parents of the treatment procedures that were currently in effect.

Although data on the child's speech behavior at home were not collected, the family reported significant improvement in his ability to use speech to communicate with them. His rate of verbalizations at home also increased, and shrieking and screaming occurred less frequently.

Results of the Treatment Program

Data records for the first few weeks that the child was enrolled in the remedial group showed that his total verbal output averaged about 42 verbalizations during the one-and-a-half-hour period that he was in the class room. On the average, 22 of these were mimics and 20 were non-mimics, consisting mostly of one-word mands. Very few nonechoic phrases were recorded during this period.

During the last three weeks of the remedial program, the data indicated that his total verbal output in the same classroom period had increased to an average of 180 verbalizations per day, more than four times the initial rate. Mimics were still occurring at an average rate of 53 per day, but appropriate verbal *phrases* were emitted approximately 112 times per sessions. He responded correctly to 85% of the cues given him and often corrected his mimics spontaneously. He also frequently amplified one-word mands without prompting, although this was not objectively measured by the observer.

The results of the remedial language training program with this echolalic child indicate that his rate of appropriate verbal behavior increased significantly during the course of treatment. This increase was reflected in all the classes of verbal behavior that were part of the training program, and indicates that controlling the environmental consequences of verbal behavior can successfully bring echoic speech under more appropriate discriminative control.

The problems encountered in working with this child demonstrate the importance of systematic observation as a corollary of treatment. Observational records of verbal behavior in both the laboratory and the classroom were essential to planning explicit procedures and evaluating their results.

Developing more effective techniques for remedial training of echolalic children will depend on continued research and experimentation. Perfecting and refining treatment procedures based on a functional analysis of the child's language behavior, and using operant procedures, should contribute to this development.

REFERENCES

Dameron, L., "Operant Therapy with an Elective Mute Autistic Child." Unpublished manuscript.

Hewett, F. M., "Teaching Speech to an Autistic Child through Operant Conditioning," *Amer. J. Orthopsychiat.*, 1965, 35, 927–936.

Lovaas, O. I., J. P. Berberich, B. F. Perloff, and B. Schaeffer, "Acquisition of Imitative Speech in Schizophrenic Children," *Science*, February, 1966.

Rimland, B., *Infantile Autism*. New York: The Meredith Publishing Company, 1964.

Risley, T. R., "The Establishment of Verbal Behavior in Deviant Children." Unpublished dissertation, University of Washington, 1966.

Rehabilitating Speech in Aphasics

The report by Holland and Harris on their work with aphasic adults points up several things. Many believe that "behavioral" procedures cannot be used with patients in which known organic pathology is the major contributor to the problem under consideration. At a rhetorical level there is really little value in disputing such an assertion (other perhaps than to ask "why?"), and Holland and Harris, as well as several others (e.g., Risley and Wolf; MacAulay), empirically demonstrate the fallacious nature of this belief.

Holland and Harris call the procedures they use "programmed instruction," while most other chapters in this book do not use this term. It would be an error to assume that there is some fundamental difference between the programmed instruction described in Chapter 10 and the procedures described by the other authors. In all of the chapters the same considerations are applied to the problems confronted — considerations related to the sequencing (programming) of the material or stimulus items, the reinforcing contingencies, and the use of stimulus control. However, when such procedures are used in an academic context that stresses paper-and-pencil tasks, or in which these sequences, response contingencies, and stimulus control are maintained by inanimate objects (teaching machines, programmed texts, etc.), the convention is to use the label "programmed instruction." When the same procedures are used, but a teacher is substituted for the machine, or the response is not written, or both, it is usually not called programmed instruction. The latter, of course, is more likely to be the case with young children. However, this minor convention should not be allowed to obscure the essential similarities.

10

Audrey L. Holland
Amy Bricker Harris

Aphasia Rehabilitation Using Programmed Instruction: An Intensive Case History

Summary. This paper describes a ten-month project using programmed instruction almost exclusively as the medium for language retraining for an adult aphasic subject. The programs used are described in detail, and an analysis is made of the effectiveness of the programs as therapeutic tools.

There are many specific speech and hearing problems that potentially can benefit from the development of appropriate teaching machine programs. Programs that successfully teach auditory discrimination to persons with defective articulation (*Holland and Matthews, 1963*) and language concepts to deaf children (*Stuckless and Birch, 1964; Falconer, 1960*) attest to this. In no area, however, do the techniques of programmed instruction hold more promise than in the area of aphasia rehabilitation. There are a number of reasons for this. Among them are the nature of the rehabilitation procedures themselves and the carefully demonstrated value of the techniques *per se*, with even extremely impaired aphasic individuals (*Filby and Edwards, 1963; Rosenberg, 1965*).

This research was supported by NIH Research Grant No. NB–06264–02.

Programs have been developed and are in clinical use for handling a number of the basic problems of the severely impaired adult aphasic. Notable in this respect is the continuing work of Taylor and her associates (*1964; 1965*); however, there is little information available on programs designed for the less severely impaired aphasic. Further, the feasibility of handling aphasic patients' language rehabilitation almost entirely by programmed instruction has not been demonstrated.

It was the purpose of the project reported here to develop programs for aphasics who are most likely to profit from traditional language retraining (Types I and II, Schuell Classification)[1] and to use those programs almost entirely as long-term language rehabilitation with a single aphasic subject. It was felt that such an experiment would result in programs with a broader application than merely to the aphasic for whom they were designed. Such an experiment, it was felt, would also furnish valuable clinical insight into the course of long-term rehabilitation using programmed instruction.

The Subject

In December, 1964, we saw for diagnostic evaluation a 23-year-old male Ph.D. candidate in clinical psychology at Harvard University. This young man had undergone surgery one month earlier, resulting in removal of an arterioveinous malformation in the posterior parietal lobe. He was subsequently aphasic.

His performance on the Minnesota Test for the Differential Diagnosis of Aphasia indicated marked word-finding difficulties, many semantic confusions, significantly impaired reading and writing skills, inability to repeat auditory material, reduced memory and retention span, and reduced comprehension for both auditory and written material. His spontaneous vocabulary was limited to a few generic nouns. His ability to use other words in controlled situations was dependent upon whether or not he could print the word. If he could do this, then he usually was able to sound the word out. He was classified as a Type II Aphasic, with moderate to severe impairment. Among this young man's strengths were the recency of

[1] For an extensive discussion of this system for describing and classifying aphasic behavior, see Schuell, Jenkins, and Jiminez-Pabon, 1964.

the aphasia, youth, a good awareness of inappropriate responses, superior intelligence, and not only motivation for overcoming his problems, but also a unique ability to look rather objectively at his problem as a fascinating clinical entity. Because of his range of deficits, he seemed a logical choice for our study. Furthermore he appreciated the experimental aspect of our work and was eager to participate in it.

The client was seen in the clinic for eight months, for approximately five hours per week of programmed instruction. In addition to this clinic work, he used programs at home for approximately 10 hours per week during this period, and received two hours of group therapy, concerned primarily with arithmetic, at another clinic.

The Program

The programs that are described in this section reflect some assumptions regarding the nature of language rehabilitation. In general, the major assumption is that effective retraining of the adult aphasic must be a more formal process than the initial acquisition of language. However, both situations reflect a process that Brown and Bellugi, in referring to acquisition of syntax, call induction of latent structure (1964). For the adult aphasic, a related process probably accounts for re-acquisition of vocabulary, morphology, etc. Aphasia retraining seldom, if ever, requires a painstaking retraining of language skills. It is rather a process of re-establishing a more circumscribed basic vocabulary and grammar, and then helping the patient to generalize from this beginning. This point of view is inherent in the programs described here.

The descriptions that follow are presented roughly in the order in which our subject was exposed to the tasks. Throughout the tasks, a constantly expanding vocabulary was incorporated, as was more and more complex grammatical structure.

The Usage Tasks. The earliest task was designed to train cross-modal language usage. It had as its criterion performance cross-modal use of the sentence, *I sit at the table on a chair.*

This sentence, in a series of programmed steps, was taught as single sounds, words, and then syntactically related components.

These steps involved repeating the above, as well as answering questions that required either the words, phrases, or the whole sentence for answers. Some of the steps required reading aloud or writing as responses, rather than speaking. Such tasks, in progressive complexity, were interwoven into a program 100 items long. This sentence was used for its high-frequency words, for its variety of parts of speech and for its grammatical structure. The reading and writing tasks were presented on 3 x 5 workbook cards; the auditory tasks were on tape. The subject was instructed to respond to an asterisk on a workbook card by starting the tape recorder. He was to turn off the tape recorder and return to the written items when he heard a taped signal to do so. Reinforcement for auditory items consisted of hearing the correct response on tape; for visual items, the correct answer was on the card following. If the patient responded incorrectly, he was instructed to replay the item, if it was auditory, and respond again. If the item was presented in writing, he was to reread it and respond again. In both cases, he was instructed not to continue on in the program until he had mastered each step. To insure that this occurred, the patient's wife was shown how the program worked, and instructed to provide additional information regarding the appropriateness of each response until he could reliably do it alone. She reported later that her participation was necessary only for a series of the earliest items.

The first program was a success. The earliest items were given in session with the patient; he was then asked to take the program cards and tape home and complete it before his next session. To our surprise, by the next session he had not only completed the task but had redone it three times.

This task served as the starting point for a similar series of tasks in the use of prepositions. New vocabulary and sentence structure were constantly incorporated. The drill necessary at the beginning of the usage task was no longer required. The prepositions thus handled included systematic cross-modal use of "on, under, beside, before, and after." The task handling "before and after" was designed to retrain appropriate use of adjectives as well. Whenever possible, the program was constructed to include remedies for possible sources of language confusions resulting from aphasic reversal problems (such as "in" for "out," "before" for "after"). The entire task involved roughly 1,000 programmed frames.

The general format of the task was again an intertwining of spoken and written items, which included both statements and questions, and which required vocal responses (reinforced by comparison with the correct answers on tape) or written responses (reinforced by comparison with correct written response). The following illustrates the section dealing with the prepositions "on, under and beside." Initial drill consisted of saying, reading, and writing the prepositions. Meaning was then gradually introduced, using sentences and accompanying illustrations in which a previously learned noun (table from the above, for example) served as the object of the preposition. A fuzzy black shape (called a "blob") served as the figure to be moved on, under, and beside the table. In this way, early meaning of the prepositions bypassed vocabulary problems. Practice with the blob led to combining new vocabulary with the prepositions. Early picture items in this sequence had only two noun-pictures in a prepositional relationship; as the program progressed, other objects were incorporated, thus requiring careful listening and observing of the relevant pictorial cues.

These tasks took us well into February. By this time the subject was using language with a great deal more facility; however, his basic difficulties in repeating, his related difficulty with retaining and comprehending auditorially presented material, and his spelling and vocabulary constriction were now more starkly apparent. We decided to handle the problems in the above order.

The Repetition and Auditory Memory Span Tasks. These programs all dealt with specifically controlled responses to spoken language. The programs were all presented auditorially and required, as responses, vocal repetition of the auditory frame. On the one hand, the programs reflect our assumption concerning the necessity of intensive auditory stimulation in aphasia. On the other hand, they reflect the assumption that the ability to repeat spoken language can serve as a parsimonious check on the effectiveness of the auditory stimulation.

The first two tasks were designed to increase the subject's ability to handle progressively longer and/or more complex units of spoken speech in this manner. Frames were tape recorded and presented on an auditory teaching machine; simultaneous orthographic representation was available on 3 x 5 cards. The subject was required to respond by repeating each item aloud. He evaluated his responses, then pushed one of two buttons on a response panel in front of him. If he evaluated his response as correct, he pushed the appropriate button and the next item was heard; if he evaluated it as incorrect, he pushed another button, which resulted in a tape-recorder rewind and a replay of the item.

Because a playback of the initial stimulus would have added a confusing variable, the evaluative technique was one of "delayed match"; i.e., after he responded, he had to judge the similarity of his response to the stimulus item. The investigators, who were present in the room, taping the sessions and making observations of his behavior, also checked his evaluations. In no instance did he evaluate a correct response as incorrect; he did occasionally evaluate an incorrect response as correct. When this occurred, the investigators simply pushed the appropriate button. Since the control circuitry operated on the last signal generated for each frame (thus allowing for a change in response), the investigator's button-press overrode the subject's, and the item replayed.

The first of these tasks was built on the single word, "turn." The task began with repeating and/or reading the verb "turn." The task then moved through a series of items involving "turn" plus prepositions, "turn" plus prepositional phrases, nouns incorporating the sounds [tɜn] or [tɚn] (for example, "pattern"), other grammatical forms of the verb, these verb forms plus prepositions, and simple sentences including at least one aspect of the preceding. All items incorporated the sequence [tɜn] or [tɚn]. When he completed this task, the 3 x 5 cards were removed and he was required to go through the task again with auditory stimulation alone.

The second task was similar. It began with the word "run" and incorporated the sequences [rʌn], [rən], [ræn]. "Run" was chosen because after the previous training a verb with an irregular past form (and therefore an additional phonetic parameter) could be utilized efficiently. The format paralleled the "turn" task in its earlier frames, although the task moved in larger and more varied frames. The last portion of the program differed in that frames were no longer specifically concerned with [rʌn, rən, ræn]. Each of these later frames incorporated words from the preceding frame, but the last word of one sentence appeared at the beginning of the next, and thus changed from object to subject. The final items began training on memory span. For example, three nouns, which the subject was required to repeat, appeared sequentially in a sentence. Again, two exposures to the task were required; in the first, the subject had the written form available; the second was auditory only.

These tasks were followed by a very long programmed task designed to increase auditory memory span. The format was similar to the above, although no written cards accompanied the task, and even its earliest items required a three-word response. The task began with a long series of frames requiring the subject to repeat progressively longer sequential units of semantically and/or structurally related material (for example, "needle and thread" . . . "I had a bowl of soup, a tuna fish salad sandwich, and a cup of coffee for lunch."). The second phase progressively faded out semantic and structural cues until the subject was repeating sequences of unrelated words such as "car, again, dishrag, lovely, swim, if." The last phase of the task dealt with digit span. Early items in this phase were preceded by a sentence designed to serve as a prompt and to give some structure to the numbers in the series. For example, the earliest item in this sequence was: "He ate three hamburgers. Repeat 8–3." Considerably later, he heard: "Pearl Harbor was bombed on December 7, 1941. Repeat 7–1–9–4–1." This was faded out, and numbers to be repeated were then grouped by appropriate pausing; this was systematically faded out. A three-digit core of numbers was then lengthened by adding numbers alternatively to each end, until a seven-digit response was required. This task was followed by a similar one using a four-digit core. Criterion items were randomly selected seven-digit numbers, presented one second apart.

The Retention Span Tasks. By the time the subject had completed the above programs, it was apparent that he could repeat quite long utterances. How well he comprehended the material he parroted back became our next concern. A series of tasks designed to help retain meaningful material presented in complex sentences followed. The subject heard a carefully constructed complex sentence, and was required to answer a simple question regarding its content. When he had heard and answered such questions for 20 sentences, he was re-exposed to the sentences and was required to answer a more complex question about each of them. For example, consider the sentence "The president reported that the gross national product was up and unemployment dropped." Following the first exposure to this sentence, the patient was asked: "Who reported that the gross national product was up and unemployment dropped?" On the second exposure he was asked, "What did the president report?" The third time through, he had to repeat the sentence (in this case a combination of the above answers) verbatim. This program was presented "live voice," and responses were evaluated by the programmer. If the patient's response was correct, the programmer so informed him and presented the next item. Incorrect responses resulted in a repeat of the item.

The "Senses" Task. During the time in which the subject was working through the initial drafts or the auditory programs in the clinic and was demonstrating to the experimenters by his performance where revisions were necessary, he was beginning to do other programmed tasks at home. One of these was a task designed basically for systematic work on semantic reversal problems, which also furnished reading practice. The subject matter that evolved for this work was a review of sensory functions and their expression in idiomatic English. This was referred to as the "senses" task and was the most typical programmed text of the series. It consisted of two hundred written frames for which the subject was required to furnish a written response. The correct response was provided in the corner of the succeeding item. The program handled the following: "hear, hear plus noun; sounds, sounds plus adjective, sounds like; feel, feel plus adjective, feels like; smell, smell plus adjective; see, see plus noun; looks, looks plus adjective, looks like." The following is an early item: You smell with your nose. You smell odors with your nose. You use your nose to smell _____. This is an item near the end of the program: An elephant: you can (1)_____ its long trunk, (2)_____ it when it trumpets, (3)_____ its rough hide, (4)_____ peanuts on its breath.

The subject was given a portion of the program at each of three successive clinical sessions, told to work through it, and then, starting from the beginning again, to read and tape record the entire task, including his filled-in responses. This furnished him an additional self-evaluative check on the adequacy of his responses, as well as giving him reading practice.

Spelling Confusion and Scrambled Words Tasks. Two programmed tasks were next evolved for correcting our subject's spelling difficulties. The first task programmed a series of alternative spellings of a given word with high probability of selection by aphasics (*Bricker et al., 1964*). The task was presented in matching-to-sample format using a teaching machine that was operated by an inductance coil. Correct answer cards, when placed on a clearly defined section of the teaching machine, closed a circuit that lit a reinforcement light on the machine. Incorrect answer cards, when placed on the section, had no consequence. The first part of the spelling confusion program involved selecting from several possible answer choices the one that matched the correctly spelled sample word. For example, "small" was written on a sample card; the matching alternatives, each on its own card and displayed beneath the sample, were "smal, swall, sval, small, snall." The second part of the program required selecting the correctly spelled choice to fit into a blank space in a sample sentence. For example, the sentence: "I can't _____ his name," had "remember, remembre, remembur, remeber, remebmer" as its alternatives.

Most frames contained the following kinds of error choices: reversal of letter order, visual configuration confusion (reversal of letter order or substitution of letter with a similar visual appearance), phonetic misspelling, and occasionally an associated word, such as "letter/write" or "believe/think." The order of presentation was arranged according to frequency of occurrence and word length. If there were several words with the same frequency of occurrence, they were presented in order of increasing length.

The first series of frames was programmed to teach the basic matching task itself and to gradually increase the difficulty of the task. The earliest frames had only three alternatives, with quite dissimilar choices visually, acoustically, and associatively. As the program progressed, the incorrect alternatives gradually increased in number of choices and in variety of errors, until the above criteria for wrong answers were reached.

This task was followed by the "scrambled word" task. Simply being able to match or pick a correctly spelled word from a series of alternative spellings does not necessarily insure that those words can then be correctly spelled spontaneously. Detecting an error is different from never making an error. The scrambled word task was designed to lead the patient into spontaneous correct spelling.

The program consisted of a series of sentence frames, each with a word missing. This missing word, with its letters in scrambled order, was written above the blank space in the sentence. The answer was presented in the upper right hand corner of the following item. The last frame of the program required the patient to make as many other words as he could out of a single word. Throughout the tasks the length of the scrambled word gradually increased.

Other Programmed Tasks. The spelling confusion and scrambled word tasks were the last completely "home-made" programs our patient worked through. By this time, early in June, our patient had progressed to a stage at which existing language skills programs could be utilized. Through the auspices of the Library of the Committee on Programmed Instruction, Harvard University, Cambridge, Massachusetts, we evaluated a large number of language skills programs on the market. Some we rejected because they were too clearly designed for use with children, others because they were too elementary, still others because they did not serve our patient's particular language needs. Some were used in modified presentation forms. Others were used in their standard forms.[2]

In one sense, there was still another class of "programmed tasks" to which our subject was exposed. These are the programming attempts we made and discarded because they were failures. Apparently logical tasks proved themselves empirically useless in some instances. For example, our earliest attempts to teach "before and after" were built around teaching the days of the week as well. The subject's performance immediately indicated that this intervention

---

[2] Among the programs which were used successfully either in modified or original forms were: *Effective Listening*, New York: Basic Systems, Inc., 1963, Gordon, E. J.; *A Programmed Approach to Writing*, Boston: Ginn & Co., 1964, Zaborska, M., and Coffroth, J.; *Vocabulary Growth: Divide and Conquer Words*, Chicago: Coronet Instructional Films, 1962, T.M.I.–Grolier Programs; *Fundamentals of Algebra, I, II*, New York: Teaching Machines Corp., 1961, Tosti, D. T., *et al.; Elementary Arithmetic, Fractions: Basic Concepts*, New York: Teaching Machines Corp., 1962, Evans, J. L., *et al.; Steps in Reading Literature*, New York: Harcourt, Brace and World, 1964, Spacks, B., *et al., Steps to Better Reading, Books 1, 2, 3*, New York: Harcourt, Brace and World, 1963, Schramm, W., *et al.*, used with *Adventures for Readers, Books 1 & 2*, Nieman, E. W., *et al.*, and *Adventures in Reading*, Lodge, E., *et al.* New York: Harcourt, Brace & World, 1964.

was too early and too difficult. The task was discarded, and a useful task combining "before and after" with a new adjective vocabulary was written. We observed our patient's inability to deal with the initial "before and after" program; we read it aloud to nonaphasic adults, and managed to confuse them, also. The practice of running nonaphasic adults through our programs before giving them to our aphasic subject became standard at this point.

Results

There are two aspects to the results of this project. The first has to do with the general nature of this patient's recovery from aphasia. The second is specifically concerned with performances on the programmed tasks. Each of these aspects is discussed below.

One year following the onset of this young man's aphasia, he was still receiving therapy predominantly geared to increasing his rate of silent reading. This appears to be his most persistent language problem. His current silent reading rate is over 300 words per minute, with 100% comprehension. It is felt that if he had been a less gifted person linguistically before he became aphasic, his present difficulties would go unnoticed. However, he reports occasional word-finding difficulties, and some difficulty in concentrating for long periods of time on language activities. He has not re-entered graduate school as of this date, but is auditing graduate courses. He intends to return to graduate school in the near future. Some indications of improvement in his general language performance are shown in Figures 1, 2, and 3.

Figure 1 represents an analysis of the subject's language in conversation with his wife in December, 1964, and in October, 1965. This figure shows increased variety in his conversational speech for both words used and length of utterances in the second sample. More adequate conversational skill is indicated by the increase in frequency of specific nouns and the concurrent decrease in generic nouns, the higher number of different words used within a similar total verbal output, the increased type-token ratio, and the statistically significant f ratio computed on mean length of conversational responses. In general, the data reported in this figure shows a less constricted vocabulary as well as less stereotyped length of conversational response.

PATIENT'S SPEECH IN CONVERSATION

MATCHED IO MIN. SEGMENTS

	DEC. '64	OCT. '65
WORDS SPOKEN	1114.	1111.
DIFFERENT WORDS	173.	264.
NOUNS	45.	116.
GENERIC NOUNS	40.	20.
NEOLOGISMS	2.	0.
TTR – NOUNS	.22	.48
MEAN LENGTH OF RESPONSE	9.52	12.72
o^{-2}	95.53	284.00

$$F = 2.94 ** $$

SIGNIF. AT .0I

FIGURE 1

Comparison of patient's speech in conversation, December, 1964, and October, 1965.

Figure 2 shows the patient's written picture descriptions and scores on the *Minnesota Test for the Differential Diagnosis of Aphasia,* obtained in February and in October, 1965. This is a five-minute timed measure. More written language was produced and,

WRITTEN PICTURE DESCRIPTION
M. T. D. D. A.

FEBRUARY 1965

a man is flying a kite while a dog stupidly stands there. — His wife (maybe) looks

TOTAL WORDS WRITTEN = 16

MTDDA ERROR SCORE = 5

OCTOBER 1965

There is a boy who is in a tree. He is trying to get his kite out of the tree. A woman or girl is pointing at the boy. A man, who also has a kite, is flying successfully. There is a dog in the picture, possibly a scottie. There is also a pond in which a

TOTAL WORDS WRITTEN = 57

MTDDA ERROR SCORE = 0

FIGURE 2

Patient's performance on the written picture description; Minnesota Test for the Differential Diagnosis of Aphasia, February, 1965 and October, 1965.

again, less constraint was apparent in the second sample. It is interesting to note the change in handwriting. Although handwriting was never worked on, improvement seems to have accompanied the general content improvement and faster rate.

Figure 3 represents an analysis of two oral descriptions of the same picture, one done in February and one in October, 1965. It shows that he is talking more rapidly, and more fluently in the

ORAL PICTURE DESCRIPTION

	FEB.	OCT.
TOTAL UTTERANCES	102.	186.
% APPROPRIATE WORDS	77.46	87.09
% DISFLUENCIES	22.54	12.91
CONCEPTS ENUMERATED	10.	17.
CONCEPT REDUNDANCIES	5.	2.
TOTAL DIFFERENT NOUNS	11.	19.
TOTAL DIF. VERB-FORMS	3.	7.

FIGURE 3

Comparison of patient's oral description of a picture, February, 1965, and October, 1965.

second sample. Further, he was able to describe the picture more fully and with fewer redundancies. He also used a greater variety of nouns and verb forms. The data shown in Figures 1, 2, and 3 adequately reflect our observation of the patient's general language improvement.

Performance on the programmed tasks, as measured by pre- and post-tests, reflects more specific improvement. For some programs, pre- and post-tests were not necessary. For example, for the earliest language usage sequences, the patient simply was unable to repeat whole words without sounding them out, or phrases, or whole sentences. He could not answer the questions used near the end of the program; he could not write the sentence. He could do all of these things following completion of the task. For other tasks, however, pre- and post-program scores were mandatory in order to measure effectiveness of the programmed tasks. Figure 4 represents pre- and post-program scores on criterion items from the preposition sequence of the language usage tasks. His post-program performance was errorless.

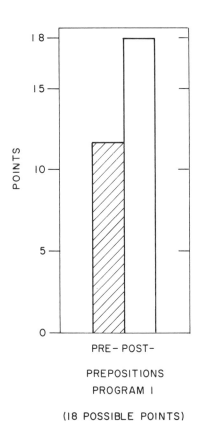

PRE- POST-

PREPOSITIONS

PROGRAM I

(18 POSSIBLE POINTS)

FIGURE 4

Performance on pre- and post-program test for preposition usage.

Figure 5 shows pre- and post-test performance on a test designed to measure the subject's ability to repeat spoken speech. The tests were constructed using items equivalent in difficulty to criterion items from each task. The same grammatical structure was employed; however, different vocabulary was used. The nearly errorless performance on both pre- and post-tests for those portions of the test furnishing written as well as auditory stimulation suggests that the subject, when allowed to, relied on visual rather than auditory stimulation for most cues. The increase in post-program scores for auditory items for the first test is maintained on the second program pretest. This suggests retention of such material from one task to the next in the series.

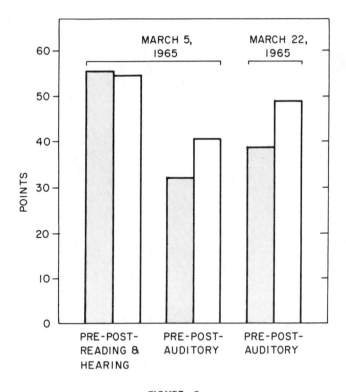

FIGURE 5

Performance on pre- and post-program tests for repetition skill.

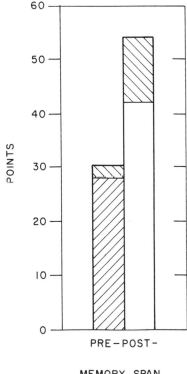

FIGURE 6

Performance on pre- and post-program tests of auditory memory span.

Figure 6 represents performance on the pre- and post-test designed for the memory-span task. The pre- and post-tests were equivalent in terms of structure, but used different vocabulary. Both tests measured related language sequences, unrelated words and digits. Cross-hatched portions represent those items on the test that measured digit span. Examination of the figure reveals increased memory span following program exposure. The post-program score was nearly errorless.[3]

---

[3] With the exception of Figure 1, all data reported here were gathered at least three months after onset of aphasia to preclude spontaneous recovery.

Discussion

The experiences gained as a result of this project, the data, and the reactions of the aphasic patient who served as the subject all strongly suggest that programmed instruction is potentially useful as a tool for recovery from aphasia. Some of the usefulness is shown in the data. Some is much more subjective, and is concerned with the rigorousness that programmed instruction forces upon the practicing clinician. By forcing careful observation, programming seems almost automatically to generate insight into the course of clinical sessions. Clinicians rarely can keep such close tabs on the effects of unprogrammed therapy sessions. With programmed instruction it is not only mandatory to do so, but it is also an extremely simple matter. The basic advantage of programmed instruction is that it furnishes measurable effects for clinical techniques.

Related to this is the manner in which a program evolves. Programmed instruction requires the programmer to make a series of "educated guesses," based both on the technology of programmed instruction and on the programmer's area of professional competency; they are tried out, the learner shows the programmer where his guesses have been correct and incorrect, the program is revised accordingly, and tried again. The learner's performance *using* the program, then, furnishes a step-by-step analysis of the way in which training works.

This unique interdependence of learner and teacher points out a third advantage we have found, not only with this patient, but with other aphasic patients and programs as well. Even our most severely impaired patients have quickly learned this interaction. Our relationships have been extremely close as a result. Part of our excellent therapeutic climate results from the ease with which patients can observe their own progress. Such feedback is a powerful reinforcement for both learner and teacher.

A fourth advantage has to do with economy. Although our preparation time was often four to six times longer than the time this one patient required to work through the material, it was warranted, since our aim was to develop programs useful to other patients as well. We are currently using these programs successfully with other patients. Given even a moderately large sample, it is clear that time-saving could be enormous. Moreover, the careful analysis required ensures that a given programmed session has a definable standard of quality.

The fifth advantage is related solely to the clinician. Using a programmed therapy session is an exhilarating experience. Not only is the clinician aware *a priori* of the direction in which a given session is going, but his time in that session can be devoted to completely free observation of his therapy and his patient. Programming serves to make two people of one clinician. The observations we were capable of making, not only of program performance but of other behavior too, suggest that it is a maximal way of learning to know a patient's strengths and weaknesses. In the long run, this is a defining characteristic of successful rehabilitation.

One more example of our patient's progress concludes this discussion. This is an unedited excerpt from the middle of a longer statement, written by him of his reactions to programmed instruction. Because of his major contribution to this work, it is necessary that his reactions be included:

"One of the very first tasks was to repeat a difficult sentence in its entirety. I didn't think it was possible, but step by step, starting with one sound, then a word, then a phrase, and finally the sentence, I did it. It was quite an achievement for me, and it lifted my spirits substantially. With the programmed approach, I could see some progress and felt that I was doing something about my aphasia.

"Flexibility was another important aspect of their techniques. If I said, for example, that prepositions were difficult for me, I might have a program on prepositions in a week. (That one was, I think, particularly successful.) It seemed that programs were set up with a very specific purpose in mind, and if one method failed there could always be another angle to be worked on. However, in a way, I was a special case, in that most of the programming was tailor-made for me — since things usually have to be more standardized, some of the flexibility may have to be sacrificed. Still, it was good to work on something which I *knew* needed work, instead of bits and pieces, some of which was too easy, some too hard. I guess that I am confounding flexibility on the one hand with plan and pattern on the other, but they seem to go together.

"One of the most valuable aspects of the programming approach, at least for me, was the fact that either the experimenter, a card, or a taped response would tell me immediately whether I was correct or incorrect in my response. Before I was aphasic, that might not have made so much difference, but since I have been so unsure of so much, the knowledge that I was either right or wrong was a boon. With that knowledge, I have felt that I am learning and could forget the constant questioning of myself."

REFERENCES

Bijou, S. W., "Systematic Instruction in the Attainment of Right-Left Form Concepts in Young and Retarded Children." In J. G. Holland, and B. F. Skinner (Eds.), *An Analysis of the Behavioral Processes Involved in Self-Instruction with Teaching Machines*, final report to U.S. Office of Education, 1965.

Bricker, A. B. (Harris), H. Schuell, and J. J. Jenkins, "Effect of Word Frequency and Word Length on Aphasic Spelling Errors," *J. Speech Hearing Res.*, 1964, 7.

Brown, R., and U. Bellugi, "The Child's Acquisition of Syntax," *Harvard Educ. Rev.*, 1964, 34.

Falconer, G. A., "Teaching Machines for the Deaf," *Volta Rev.*, Reprint No. 730, 1960.

Filby, Y., and A. E. Edwards, "An Application of Automated Teaching Methods to Test and Teach Form Discrimination to Aphasics," *J. Progr. Inst.*, 1963, 2.

Holland, A. L., and J. Matthews, "Application of Teaching Machine Concepts to Speech Pathology and Audiology," *Asha*, 1963, 5.

Rosenberg, B., "The Performance of Aphasics on Automated Visuo-perceptual Discrimination, Training and Transfer Tasks," *J. Speech Hearing Res.*, 1965, 8.

Schuell, H., J. J. Jenkins, and J. Jiminez-Pabon, *Aphasia in Adults*. New York: Hooker, 1965.

Stuckless, R., and J. Birch, "Programmed Instruction in Written Language for the Deaf," *Except. Child*, 1964, 30.

Taylor, M. L., "Language Therapy." In H. G. Burr, (Ed.), *The Aphasic Adult: Evaluation and Rehabilitation*. Charlottesville: Wayside Press, 1964.

Taylor, M. L., and E. S. Sands, "Application of Programmed Instruction Techniques to the Language Rehabilitation of Severely Impaired Aphasic Patients" (Abstract), *Asha*, 1965, 7.

V

Reinstating Speech in Mute Children and Adults

As used in this book, the term "mute" is given a restricted meaning. It does not refer to all persons who do not speak. The mute child or adult, as differentiated from the speech-free individual, talks in some situations but not in others, or spoke at one time but currently does not. The term is also used with the implication that the lack of speech is not due to damage to the speech mechanism or to structures that support speech. Thus, mutism refers to the situation in which environmental variables no longer maintain speech behavior, or where the environment actively suppresses speech. Remedial measures do not, therefore, involve training the individual to make the differentiated responses or the discriminations involved in speaking, but in changing the environment so that a repertoire that it is assumed already exists will be emitted. Psychotherapeutic approaches to mutism stress assessing the "causes" of the loss of language and manipulating these. The approaches reported in this section do not place any emphasis upon determining (if this is in fact possible) the historical basis of the mutism, but are oriented towards changing current factors that may control speaking.

In the paper by Sherman, although shaping procedures are used initially to produce verbal behavior, there is clear evidence that a repertoire already exists. In this paper, after the first few sounds or words were obtained by shaping procedures, the previously mute individual started emitting sounds and words, often appropriately, that the experimenter had not shaped. Apparently, reinforcing some members of the class of verbal operants strengthened a wide range of responses in this class.

Straughan discusses a somewhat different kind of problem — that of the adolescent who does not speak in specific situations. His paper, as well as other chapters in this book, illustrates a current trend in behavior modification — treating a problem in the environment in which the problem actually occurs. Thus, with children who are mute in class, Straughan works in the classroom. Using a procedure adapted from Patterson (1964), Straughan attempts to manipulate the manner in which other children in class respond to the speech, or lack of it, of the individual under study. This is quite different from the traditional psychotherapy approach to such problems, in which the individual and a highly trained professional interact in a special environment isolated from other persons.

11

James A. Sherman

Use of Reinforcement and Imitation To Reinstate Verbal Behavior in Mute Psychotics

Verbal behavior was reinstated in 3 long-term, mute psychotics using reinforcement procedures. For 2 Ss, shaping and fading techniques were used to establish limited verbal repertoires. With a 3rd S, the shaping technique was ineffective; however, a reinforced imitation technique succeeded in developing imitative vocalizations which were then established as verbal responses. For all Ss, the functional role of contingent reinforcement in maintaining the recently developed verbal behavior was demonstrated: when Ss received reinforcement only when they were not responding verbally, their rates of verbal responding showed marked decreases, but recovered when contingent reinforcement for verbal behavior was resumed.

Reprinted from Journal of Abnormal Psychology, Vol. 70, No. 3, June 1965.

This investigation was supported in part by a Public Health Service fellowship (1–F1–MH–20, 426–01) from the National Institute of Mental Health. This paper is a portion of the research submitted in partial fulfillment of the requirements for the PhD degree at the University of Washington, 1964. The author is grateful to Donald M. Baer for his advice and encouragement throughout the course of this study.

Behavior therapy is a term currently used to label the modification of abnormal human behavior through procedures developed by experimental psychology. In recent years behavior therapy studies have begun to appear with increasing frequency. A critical review of this area has been presented by Sherman (*1964*).

A major problem in the area of behavior therapy has been the lack of experimentation. Certainly it is worthwhile to provide examples that a certain procedure may be useful for therapeutic purposes. However, it seems more valuable first to demonstrate experimentally that the procedure used was indeed responsible for producing this changed behavior. With individual cases, such an experimental demonstration can be provided by showing that systematic manipulations of the procedure repeatedly result in reliable changes in the problem behavior (*Sidman, 1960*).

Two examples of successful but nonexperimental behavior-therapy studies are provided by Isaacs, Thomas, and Goldiamond (*1960*) and by Sherman (*1963*). In the Isaacs et al. study, a shaping procedure was used to reinstate verbal behavior in two previously mute psychotics. For one subject the reinstated verbal behavior was obtained only in response to questions posed by the experimenter in the experimental situation. The subject apparently did not respond to questions asked by others; nor did he respond on the ward to questions even when asked by the experimenter. In the other case, verbal behavior was reinstated both in the experimental situation and on the ward, but only in response to the experimenter. An attempt was made to generalize this verbal responding to other people by bringing another person into the experimental situation. After a period of a month, the subject began to respond verbally to the second person. He also began to respond to people on the ward when the ward situation was arranged so that his nonverbal requests had no reinforcing consequences.

In the Sherman study, the subject was a mute psychotic who communicated with ward attendants by writing notes. The experimenter refused to read the subject's notes and used a shaping procedure to establish a verbal response. The reinstatement of one verbal response was accompanied by an almost total reinstatement of other verbal behavior in response to the experimenter. In addition, once ward attendants refused to read the subject's notes, he responded verbally to them on the ward.

Unfortunately, in neither study were systematic manipulations of procedure performed to determine their effect on verbalizations. While it appeared highly likely that the reinforcement procedures were responsible for the subjects' verbal behavior, this could not be stated with complete confidence. It could have been, for example, that the extrinsic reinforcement was irrelevant, and that some other unspecified "social relationship" was responsible for the increase in verbalizations. Or, in the Isaacs et al. study, since the subjects were concurrently participating in group therapy, this might have contributed to the verbal reinstatement.

The purpose of the present study was (a) to use positive reinforcement procedures to reinstate some verbal behavior in long-term, mute psychotics, and (b) to manipulate conditions to demonstrate experimentally that the contingent use of reinforcement was essential to this reinstatement. A secondary goal was to evaluate the generalization of the verbal behavior to persons other than the experimenter and to situations other than the experimental one.

Methods and Results

The subjects were three hospitalized psychotics at a state hospital.[1] All subjects had been hospitalized continuously for 20 years or longer and all had had long histories of mutism. A complete description of each subject is given below.

General Procedure

In general, three separate procedures were employed to establish verbal behavior in the subjects: shaping, reinforced imitation, and fading. Shaping procedures are used when it is necessary to develop behavior which is not currently exhibited by a subject, either because of the complexity of the behavior or because of the impoverished behavioral repertoire of the subject. In shaping, the experimenter at first reinforces responses which may have little similarity to the desired behavior, but which are clearly within the subject's current behavioral repertoire. The variability of the subject's behavior allows the experimenter to reinforce successively

---

[1] The author is indebted to Giulio di Furia, Superintendent, Western State Hospital, and John B. Marks, Director, Mental Health Research Institute, Fort Steilacoom, Washington, for their assistance in making space and subjects available for this study.

only behaviors which are increasingly similar to the desired behavior. Finally, only the desired behavior is reinforced until it attains suitable strength.

Although imitation has often been cited as having important functions in behavior development, it rarely has been used to modify abnormal human behavior (for one of the few examples see *Jones, 1924*). In the present study, a reinforced imitation technique was employed with one subject (Subject 3) with whom shaping techniques appeared to be ineffective. An imitation procedure was chosen because a study by Baer and Sherman (*1964*), with children, demonstrated that the probability of occurrence of an imitative bar-pressing response could be changed by contingent reinforcement, not directly of bar pressing, but of other imitative responses. This study thus suggested that a class of imitative responses could be established such that the strengthening of a few members of the class would result in the strengthening of other members of the class.

The implications of the Baer and Sherman study for the establishment of verbal behavior in a subject seemed clear: if a repertoire of various nonverbal imitative behaviors could be established, it might result in an increased probability of occurrence of imitative vocal and verbal behavior. In the imitative procedure used in the present study, the subject initially was required to imitate various nonverbal behaviors in order to receive reinforcement; gradually the behaviors to be imitated progressed to behaviors associated with vocalizations (e.g., mouth movements), and then to vocalizations and verbalizations.

Fading procedures may be used to change the stimulus conditions in which a behavior is exhibited, without changing the form of the behavior and without repeated extinction trials and consequent errors. The procedure is to introduce the stimulus change very gradually, at a rate which produces no disruption in correct performance. In this manner, an already established behavior may be errorlessly brought under the control of new discriminative stimuli. For example, in programed instruction a verbal response of the subject may be obtained by providing that assortment of textual cues which invariably leads to the emission of the correct response. Then the textual cues are gradually changed so that the subject responds correctly to what was a complex question without the presence of the textual cues which originally controlled the response. Fading procedures may also be used to program, rapidly and with few errors, the learning of stimulus discriminations, where standard discrimination procedures would involve more errors and longer time periods (*Moore & Goldiamond, 1964; Terrace, 1963a, 1963b*).

In the present study, once subjects were mimicking some of the experimenter's verbalizations, fading procedures were used to establish the subjects' verbal behavior in response to the experimenter's questions.

Once shaping, reinforced imitation, and fading procedures had established stable rates of verbal behavior in the subjects, periods of differential reinforcement for other behavior (DRO) were programed to investigate the role of contingent reinforcement in maintaining the verbalizations. During DRO periods all conditions in the experimental sessions were kept the same as in the preceding sessions, except the reinforcement contingencies. Reinforcement was delivered only when the subjects were not responding verbally, but was delivered in the same amount and at approximately the same rate as previously. Thus, any changes in a subject's rate of verbal behavior during the DRO period could be directly attributed to the changed reinforcement contingencies rather than any other factor in the experimental situation.

Following the DRO periods, contingent reinforcement for verbal behavior was resumed until the subjects again showed stable rates of verbalizations. Further reinforcement procedures were then used to expand the subjects' verbal repertoires.

A test of the generalization of the subjects' responding to other people was made by having a second experimenter come into the experimental situation and take over the sessions, both in the presence and absence of the first experimenter. The generalization of the subjects' verbal behavior to other situations was evaluated by their verbal responses to both the first experimenter and the second experimenter on the ward.

The responses of the subjects during sessions were recorded both with a tape recorder and in writing by the experimenter. Checks upon the reliability of the experimenter's recording were not attempted since the responses of the subjects (once they were responding with words) were easily and clearly discriminable. One indication of the reliability of recording was obtained from the generalization test periods when a second experimenter took over the experimental sessions and recorded the responses of the subjects, both in writing and by tape recording. The tapes of these sessions were later scored by the first experimenter. There were no differences between the two records, either in type or in number of words.

Specific Procedures and Results

Since the specific application of the procedures varied among subjects, a detailed description for each subject is required. The experimental room which was used for sessions contained a desk, three chairs, and a tape recorder.

Subject 1

Subject 1 was a 63-year-old man, diagnosed, in 1916, as dementia praecox, hebephrenic type. He had been in the hospital continuously for 47 years, with a history of mutism for 45 of those years. At the time of this study, he was not receiving any medication or participating in psychotherapy. Periodically, when seen on the ward, Subject 1 could be observed walking around mumbling softly to himself. However, all of this mumbling appeared to be nonsensical vocal behavior. In his 45-year history of mutism, Subject 1 had not exhibited any recorded instance of appropriate verbal behavior.

Sessions 1–2. Sessions were held 3 times a week and were approximately ¾ of an hour in length. Initially, candy and cigarettes were used as reinforcers. When a reinforcer was presented, it was accompanied by a statement from the experimenter such as, "Good" or "Very good."

Since the subject did not attend to the experimenter most of the time, and since it was felt that the refinement of later verbal behavior would, to some degree, be dependent upon keeping the subject's attention, the first response reinforced was making eye contact with the experimenter for a 1-second period. By the end of Session 2, the subject was making eye contact with the experimenter an increasing amount of time.

Sessions 3–8. At the start of Session 3, the subject spontaneously emitted a vocalization (a grunt) and was reinforced for it. Thereafter, reinforcement was made contingent upon vocalizations. Vocalizations were defined as any audible sound, including moans, grunts, burps, and coughs. Had words occurred, they too would have been reinforced, of course. However, words never did occur until after direct shaping during the early sessions.

By Session 6 the subject exhibited a low rate of vocalizations (five to eight per session); however, by Session 8 there was no indication of any further increase in rate.

Sessions 9–11. To increase the effectiveness of the reinforcement procedure, portions of the subject's lunch were made contingent upon vocalizations. Each lunch 3 days a week was divided up into approximately 50 portions; and when a vocalization occurred, the experimenter said, "Good," and handed a bite of food to the subject. Concurrently, checks were made of the subject's weight before each session. The subject showed only minor weight changes between sessions; he weighed 150 pounds at the start of the experiment and 151 pounds at the end.

Sessions 12–25. At the beginning of Session 12, the experimenter started to use instructions. A bite of food was held up and the experimenter said, "Say food." At first, any vocalization which temporally followed these instructions was reinforced. Gradually, however, the requirements for reinforcement were changed so that an increasing similarity to the word "food" was required.

Between Sessions 12 and 22, the responses of the subject progressed from indistingishable mumbles and grunts to drawn out "o͞o"[2] sounds, to "o͞od" sounds, and finally to a distinct "food." When the response "food" occurred, the subject also began to repeat other simple words said by the experimenter, such as "water," "pie," and "Jello." By Session 25, in addition to the word "food," the subject had repeated 12 different words. However, the experimenter's control over the subject's responding was weak. Frequently, the subject did not respond when the experimenter held up a bite of food and said, "Say food."

Sessions 26–43. To increase the experimenter's control over the subject's verbal responding, all three of the subject's meals for 3 consecutive days were made contingent upon verbal behavior. The experimenter continued to use the instructions, "Say food," while holding up a bite of food. If the subject responded, he was reinforced. If he did not respond within 10 seconds, the experimenter silently read a book for 1 minute before starting the next trial.

By Session 43 the experimenter had good control over the subject's verbal responding. Almost every time the experimenter used the instructions, the subject responded, "Food." In addition, the subject consistently repeated any one of approximately 20 words (such as "meat" or "pie") the experimenter might use instead of the word "food." However, the subject did not respond with a nonimitative word. For example, when the experimenter held up a bite of food and said, "Say food," the subject responded, "Food." If on the next trial, the experimenter held up a bite of food and asked, "What is this?" the subject did not respond.

Sessions 44–79. To obtain the word "food" from the subject when the experimenter asked, "What is this?" a fading procedure was used. With the fading procedure, the experimenter continued to hold up a bite of food each time and to deliver instructions to the subject. The behavior of the subject — that is, saying "Food" — was maintained with reinforcement while the instructions to the subject were gradually changed in

---

[2] Standard dictionary phonetic symbols are used to indicate pronunciation.

the following steps: (a) "Say food"; (b) "Say foo_"; (c) "Say f_____";
(d) "What is this? Say f_____"; (e) "What is this? Say _____"; (f)
"What is this?"

By Session 79 the subject was saying the word "food" with great
regularity as soon as the experimenter held up the bite of food. In fact,
between Sessions 72 and 79 the subject was responding regularly enough
so that he consistently received almost all of every experimentally controlled meal. In addition to the word "food," the subject occasionally
named specific foods. When he did so, he was reinforced. Nevertheless,
approximately 95% of the words he emitted were the word "food."

Sessions 80–85. To determine whether contingent reinforcement was
essential in maintaining the subject's verbal behavior, a period of DRO
was programed. Now, if the subject responded verbally when the bite
of food was held up, he did not receive the food reinforcement until 30
seconds after his response (or if he responded more than once, 30 seconds after his last response). If the subject did not respond, he received
the food 30 seconds after it was held up. Thus, the subject received the
food (accompanied by "Good" from the experimenter) whether he responded or not. All other conditions were kept the same as in the immediately preceding sessions. The experimenter continued to hold up
the bite of food and ask, "What is this?" at the same rate, and the food
was delivered at approximately the same rate and in the same amount
as previously.

Figure 1 shows the effect of DRO sessions on the subject's previously
stable rate of verbal responding. This graph is a cumulative plot of the
total number of nonimitative words emitted by the subject each session
(mainly "food"). As can be seen from the figure, the DRO period
(dotted line) resulted in a marked and stable decrease in verbal responding.

Sessions 86–92. Contingent food reinforcement for verbalizations was
resumed. However, now when the experimenter held up the bite of food
and asked, "What is this?" there was no response from the subject to be
reinforced. Therefore, at the start of Session 86, the experimenter returned to an earlier step in the reinforcement procedure. The experimenter held up the bit of food and said, "Say food." The subject responded and was reinforced. After this had been repeated three times,
a brief fading procedure, similar to that used during earlier sessions, was
used until, after about 15 minutes, the subject said "Food" when the
experimenter merely held up the bite of food. Thereafter, verbal behavior was simply reinforced as before.

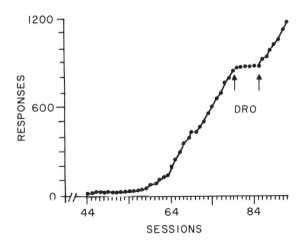

FIGURE 1

A cumulative record of the number of verbal responses per session for S1 under reinforcement for responses and DRO conditions.

As can be seen from Figure 1, the reinstitution of reinforcement for verbal behavior, plus the brief fading procedure, resulted in a recovery of the subject's former rate of nonimitative verbalizations.

Sessions 93–122. Up to this time the subject's verbal behavior consisted primarily of one word, the word "food." Next, an attempt was made to see how long it would take to establish 10 new words in his repertoire. For this, 10 picture cards were employed. Each of these cards contained a picture of some common object or animal such as a ship, a dog, a rabbit, or some grapes. To establish these 10 new verbal responses, food reinforcement was continued and a fading procedure was used. First, the experimenter pointed to the picture of the dog and said, "Say dog." When the subject repeated the word, he was reinforced. Gradually the word "dog" was faded out from the experimenter's instructions until the subject was responding with "Dog" when the experimenter pointed to the card and said, "What is this?" A similar fading technique was used for the other 9 cards, and by Session 122 the subject was responding appropriately and reliably to each of the 10 cards.

Total verbal behavior. At the end of the experimental sessions, the subject's verbal repertoire consisted of approximately 30 words which could be reliably obtained. The subject would say "Food," "Candy," "Cigarette," name the 10 picture cards, read his name and read the numbers from 1 to 20 printed on a card. The name and number reading responses appeared to be indirect effects of the reinforcement of other verbal behavior, since these responses were never directly shaped.

Six months after the experimental sessions had been terminated, the subject was tested to see whether his verbal behavior could still be obtained. All the verbal behavior which the subject exhibited at the end of the experimental sessions was still obtainable after this 6-month delay.

Subject 2

Subject 2 was a 45-year-old man diagnosed as schizophrenic. He had been hospitalized continuously for 20 years and had had a history of mutism for 16 of those years. During this study Subject 2 was not taking part in psychotherapy, but was receiving medication (tofranil, 25 milligrams, three times a day).

From ward reports and questioning of the attendants, it appeared that Subject 2 had emitted approximately six words in the 6-month period prior to the study. All of these words were either "Yes" or "No" in response to the attendants' questions.

Sessions 1–4. Candy was used as the reinforcer, accompanied by "Good" or "Very good" from the experimenter. Sessions were held two times a week and were approximately ¾ of an hour in length.

The word "candy" was shaped through reinforcement of the subject's increasing approximations to the word when the experimenter held up a piece of candy and asked, "What is this?" By Session 4 "Candy" could be reliably obtained from the subject whenever the experimenter held a piece of candy up. In addition, during these early sessions the experimenter periodically asked the subject various conversational-type questions such as, "What is your name?" "What do you like to read?" "What did you do yesterday?" and the like. At first, any type of vocalization following one of these questions was reinforced; gradually, however, the subject was required to say at least one intelligible word in order to receive reinforcement. During Session 4 the subject responded for the first time with distinct words to some of the conversational questions.

Sessions 5–17. Since the subject was responding perfectly when candy was held up, beginning with Session 5, the experimenter began to ask the subject to name various objects in the experimental room such as a chair, a table, a pencil, and so forth. Each time the experimenter would point to the object and say, "What is that?" In addition, mixed in with object questions, the experimenter continued to ask the conversation questions. For both types of questions, if the subject responded appropriately he was reinforced; if not, the experimenter silently read a book for 1 minute before asking the next question.

Figure 2 shows the results of this procedure. This figure is a plot of the percentage of each type of question, object and conversation, to which the subject replied each session. A reply to a question consisted of one or more intelligible words that were appropriate to the question being asked. As can be seen from Figure 2, the subject exhibited an increased percentage of questions answered for both object and conversation questions.

Sessions 18–35. To determine whether contingent reinforcement was functional in increasing the subject's verbal behavior, several DRO periods were programed. In these periods the experimenter continued to ask both object and conversation questions at the same rate as previously. During DRO conditions, if the subject responded, the experi-

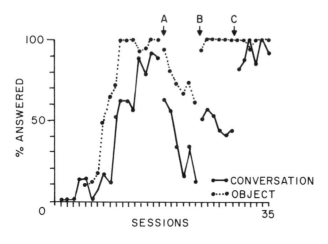

FIGURE 2

A record of the percent of verbal responses per session for S2 to two types of questions under reinforcement for responses and DRO conditions. (At (a) answers to both types of questions were put under the DRO condition; at (b) answers to object questions were reinforced, with answers to conversation questions kept under the DRO condition; at (c) answers to both types of questions were reinforced.)

menter waited until 30 seconds after the response and then reinforced the subject with candy and a verbal "Good." If the subject did not respond, he received reinforcement 30 seconds after the experimenter's question. All of the object questions used were ones that had been asked in the immediately preceding sessions. (The differences in the experimenter's conversation questions between sessions were due to differences in the subject's answers which necessitated slightly different follow-up questions.)

In Sessions 18–23, responses to both types of questions were under the DRO conditions. Figure 2 shows the effect upon the percentage of questions answered: answers to both object and conversation questions showed a marked decrease, with the conversation answers showing the greater decrease.

During Sessions 24–29, contingent reinforcement for answers to object questions was resumed, while DRO procedures were left in effect following answers to conversation questions. With this procedure, percentage of answers to object questions rose to its former rate, while percentage of answers to conversation questions showed an initial rise, although not to its former rate, and began to drop.

In Sessions 30–35, contingent reinforcement was resumed for answers to conversation questions, with contingent reinforcement for answers to object questions kept in effect. The results, plotted in Figure 2, show that responding to conversation questions rose markedly, while responding to object questions remained high.

Sessions 36–44. Up to this time the subject had responded to conversation questions primarily with one or two word answers. To increase the number of words spoken per answer, object questions were discontinued and a fading procedure was used for conversation questions. For example, when the experimenter would ask the subject, "What did you do yesterday?" the subject might respond "Walk." The experimenter would then reply, "No, make a sentence. Say, *I went for a walk.*" If the subject repeated the sentence, he was reinforced. Each time the subject responded to the experimenter's questions with one or two words, the experimenter made a sentence out of the subject's response and told the subject to repeat the sentence. Gradually, the verbal cues supplied by the experimenter were faded out until, when the subject responded with one or two words to a question, the experimenter only had to say, "Make a sentence," to obtain a sentence or complete phrase from the subject. Finally, by Session 44 even these last instructions were dropped. The subject was regularly responding to common conversational questions with full-sentence answers, averaging about five to six words per answer.

Subject 3

Subject 3 was a 61-year-old woman, diagnosed (in 1926) as dementia praecox, simple type. She had been hospitalized continuously for 37 years and had a history of complete mutism for 33 of those years. During this study Subject 3 was not participating in psychotherapy, but was receiving medication (equanil, 400 milligrams, two times a day).

From the ward reports and questioning of the attendants, it appeared that the subject had not exhibited any verbal behavior in the last 33 years. In fact, the attendants reported that they had never heard the subject emit any type of vocalization.

Sessions 1–10. Initially, candy accompanied by "Good" or "Very good" from the experimenter was used as the reinforcement. Sessions were held three times a week and were approximately ¾ of an hour in length.

Since it appeared that the subject did not exhibit a rate of vocalizations, the first response chosen for reinforcement was lip movement. It was hoped that as lip movements increased in probability of occurrence, vocalizations also would occur. At first, reinforcement was presented whenever very slight lip movements occurred; later, reinforcement was contingent upon a distinct parting of the lips. Once a steady rate of parting the lips was exhibited, this response was put on a variable ratio schedule of reinforcement (VR 3) to further increase its rate.

Sessions 10–23. During the last part of Session 10, the subject emitted a vocalization for the first time (a low moan), and was reinforced for it. Thereafter, the experimenter began to use instructions of "Say candy" while holding up a piece of candy. Reinforcement was presented contingent upon any type of sound which followed these instructions, including soft vocalizations, burps, cough, and audible sighs. If the subject did not respond to the instructions within 20 seconds, the experimenter silently read a book for 1 minute before starting the next trial.

Between Sessions 10 and 23 the subject exhibited a number of sounds; however, the rate of these sounds was extremely low. They also were of very low intensity, so low that the experimenter had difficulty in hearing them even though he sat with his ear approximately 8 inches from the subject's mouth.

Sessions 24–35. In an attempt to increase the effectiveness of the reinforcement procedure, the subject's meals were used as reinforcers. For 3 consecutive days each week the subject's breakfast, lunch, and dinner were each divided up into approximately 60 portions. These portions were presented to the subject, accompanied by "Good" from the experimenter, whenever she emitted a sound following the experimenter's instructions, "Say food."

As in the case of Subject 1, with the introduction of food reinforcement, weight checks were taken before each session. It was found that as experimental sessions progressed, the subject showed a slight decrease in her weight. However, since she was quite overweight at the start of the experimental procedure, this was not of great concern. (The subject was 5 feet, 1 inch tall, and at the start of the experiment weighed 178 pounds; at the end of the experiment she weighed 168 pounds.)

The introduction of food reinforcement failed to increase substantially the subject's low rate of emitting sounds, and by Session 35 it appeared doubtful that continued application of the same procedure would be useful, at least without better methods of detecting faint sounds emitted by the subject.

Sessions 36–57. In order to obtain a rate of sounds from the subject, the imitative procedure described earlier was devised. Again, the purpose of using an imitative procedure was to attempt to establish a functional class of imitative behavior, such that strengthening imitative nonverbal responses would result in the strengthening of imitative vocal and verbal responses.

As a starting point for the imitative procedure, various nonverbal behaviors of the subject which were under the experimenter's verbal control were used. These responses were those of standing up, sitting down, picking up a spoon, and touching the table. Initially, the experimenter said to the subject, "Do this. Stand up." The experimenter then stood up. If the subject performed the response, she was reinforced with a bite of food and "Good" from the experimenter. If she did not perform the response, the experimenter sat down and read for 1 minute before starting the next trial. Gradually, the experimenter changed two aspects of the procedure: first, the verbal description of the action was dropped until the experimenter merely said, "Do this," and performed the response to be imitated; second, the responses exhibited by the experimenter to be imitated were gradually changed until they became more and more similar to vocal behavior. At first, the responses exhibited by the experimenter to be imitated were those of standing up, sitting down, picking up a spoon, and touching the table. Next, other responses such as nodding the head, looking up at the ceiling, and opening the mouth were introduced. After this, responses of blowing out a match and clearing the throat were included.

By Session 40 the subject reliably imitated any of the above responses when the experimenter said, "Do this," and performed the response. At this point the experimenter introduced a vocalization to be imitated —

an "ââä" sound. Not only did the subject fail to imitate this sound, but following its introduction, she did not imitate any of the responses which had been introduced during the previous two sessions. Sessions 41 and 42 were spent re-establishing the imitative repertoire the subject had exhibited prior to Session 40. At Session 43, instead of again moving to vocalizations, several intermediate responses were introduced. These responses progressed from blowing (without the match present), to making a hissing sound, to an aspirate "h" sound, to a "ppph" sound, and finally, to an "ââä" sound. By Session 45 these responses were under good imitative control and further sounds were introduced without difficulty.

By Session 48 the subject was imitating the sounds of "fff," "ōō," and "da," which, when combined, make up the word "food." Since the subject did not, at this point, imitate the entire word, Sessions 49 to 57 were spent chaining these sounds together to make a functional verbal unit. Initially, the experimenter said to the subject, "Say fff (pause while the subject responded) Say ōō." When the subject imitated first "fff" and then "ōō," she was reinforced. Gradually, the instructions were changed to, "Say fff (pause while the subject responded) ōō," and then, "Say fffōō." In a similar manner, "da" was added onto the previously built chain of "fffōō" until, at Session 57, the subject consistently imitated the entire word "food." In addition, it was noted at this point that the subject would consistently imitate many other simple words said by the experimenter.

Sessions 58–78. Since the subject at this point was simply repeating words said by the experimenter, the next step was to have her emit "Food" when the experimenter held up a bite of food and asked, "What is this?" To establish this response, a fading procedure identical with that used for Subject 1 was used, and by Session 66 the subject was responding regularly with "Food" when the experimenter asked, "What is this?" As the reinforcement procedure continued, other words began to appear in the subject's repertoire. She no longer always answered "Food" in response to the experimenter's question, but on occasion named specific foods. These words which appeared were ones which had never been directly shaped by the experimenter. However, if they were appropriate to the kind of food being held up, the subject was reinforced.

From Sessions 65 to 78 the subject responded regularly enough to receive almost all of each experimentally controlled meal. Figure 3 is a plot of this responding. It is a cumulative plot of the total number of responses emitted by the subject each session in response to the experimenter's question, "What is this?" Each of these responses consisted either of "Food" or of the name of a food. In general, as sessions pro-

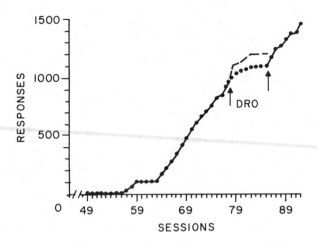

FIGURE 3

A cumulative record of the number of verbal responses per session for S3 under reinforcement for responses and DRO conditions.

gressed the response "Food" became less frequent and, with increasing regularity, the subject responded to the experimenter's question with the name of a specific type of food. Thus, the plot of the responses for Sessions 68 to 78 in Figure 3 represents the combined totals of approximately 40 different words.

Sessions 78–85. Since a stable rate of verbal responding was established, DRO procedures were programed to examine the role of reinforcement in maintaining the verbal behavior. This DRO period was put into effect during the second half of Session 78. While it was in effect the experimenter continued to hold up bites of food and ask, "What is this?" at the same rate as he had before. If the subject responded, she received reinforcement 30 seconds after her response (or if she responded more than once, 30 seconds after her last response). If she did not respond, she received reinforcement 30 seconds after the experimenter said, "What is this?"

Figure 3 shows the results of the DRO period (dotted lines) upon the subject's rate of verbal responding. The two dotted lines shown in the figure representing the DRO period were necessary because of the subject's type of response under this condition. The upper dotted line shows the total number of responses, including repeated responses, emitted by the subject each session. At first, when the experimenter held up the bite of food and asked, "What is this?" the subject might respond "Meat." When reinforcement was not forthcoming, the subject again responded "Meat," and then again and again. On some trials the subject responded over 20 consecutive times before pausing long enough (30 seconds) to receive reinforcement. Thus, because of the repeated responses, the upper dotted line shows an initial increase over the previous rate of verbal responding. These repeated responses, however, soon ceased to be emitted. The lower dotted line of Figure 3 represents the total number of trials responded to with one or more appropriate words per session during the DRO period. In spite of the differences in plotting, both lines show essentially the same characteristic: during the DRO period the subject's rate of verbal responding gradually decreased.

Sessions 86–92. Contingent reinforcement for verbalizations was resumed. Initially, the experimenter had to name several foods in order to obtain a response from the subject to reinforce. After several trials of this, however, the subject again began to emit naming responses when the experimenter held up a bite of food and asked, "What is this?"

The marked increase in the rate of verbal behavior (shown in Figure 3) following the resumption of contingent reinforcement, further demonstrated the functional role that reinforcement played in reproducing the subject's verbal behavior.

Sessions 93–99. These sessions were spent expanding the subject's verbal repertoire. A number of objects and pictures of objects were introduced into the experimental sessions, and the subject was required to name them in order to receive reinforcement. For the most part, the subject named these objects immediately, and it was not required for the experimenter to name them first. In addition, a limited variety of conversational questions and comments were included in each session. These questions and statements were ones such as, "What is your name?" "What ward are you from?" "How are you today?" "Hello," and "Goodby." If the subject responded to these appropriately, she was reinforced.

By the end of Session 99 the subject was consistently naming scores of objects. She also was responding regularly with appropriate replies to the simple questions and statements made by the experimenter, although her replies consisted only of one or two words.

Generalization Tests

Responding to other people. At the end of the experimental procedure, a test of the generalization of the subjects' responding to other people was made by having a second experimenter (a male for Subject 1 and a female for Subject 2 and Subject 3) come into the experimental situation and take over the sessions. The second experimenters were given instructions to duplicate as much as possible the behavior that the first experimenter exhibited during the last experimental session with each subject (including reinforcement for subjects' verbalizations).

The responses of all three subjects in response to the second experimenter were quite similar to their verbal behavior toward the first experimenter. Subject 1 continued to name the 10 picture cards accurately; Subject 2 responded with full sentence or phrase answers to conversation questions and named all the objects he was asked to name; Subject 3 named objects and gave one-word answers to certain conversational questions and statements. These responses from the subjects were obtained both with the first experimenter present and with him absent from the room. Thus, the newly reinstated verbal behavior of the subjects was not limited to a specific person.

Responding in other situations. During the course of the study it had been noted that the subjects' verbal behavior was not limited to the experimental room. In fact, each of the subjects exhibited all the verbal behavior on the ward that they exhibited in the experimental room as long as at least a partial reinforcement schedule was maintained. For example, when Subject 1 was repeating simple words in the experimental room he also repeated these words on the ward; when he was naming picture cards in the experimental room, he named them on the ward. The same type of effect was noted for Subject 2 and Subject 3. With all three subjects, this verbal behavior on the ward was exhibited both toward the first experimenter and toward the second experimenter.

In spite of the verbal behavior which was exhibited toward both the experimenters on the ward, the subjects' responding did not seem to generalize greatly to ward attendants. Subject 1 apparently did not ever exhibit any verbal behavior toward attendants on the ward after the experiment was completed. With Subject 2, ward attendants reported that he responded verbally to their questions several times a week, whereas he had exhibited only about six words on the ward in the 6-month period prior to the study. Subject 3, on at least one occasion, exhibited verbal behavior in the presence of an attendant.

Part of the reason for the failure of subjects' verbal behavior to generalize to ward attendants may have been due to a lack of reinforcement for verbalizations. When the subjects responded verbally to the experimenter on the ward, at least a partial reinforcement schedule had to be in effect to maintain this responding. If reinforcement was completely discontinued, the subjects quickly stopped responding. Nevertheless, it seems possible to overcome this rapid cessation of responding by scheduling the reinforcements. At one point with Subject 3, the experimenter started to schedule the reinforcements, gradually increasing to a variable ratio four, with no noticeable decrease in the subject's responsiveness. Thus, it would seem possible that further scheduling might result in sustained verbal behavior with only an occasional reinforcer delivered. Also, perhaps the use of ward attendants to deliver reinforcers for subjects' verbalizations would have increased their responding to the attendants.

Discussion

With the three subjects in this study, an increase in verbal behavior was obtained through the use of reinforcement procedures. In the case of Subject 1, shaping and fading techniques were employed to establish a verbal response, which was then maintained with reinforcement. For Subject 2 a shaping technique was used initially to establish a verbal response. Thereafter, reinforcement was used to maintain and expand the verbal repertoire exhibited by the subject in response to the experimenter's questions. With Subject 3 a shaping technique appeared to be ineffective in establishing behaviors approximating verbal behavior. However, a reinforced imitative technique succeeded in developing imitative vocalizations, which were then chained together to form an imitative verbal unit. Through the use of fading, this imitative verbal unit was established as a verbal response.

For all subjects, once a rate of verbal responding had been established, DRO procedures were put into effect. The results of the DRO periods demonstrated the functional role that contingent reinforcement played in maintaining the subjects' rate of verbal responding, since the rates of all three subjects showed marked decreases under the DRO condition. By extension, these results imply the functional role that reinforcement played in producing the subjects' verbal behavior. In addition, when contingent reinforcement for verbalizations was resumed following the DRO periods, the rates of all three subjects showed marked increases. This provides further evidence regarding the functional role of contingent reinforcement in re-establishing the subjects' verbal behavior.

The intrasubject reversals of the rate of verbal behavior described for Subject 1, Subject 2, and Subject 3 show the reliability of the results for each case. That is, for each of these three cases they demonstrate that the increases in verbal behavior which were obtained were not due to unknown or chance factors, but were due specifically to the contingent use of reinforcement.

Information about the generality of the present results, that is, the typical applicability of positive reinforcement procedures to the reinstatement of behavioral repertoires in disturbed subjects, is provided by an accumulation of many individual cases in which the functional efficacy of such procedures has been demonstrated for each case (*Sidman, 1960*). Thus, information on generality is provided by the results of the intersubject replications of the use of positive reinforcement procedures with Subject 1, Subject 2, and Subject 3. With each of these subjects, positive reinforcement procedures resulted in an increase in verbal behavior.

Further information on generality is suggested by previous non-experimental studies which have used positive reinforcement to reinstate behavioral repertoires in hospitalized patients (*Ayllon, 1963; Bachrach, Erwin, & Mohr, in press; Brady & Lind, 1961; Isaacs et al., 1960; Sherman, 1963*). In addition, there have been several studies which have used positive reinforcement procedures to develop new behavioral repertoires which previously were lacking in subjects (*Fuller, 1949; Wolf, Risley, & Mees, 1964*).

The similarity of the results reported in the studies cited above lends generality to the findings of the present study; in each of these studies the use of positive reinforcement procedures has been followed by the development of some appropriate behavior. Thus, it can be stated with increased confidence that positive reinforcement procedures can have wide applicability to problems of instatement and reinstatement of normal behavioral repertoires in humans.

One further similiarity between the results of the present study and those obtained by Isaacs et al. and by Sherman was the effect of reinstatement of one verbal response upon other verbal responses. For both subjects in the Isaacs et al. study, the reinstatement of the first verbal response was accompanied by the reappearance of many other verbal responses. In the Sherman study the reinstatement of one word was accompanied by an almost total reinstatement of all other verbal behavior. The same type of effect was noted for all three subjects in the present study.

In the cases of both Subject 1 and Subject 3, the establishment of the mimicking response "Food" was accompanied by mimicking responses of other simple words said by the experimenter, even though these latter verbal responses had never been directly shaped. During later sessions with both of these subjects, the establishment of "Food" in response to the experimenter's question, "What is this?" was accompanied by unshaped naming responses of specific types of food.

With Subject 2 there are two observations which are relevant to this point. The first is that during the earlier sessions when he exhibited a naming response to candy, he also began to answer some conversational questions. The second was noted during the subject's DRO periods (see Figure 2). When the DRO condition was first instituted, percentage of responses to both object and conversation questions dropped. Then, when contingent reinforcement was resumed for responses to object questions, the percentage of responses to these questions arose. However, the percentage of responses to conversation questions also rose even though they were still under the DRO condition and were not being reinforced.

Thus, the results of the present study, of Isaacs et al., and of Sherman strongly indicate that, for such subjects, verbal behavior is a functional class: variables which produce changes in one member of the class thereby affect the other members of the class similiarly.

There are two main restrictions relating to the generality of the results obtained in the present study. The first is the wide variation among subjects in the amount of verbal behavior obtained following the reinforcement procedures. In the case of both Subject 1 and Subject 3 a quite limited verbal repertoire was reinstated, while with Subject 2 a fairly wide verbal repertoire was re-established. It is difficult to account for the wide differences in amount of reinstatement among subjects through an analysis of the experimental procedures which were used for them.

The second restriction on the generality of the results of this study is the apparent ineffectiveness of shaping procedures to establish vocal behavior in the case of Subject 3. However, the primary reason for this ineffectiveness may have been a result of the difficulty of response detection rather than a lack of applicability of the technique. In shaping, the experimenter must be sensitive to slight differences in the topography of the behavior being shaped. During the early sessions with Subject 3, her vocalizations were of such low intensity that it was difficult to detect their presence; thus reinforcement was likely to be unreliable. One technique which might have alleviated this problem would have been the use of a throat microphone and an amplifier by which these low intensity sounds could be made clearly audible.

Nevertheless, the reinforced imitative technique which was developed for Subject 3 seemed to provide an adequate method of establishing a reliable vocal mimicking repertoire as a starting point from which verbal behavior could be developed. This, after all, is still an example of programing operant behavior with positive reinforcement; it is just a different program.

It seems possible that the type of imitative technique used for Subject 3 could have rather extensive applications. For example, a common behavioral deficit of both autistic and retarded children is their lack of adequate verbal behavior. In cases where these children exhibit vocal mimicking behavior, the use of reinforcement procedures may result in rather rapid progress in verbal training. However, if the children do not exhibit any type of vocal mimicking, or have an extremely low rate of vocalizations, the shaping of verbal behavior may be an arduous process even with relatively powerful reinforcers (*Wolf et al., 1964*). In these latter cases an imitative procedure similar to that used for Subject 3 may well be useful, in that the development of nonverbal imitative behaviors and subsequent progression toward imitative vocalizations and verbal behavior may be relatively more efficient than the direct shaping of vocalizations and subsequent discrimination training necessary to bring them under the control of other people's verbal behavior.

REFERENCES

Ayllon, T., "Intensive Treatment of Psychotic Behavior by Stimulus Satiation and Food Reinforcement," *Behav. Res. Ther.*, 1963, 1, 53–61.

Bachrach, A. J., W. J. Erwin, and J. P. Mohr, "The Control of Eating Behavior in an Anorexic by Operant Conditioning Techniques." In L. Ullmann and L. Krasner (Eds.), *Case Studies in Behavior Modification*. New York: Holt, Rinehart and Winston, 1964.

Baer, D. M., and J. A. Sherman, "Reinforcement Control of Generalized Imitation in Young Children," *J. exp. Child Psychol.*, 1964, 1, 37–49.

Brady, J. P., and D. L. Lind, "Experimental Analysis of Hysterical Blindness," *Arch. gen. Psychiat.*, 1961, 4, 331–339.

Fuller, P. R., "Operant Conditioning of a Vegetative Human Organism," *Amer. J. Psychol.*, 1949, 62, 587–590.

Isaacs, W., J. Thomas, and I. Goldiamond, "Application of Operant Conditioning to Reinstate Verbal Behavior in Psychotics," *J. Speech Hearing Dis.*, 1960, 25, 8–12.

Jones, Mary C., "A Laboratory Study of Fear: The Case of Peter," *Pedagogical Seminary and J. gen. Psychol.*, 1924, 31, 308–315.

Moore, R., and I. Goldiamond, "Errorless Establishment of Visual Discrimination Using Fading Procedures," *J. exp. Anal. Behav.*, 1964, 7, 269–272.

Sherman, J. A., "Reinstatement of Verbal Behavior in a Psychotic by Reinforcement Methods," *J. Speech Hearing Dis.*, 1963, 28, 398–401.

Sherman, J. A., "Use of Reinforcement and Imitation to Reinstate Verbal Behavior in Mute Psychotics." Unpublished doctoral dissertation, University of Washington, 1964.

Sidman, M., *Tactics of Scientific Research*. New York: Basic Books, 1960.

Terrace, H. S., "Discrimination Learning with and without 'Errors,' " *J. exp. Anal. Behav.*, 1963, 6, 1–27 (a).

Terrace, H. S., "Errorless Transfer of a Discrimination across Two Continua," *J. exp. Anal. Behav.*, 1963 6, 223–232 (b).

Wolf, M. M., T. Risley, and H. Mees, "Application of Operant Conditioning Procedures to the Behaviour Problems of an Autistic Child," *Behav. Res. Ther.*, 1964, 1, 305–312.

James H. Straughan

The Application of Operant Conditioning to the Treatment of Elective Mutism

The author's intent in this chapter is to describe and discuss a method that has been used successfully for the classroom treatment of one case of elective mutism and used with partial success in a second case. In this method, both the mute and his peer group are reinforced for his vocal responses; i.e. their reinforcement is contingent on his behavior.

Elective mutism is a label that is most appropriately applied to the lack of speech in those cases where the person under treatment shows adequate speech and reasonably normal behavior with some of the persons with whom he comes in contact, but where he is mute with other important persons. These criteria will serve to differentiate elective mutism from mutism involving organic pathology or severe emotional disturbance where speech and/or other behavior is consistently abnormal. Sloane and MacAulay (1966) have suggested the term "temporal mutism" to distinguish the person who previously spoke but no longer does from spatial or situational mutism as described above. It would be much more difficult to determine whether temporal mutism was elective in the sense that speech remained a possible response in the mute's behavioral repertoire. In many cases the mutism appears with a variety of other more-or-less obvious behaviors which have been

242

described by others with terms such as low intelligence (*Reed, 1963*), autism (*Wolf et al., 1963*), or withdrawal (*Strait, 1958*). These other behaviors are not usually offered as the cause of the mutism, but as associated reactions that have been acquired with it. Reed summarized existing knowledge well when he wrote: "It is concluded that elective mutism is not, as has been suggested, a clinical entity but rather an abnormal psychogenic reaction which may be viewed as learned behavior dependent on a variety of precipitating factors in differing personality types."

As with many disorders, the point at which those responsible for the child should become concerned about his refusal to talk and seek professionable help is debatable. It is likely that most children (and many adults) develop transitory mutism to some persons during their lives. The condition tends to disappear as social conditions, parental manipulations, or other influences extinguish mutism and elicit or reinforce the competing behavior of talking. A father recently described this example to the author. When the father had returned from a business trip of several days' duration, his second oldest son, a boy of about seven, had refused to speak to him. Believing that the child should be treated gently lest his antipathy towards him should become worse, the father had tolerated the mutism for about two years. The child spoke with other members of the family and performed his school work adequately. At this time the father became exasperated, told his son that the nonsense must stop, and refused to allow him any privileges unless he asked his father for them. According to the account, the nonsense did stop and communication with the father became normal.

In those cases when persuasion, threats, or other attempts to elicit speech fail, and, in particular, when mutism occurs in the classroom, an adaptation of the method devised by Patterson (*Patterson, 1964; Patterson et al., 1964; Patterson and Ebner, 1965*) for the treatment of hyperactivity in the classroom appears to offer promise. In Patterson's procedure a small box containing a signal light, a counter and (sometimes) a buzzer was placed on the hyperactive child's desk to serve as a secondary reinforcer for the nonoccurrence of hyperactive behavior over a set time interval. The treatment or conditioning period, lasted 20 or 30 minutes each school day. During this treatment period each brief period of time, e.g., 10 seconds, in which no hyperactive behaviors occurred, was reinforced by activation of the signal box. The child was told or taught beforehand that each activation of the signal box meant that another candy, penny, or some other reward was earned. This other reward was given each day immediately following the treatment period and, in the case of candies, was most often shared with other members of the class. When the reinforcements were to be shared with the class, an explanation was also given to the class just before treatment on the first day, in order to inform them of the contingency between the hyperactive child's behavior and reinforcement.

Case 1

This case has been separately described in another report (*Straughan et al., 1965*). Gene was a 14-year-old boy who was attending a day school for the mentally retarded. He was the youngest of 11 children, showed no diagnosed physical abnormalities other than a slight hearing loss in one ear, and had no history of injuries, illnesses, or other disorders which could account for his mutism. He had entered public school at the age of six but had been referred to a school for the mentally retarded two years later because of poor academic performance and muteness. Several intelligence tests during the next few years resulted in measured IQ's in the 50's and 60's. The combination of apparent subnormal intelligence, poor family environment, mutism, and long history of the disorder confused the picture by making it difficult to decide whether the mutism should be treated with hoped-for improvements in other behavior or whether the mutism was merely one more undesirable reaction shown by a mentally-retarded adolescent for whom little could be expected in the way of improvement.

Many aspects of Gene's behavior were observed which could be called negativistic. For example, when his teacher persisted in trying to elicit a vocal response from him, he would almost invariably remain mute and unresponsive. When the teacher would eventually give up and move away, he would glance from the corner of his eyes at the observers and smile. The observers were unanimous in agreeing that Gene was "enjoying a victory."

The students in Gene's class were already somewhat familiar with the signal box because they had seen it used in the classroom for the treatment of a hyperactive boy (*Anderson, 1964*). In this previous use the reinforcements had been candies which had been given only to the hyperactive boy and had not been distributed to the others in the class. For Gene the decision was made to use points earned towards a class party as reinforcements. The procedure was begun by bringing the signal box into the room and explaining and demonstrating its use to the class. They were told that the box would help Gene learn to talk in the classroom, that they could help him by encouraging him, and that he would be earning a party for the class by talking. A chart was hung on the wall in front of the classroom upon which each day's progress could be recorded. The box was left in the room only during the 20 minutes a day when talking was being reinforced.

Progress was rapid and satisfactory. The party was earned at the end of two weeks after nine days of treatment. It had been estimated that it would take Gene a month to earn the number of points which had been set for the party. Because it was felt that more time was needed to establish talking in the classroom, additional reinforcements (M & M candies) were given to Gene during another nine days of treatment. These candies were given to Gene only and were not distributed to the other members of the class. It is quite possible that other methods for continuing the reinforcement would have been effective also.

Data were collected each day during 20-minute observation periods on the days before treatment started, during 10-minute observation periods during treatment days, and during 30-minute observation periods on follow-up days after treatment. Before treatment, Gene spoke about 11% of the time when the teacher requested a response. During the days of treatment a spoken reply occurred 54% of the time, and following treatment, 61% of the time. Increases in the total frequency of talking were even greater, that is talking in response to all stimulation including that from the teacher.

In line with the theory that peer reinforcement is often an important part of such changes, it was noted that peer verbalizations to Gene also increased. During the observation periods before treatment, peers spoke to Gene about once each 30 minutes. During treatment this rate increased to one and a half times per 10-minute interval; following treatment, the rate increased to over five times per 10 minutes. Peer responsiveness was recorded as a gross count of the number of peer comments directed towards Gene.

The following data (Figure 1), show Gene's responsiveness to the teacher in more detail. The data are presented as the daily cumulative average response frequencies to the teacher per 10-minute observation period. The number of the teacher's questions to Gene varied from a low of one question on day 19 to a high of 143 questions during the observation period on day 44. It will be noted that even after 15 days of treatment there were still some days when Gene did not respond during the few minutes of the observation period. Obviously Gene's vocal responses cannot be treated as independent events; i.e. the likelihood of making a verbal response to a stimulus is related to the response to the preceding stimulus. School reports a year later indicated that Gene's classroom verbal responsiveness was still improved although not as good as when treatment was terminated. Perhaps occasional periods of reconditioning would be helpful with some cases in maintaining change.

Case 2[1]

The results of the treatment of a more serious case serve to support the argument that the classroom reinforcement procedure is effective without having unsatisfactory side effects. Mary was a 15-year-old girl whose behavioral disorder might more appropriately be called delayed speech or schizophrenic mutism rather than elective mutism, because the loss of speech occurred at a very early age, and speech continued to be limited even with close friends and relatives.

Mary's birth was described in her physician's records as difficult, with about 18 hours of labor, although no other problems and no defects were noted either before birth or during infancy. Withdrawal is reported by her mother to have begun just before Christmas at about the age of 2 years, 11 months, following an incident when she was reprimanded by her mother for an action in connection with cooking. Until this time she was described as developing

---

[1] The author is indebted to Dr. Barbara Etzel for her assistance with this case.

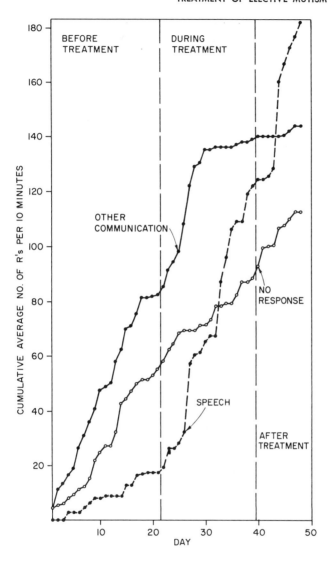

FIGURE 1

Daily cumulative average response frequencies to the teacher per 10-minute observation period. "Other communication" consisted of smiling or looking at the teacher or making an appropriate motor response.

normal speech and using words, phrases, and short sentences. Following the start of the withdrawal, she whispered for a few weeks and finally ceased talking completely. She would sit in a corner for hours or squat in the middle of the floor while rocking back and forth, seemingly oblivious to her surroundings.

During her childhood years Mary was taken to a variety of diagnostic and treatment centers. She was first diagnosed tentatively — and briefly — as deaf, and an abortive attempt was made to teach her sign language. She was placed for two years as an in-patient in a special school for disturbed children, without satisfactory progress. Finally she was brought home and treated briefly at an out-patient psychiatric clinic and enrolled in the special class of a local school. None of the special treatments, including speech therapy and psychotherapy, seemed to be noticeably effective, although her most bizarre reactions diminished as she approached adolescence. The consensus of opinion based on the various tests and evaluations was that Mary was not retarded, but had normal or higher intelligence.

At the time conditioning was attempted, Mary had been in the special class at the local school for about five years. There were six other young teenagers in the class, all of whom were diagnosed as mentally retarded. The teacher asked for help with Mary because he felt encouraged by some slight increase in her responsiveness to him but he felt that more powerful methods were needed to increase talking. Her progress seemed to have been due to two occurrences. First, a sister had been born and, consequently parental reinforcement of mutism had decreased. Before the sister's birth the parents had reinforced many of Mary's withdrawn, mute behaviors. They had responded quickly to her non-verbal cues by providing for her needs or speaking for her, and they had neither punished nor withheld reinforcements for withdrawal or muteness. Second, the teacher in the special class had been careful not to reward or encourage mutism or withdrawal but to reward responsiveness. Even so, when first seen, Mary would attempt to use words in the classroom only occasionally.

Observations of Mary illustrated a major source of difficulty in attempting to treat a well-established habit such as mutism. Ordinarily, a teacher who asks a child a question expects an answer. Appropriate answers are rewarded, silence is reprimanded by words or actions. If an answer is *not* expected, the question may be asked rhetorically; i.e. little or no time is given for the reply to be formulated, and silence is not reprimanded. Rhetorical questions may have two effects: they protect the questioner from the embarrassment of a nonresponsive audience, and they allow a nonresponsive audience to remain silent. Preliminary observations showed that Mary's teacher used many rhetorical questions. In this situation the use of a simple positive reinforcement, administered by a machine and controlled by an observer, had the advantage of keeping the observer from becoming involved in the educational or social processes during which adventitious, haphazard social reinforcements are often dispensed.

The procedure used with the present case was very much like that for the preceding case. After informal preliminary observations in the classroom, systematic observations and data collection were carried out for three weeks. The following six types of events were recorded for 25 minutes at the same time each day: (a) requests for the patient to talk or respond made by (1) the teacher, (2) a peer, or (3) some other or unknown stimulus, and (b) responses classified as either (4) vocal, (5) behavior such as gestures, etc., or (6) no noticeable response.

A training period for the purpose of establishing the signal box as a secondary reinforcer was not used for these reasons. First, none of the persons working as experimenters or therapists was sure that he could obtain speech from Mary when working with her alone. The teacher was able to obtain speech from her at times, but most of her communication, even in the classroom, was by other signals. Second, the therapists thought that Mary may have been too frightened to have responded to the candies when she was not with her classmates. For these reasons the procedure was introduced directly into the classroom.

On the first day of training the signal box was set in the middle of the table around which the children sat, and its use was explained to them. They were told that each time the signals operated, it would mean that Mary had earned another piece of candy (M & M's) for the class, and that these would be divided among them after the observers had gone. It was also pointed out that it was very important for Mary to learn to speak freely and that they could help by not responding to her other efforts to communicate.

On many subsequent treatment days either the teacher or the therapist again explained to the class that it was important for them not to respond to Mary's efforts to communicate by means other than speech. At the close of each treatment period, the class's attention was drawn to what Mary had earned that day by talking. During each day's conditioning period, the teacher made a special effort to give Mary opportunities to talk. The teacher described Mary as very happy with the procedure and extremely fond of sharing the candy with the class after a first day's reluctance.

Data on Mary's talking were collected 25 minutes a day on 10 days over a period of three weeks before treatment began. The reinforcement procedure was also carried out for 25 minutes a day for a total of 20 days distributed throughout two months. Data were collected for only 15 of these 20 days. Treatment was terminated without follow-up observations because of the end of the school year. During the first 12 days of treatment the reinforcements were the candies distributed as described. During the remaining days of treatment Mary was earning points towards gifts for the members of the class. Each day's accumulation of points was recorded on a chart posted at the front of the classroom. The gifts were small items purchased at a local variety store. Each member of the class was allowed in advance to choose from an assortment the item that he would have after enough points were earned.

Mary's responses to the teacher before and during training are shown in Figure 2 and Table 1. The number of teacher's questions during the observation period ranged from a low of 2 on day 14 to a high of 66 on day 16. Responses to her peers are shown in Figure 3 and Table 2.

	Speech	Other Communication	No Response	No. of Teacher's Questions*
Before Training	8.1	6.2	12.2	26.5
During Training	22.9	3.7	5.5	32.1

* Teacher's "questions" include questions, requests, and other verbalizations which would be likely to evoke speech in a normal child.

TABLE 1
Average Number of Mary's Responses to the Teacher
During Each Observation Period

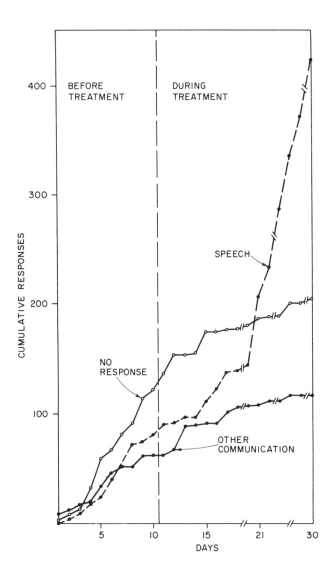

FIGURE 2

The cumulative frequencies of Mary's responses to the teacher. Data were not recorded on days 19, 23, 24, 28, and 29. "Other communication" consisted of nodding, whispering, pointing, etc.

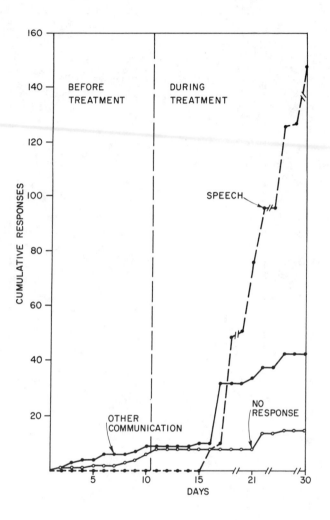

FIGURE 3

The cumulative frequencies of Mary's responses to peers. Data were not recorded for days 19, 23, 24, 28, and 29. "Other communication" consisted of nodding, whispering, pointing, etc.

	Speech	Other Communication	No Response	No. of Peer Questions*
Before Training	—	0.9	0.6	1.5
During Training	9.9	2.3	0.6	12.7

* Peer's "questions" include questions, requests, and other verbalizations which would be likely to evoke speech in a normal child.

TABLE 2

Average Number of Mary's Responses to Peers
During Each Observation Period

It is clear that her frequency of talking increased and that peer behavior toward her also changed. Indirect evidence suggests that her increased talking was specific to the special class and generalized little to other situations. Although she spent time each day in two other classes — typing and art — she did not begin to talk in these classes. Her mother, however, gave an unsolicited testimonial when she reported that her daughter had begun to talk more freely at home and that such improvement had not followed previous attempts at treatment. In the following school year Mary began attending regular classes in high school where she was reported to have remained mute.

Discussion

Work with the foregoing two adolescents and with hyperactive children indicates that classroom conditioning can be effective when the responses to be conditioned are in the person's repertoire of behavior. Generalization to other situations, such as other classes, will not necessarily follow conditioning in one class. It seems reasonable in the light of what is known about generalization that conditioning in more than one situation may be necessary at times.

It has been suggested in the foregoing presentation that the behavior of the peers or others who come in contact with the person being conditioned is an important part of the treatment. The evidence presented does suggest that peer behavior changed rather markedly. Although classroom conditioning has been carried out without involving the peers, as in the study by Anderson (1964) and in part of the treatment of Case 1 presented above, there is some evidence to suggest that peer behavior must change if treatment is to be effective. This is in contrast to theories that emphasize insight or other mediational variables to account for persistence and generalization of treatment effects. Ebner (1965) has collected data showing that changes in hyperactive behavior on the playground are accompanied by changes in peer social reinforcements, with more social reinforcements being dispensed on the patient's less active days. These playground changes generalized from classroom treatment.

Finally, it may be pointed out that other methods may also be effective with elective mutes as with any other behavioral disorder; however, traditional psychotherapy appears to be one of the least effective methods. Reed (1963) commented on the intractability of mutism and attributed improvement in his cases to the re-learning of social responses. For two of the mutes his aim was to extinguish mutism by ignoring it and to build up self-esteem by openly appreciating other aspects of the girls' behavior, personality, and appearance. Follow-ups showed good improvement with one girl, who was able to live a normal life, and some improvement with the other, who lost her mutism but remained shy with strangers. For two other mutes, therapy was designed to extinguish or diminish fear of the therapist and then to generalize this changed reaction to other people and circumstances. Self-expression was reinforced. For one of these mutes, progress was slow, but she eventually made a reasonably normal adjustment. For the other, a boy of 12 when treatment began, little change occurred during three years of therapy although, at 23, he was described as "taciturn but amiable."

Speech therapy by itself, or in conjunction with psychotherapy, has been used with some success in the treatment of elective mutism. Smayling (1959) presented six cases of what she called voluntary mutism; in each of these there were speech defects in addition to mutism in the classroom. In each of these cases speech occurred at home, there were no physical defects, and conventional speech training was used. She reported success in five of the six cases; i.e., speech appeared in the classroom. The changes in classroom speech may be considered to be examples of generalization. In one case Smayling facilitated generalization by gradually bringing members of the class into the speech therapy room while the patient was reading aloud.

Strait (1958) also presented a case where generalization was facilitated by gradually bringing other persons into the therapy room. These other persons were encouraged to socially reinforce the elective mute for his reading aloud. Eventually he read to the entire class in his own classroom following which he was reported to have participated more and more in regular class speech.

It is obvious, then, that the method presented in this paper is not by itself always successful with elective mutism. It is likely that speech defects will be present in many cases, and these defects should be treated. The present cases, however, do suggest that the therapist should concern himself with preparing or changing the social environment to support and encourage speech when it does occur.

REFERENCES

Anderson, D., "Application of a Behavior Modification Technique to the Control of a Hyperactive Child." Unpublished master's thesis, University of Oregon, 1964.

Ebner, M. J., "Role of the Social Environment in Behavior Modification." Unpublished doctoral dissertation, University of Oregon, 1965.

Patterson, G. R., "An Application of Conditioning Techniques to the Control of a Hyperactive Child." In L. P. Ullmann and L. Krasner (Eds.), Case Studies in Behavior Modification. New York: Holt, Rinehart and Winston, 1964.

Patterson, G. R., "Applications of Learning Principles to the Treatment of Deviant Children," Amer. Psychologist, 1965, 20, 520 (abstract symposium).

Patterson, G. R., R. Jones, J. Whittier, and Mary A. Wright, "A Behavior Modification Technique for the Hyperactive Child. Unpublished manuscript, 1964.

Reed, G. R., "Elective Mutism in Children: A Re-appraisal," J. Child Psychol. Psychiat. 1963, 4, 99–107.

Sloane, H. N., and B. D. MacAulay, Personal Communication. 1966.

Smayling, L. M., "Analysis of Six Cases of Voluntary Mutism," J. Speech Hearing Disord., 1959, 24, 55–58.

Strait, R., "A Child Who Was Speechless in School and Social Life," J. Speech Hearing Disord., 1958, 23, 253–254.

Wolf, M., T. Risley, and H. Mees, "Application of Operant Conditioning Procedures to the Behavior Problems of an Autistic Child," Behav. Res. Ther., 1964, 1, 305–312.

VI

Articulation Difficulties

As most people know, speech correctionists spend a greater amount of time treating children with faulty articulation than on any other type of speech problem. Any procedures that reduce the amount of professional time required in this endeavor, let alone increase the effectiveness of remedial training, are therefore quite significant. Two of the chapters in this section present methods that do reduce the amount of individual professional attention required for effective modification of articulation, and both chapters rely upon the technology of programmed instruction (see introduction to Part IV). Chapter 13, by Holland and Matthews, places relatively greater emphasis upon the reinforcement contingencies programmed than the McDearmon chapter. The chapter by McDearmon stresses the sequence of stimulus materials and responses required in an overall phonics (or auditory discrimination or production) program. The Holland and Matthews chapter describes a series of programs based upon behavioral analysis of the problems involved in [s] discrimination; although other problems are not discussed, the general procedures have implications for learning to discriminate all sounds. McDearmon presents a program that has been carefully worked out over a number of years for teaching allograph discriminations both in isolation and in different word and letter contexts. Concurrently, the student learns to pronounce the associated phoneme and to discriminate the verbal productions of the teacher.

Chapter 15, by Mowrer, Baker, and Schutz, describes several studies that investigated the efficacy of operant procedures in correcting articulatory problems. The authors also explore the roles played by various aspects of the procedures.

Several chapters in Parts II, III, and IV also discuss articulation training.

13

Audrey L. Holland
Jack Matthews

Application of Teaching Machine Concepts to Speech Pathology and Audiology

Speech pathology and audiology is a borrowing field. We borrow from psychology, physics, anatomy, physiology, linguistics, anthropology — ad infinitum. A breakthrough in any of the areas from which we borrow may revolutionize concepts and procedures in speech pathology and audiology. Those of us responsible for the training of tomorrow's speech pathologists and audiologists must be alert to the applications of today's discoveries in the many disciplines related to communication processes and their disorders. On the basis of our research and clinical experience we feel that the recent work of B. F. Skinner and his associates (5, 9, 10, 11, 12, 13) may be a breakthrough in the science of behavior which can significantly influence the field of speech pathology and audiology.

To many, the name B. F. Skinner immediately calls to mind teaching machines. Teaching machines did not originate with B. F. Skinner, nor are they a product of this decade in the history of psychology. The first teaching machine was patented in 1866 by Halcyon Skinner. In spite of many other patents in the area of automated teaching, there followed 60 years of relatively unsuc-

Reprinted from *Asha,* Volume 5, No. 1, January, 1963.

cessful history interrupted briefly by the work of Sydney L. Pressey in the 1920's (8). Pressey envisoned a revolution in education as a result of the application of teaching machines. The revolution did not occur. Skinner attributes this failure to "cultural inertia — a world which was not ready for it," and to a lack of scientific interest in how the organism learns, of what variables learning is a function, and of how to control those variables (11).

Holland points out that the current interest and progress in teaching machines stems directly from the incorporation into them of principles developed in the science of behavior which permit precise control of behavior. "The movement today is not simply the mechanization of teaching, but instead the development of a new technology — an attempt to obtain the kind of behavioral control shown possible in the laboratory" (5). In effect, present-day teaching machines are grounded in some of the better established facts of behavioral control.

This new technology was initiated by B. F. Skinner (10, 11), and the principles involved in teaching machines have emerged from the work of Skinner and his associates (5, 9, 12, 13). Their discovery of the functional variables of learning has made possible a new applied technology — teaching machines. In an effort to explain why teaching machines of today provide both efficient and effective learning, their characteristics will be briefly discussed from the standpoint of the principles of learning incorporated in them:

Immediacy of Reinforcement. Immediacy of reinforcement is a feature of the teaching machine. Correct responses are known to be reinforcers for human beings. When the student compares his answer to the correct answer on the machine, the reinforcement is immediate. Laboratory work shows that a delay between a response and its reinforcement greatly reduces the effectiveness of reinforcement (5).

Emitting and Reinforcing Behavior. In order that behavior be learned, it is necessary for it to be emitted and reinforced. Concerning this principle, Holland says:

> ... in the classroom, the student provides little verbal behavior. However, while working with a machine, the student necessarily

emits appropriate behavior and this behavior is usually reinforced since the material is designed so that the student is usually correct. Not only is reinforcement needed for learning, a high density of correct items is necessary because material which generates errors is punishing. Laboratory experiments have shown that punishment lowers the rate of punished behavior (5).

Successive Approximation (Gradual Progression) in the Development of Complex Repertoires. Learning a subject-matter is not simply learning a response. It is a complex operant behavior. Teaching machines use exactly the same approach as that of the laboratory in attempting to develop complex operant behavior. First, a very, very simple behavior, a quite rough approximation to the behavior we wish to obtain in the end, is reinforced. On successive performances, we reinforce successively closer approximations to the criterion behavior. The teaching machine program runs through finely graded steps, working from simple to an ever higher level of complexity. Not only does gradual progression serve to make the student correct as often as possible (and thus be reinforced), but also it has been shown through laboratory research to be the fastest way to develop complex repertoires (4, 5).

Gradual Withdrawal of Stimulus Support (Fading). Gradual withdrawal is similar to the above principle of gradual progression. This principle insures that the student learning from a program is actually "interacting" with the subject-matter. Skinner gives an example of teaching a student to recite a poem:

> The first line is presented with several unimportant letters omitted. The student must read the line "meaningfully" and supply the missing letters. The second, third and fourth frames present succeeding lines in the same way. In the fifth frame the first line reappears with other letters also missing. Since the student has recently read the line, he can complete it correctly. He does the same for the second, third and fourth lines. Subsequent frames are increasingly incomplete, and eventually, . . . the student reproduces all four lines without external help. . . . responses are first controlled by a text, but it is slowly reduced . . . until the responses can be emitted without a text, each member in a series of responses being now under the "intraverbal" control of other members (11).

Control of the Student's Observing and Echoic Behavior. The experimental analysis of behavior has pointed out that observing behavior, or "attention," is subject to the same forms of control as other behavior. Classroom methods are effective only insofar as the student has some behavior with respect to the material being taught. Teaching machines control observing behavior in much the same manner as does the laboratory. For example, when the student becomes "inattentive in the classroom," the teaching material flows on; with a machine, he moves ahead only as he finishes an item. Lapses in active participation result in nothing more than the machine sitting idle until the student continues. Further, it is simple to control the student's observing behavior by constructing items in which correct answers depend only upon his careful observation of the material in front of him (5).

Discrimination Training. Obviously, teaching machines can reinforce correct discriminations. However, little education consists of simple discrimination training. More often, it is abstraction or concept formation which is the subject of education. An abstraction is a response to a single isolated property of a stimulus which cannot exist alone. Through providing many examples employing the common property embedded in a wide range of other properties, the teaching machine program is a powerful device for accomplishing the teaching of concepts (3, 5).

The above are direct applications of laboratory principles. However, there are other advantages to the use of teaching machines, stemming from laboratory methodology. One of the most important of these is that of the ease of revision of teaching machine programs. The student's answers provide a detailed step-by-step record of his progress in learning the material, pointing up weaknesses and strengths in the program. The programmer is able to revise his material in view of the student's particular difficulties, as is not possible in other teaching techniques. In effect, the student writes the program; he cannot write the textbook. One further facet of teaching machines, inherent in most of the above discussion, should be emphasized. That is the ability of teaching-machine teaching to progress as the student is ready for it. Slow students can move through a program at a pace geared to their learning abilities without penalty. Brighter students may also move at their own best speed without having to wait for the slower students to "catch up" before going on to a new topic.

Automated teaching today is effective because it is the result of the application of a scientific technology to the process of education, a process which Glaser calls "the applied psychology of education" (4). Similar technology is at work experimentally in the fields of psycho-pharmacology, neurology and nutrition — to name just a few (9).

We will describe an application of the technology to the field of speech pathology and audiology. Because much of the literature in the area of teaching machines devotes little attention to details of program construction and because we feel such information may be valuable to those interested in further research in this area, we have devoted considerable space to explaining how our program was constructed.

The Problem and Purposes

This study is a preliminary evaluation of the effectiveness of self-instruction techniques for teaching speech sound discrimination to children with defective articulation. The training of speech sound discrimination was chosen for programming, not only because it is recognizedly useful for the early phases of articulation therapy (1, 7, 17), but also because it appears especially suited to teaching machine programming.

The purposes of this study were to develop a series of experimental teaching machine programs for teaching discrimination of the [s] phoneme to children with defective [s] articulation, to develop an experimental teaching machine suitable for presenting the programs, and to evaluate the relative effectiveness of each of the programs. The study compared (a) a program which was patterned after the procedure suggested by Powers (7); (b) a program which provided extensive training on discrimination of phonemes which were not embedded in phonetic context (isolated speech sounds); and (c) a program which trained exclusively in discriminating correct from misarticulated sound production within words. It was felt that the program which proved most effective should provide a close approximation to a useful automation of the early phases of articulation correction.

The Teaching Machine

The teaching machine developed for this study presented the auditory problem (single words, pairs of words or isolated sounds) by tape recorder. The subject's response to each problem (item) was to press one of three buttons. An incorrect response resulted in the tape recorder's immediately rewinding and replaying that problem. On correct responses the tape recorder simply continued to play uninterrupted. The clatter of the rewinding recorder was sufficient to delineate incorrect items without the assistance of auxiliary stimuli. Hence, the instrument meets qualifications for a teaching machine in presenting short problems, requiring the student to respond, and giving immediate information as to whether the response was correct or incorrect.

A Wollensak Model T-1600 tape recorder was modified for the purpose. This recorder was particularly adaptable because it contained internal wiring for rewinding as long as a switch was closed. An erroneous response resulted in the operation of a Hunter timer with its output switch in parallel with the rewind switch. The timer interval was adjusted to rewind the recorder past the missed item and into the silent period preceding it. At the end of the timed interval the recorder automatically resumed its forward motion, repeated the missed item, and if the response was then correct continued on to the next item.

The subject depressed one of the three large wooden buttons which operated electrical switches. The buttons, which were colored blue, red and green and had large white numerals (1, 2, and 3 respectively) painted upon them, were placed in a row on a metal panel. Each of the three types of response labeling (position, color and number) was of use in some particular phase of at least one of the programs.

Coding for the correct response was controlled manually by four keys on a small panel held in the experimenter's lap. This panel was always out of the subject's sight. Three of the experimenter's keys corresponded to the three keys on the subject's panel. The experimenter pressed the appropriate key at the beginning of each item. If the subject pressed either of the buttons which did not correspond to the key depressed by the experimenter, a simple switching network caused a pulse to be delivered to the Hunter timer and the rewinding operation ensued. The fourth key directly pulsed the timer. It was used only in the few cases when a subject failed to respond within the allotted time and resulted in repetition of the item.

The Programs

Each of the three programs developed for teaching auditory discrimination of the [s] phoneme will be discussed separately.

Program I. Program I followed Powers' outline and had four distinct phases. Phase 1 involved discrimination of [s] in isolation from other isolated speech sounds. This was the grossest type of auditory discrimination within the program. For the 62 items in this phase, the subject pressed the blue button every time he heard [s] and pressed the red button when he heard any other sound. Isolated sounds were recorded so that there was a period of 5 seconds between the presentation of one sound and the sound following it. Good teaching machine programs are constructed so that in as many instances as possible the student is right. They attempt to shape complex forms of behavior by proceeding in small steps from quite simple material to more and more difficult material. The material in Phase 1 was thus constructed so that early presentations of [s] were longer and louder than non-[s] sounds. This was gradually faded until all the sounds were of roughly equal length and loudness. The earliest discriminations involved [s] and other speech sounds phonetically quite different from [s]. As this phase of the program continued, sounds which required finer discriminations were incorporated into the program.

In Phase 2, the subject was required to discriminate the sound in words. Again, an attempt was made to evolve from simplest to more complex discriminations. Since it is easier to discriminate sounds at the beginning of words, the first 83 items in this part of the program required the child to determine which one of a pair of words began with the [s] sound. If word number 1 began with the [s] sound, pressing button number two was correct. Early items in the program stressed the word which began with the [s] sound. This emphasis was gradually eliminated (faded) as the program progressed. This part of the program began with items in which the whole phonetic structure of the non-[s] words was much different from the [s] words, gradually progressed through items in which the non-[s] words rhymed with the [s] words but began with much different sounds, went on through items where the initial sound of the non-[s] words was similar to [s] but which differed in the remaining phonetic context, and finally included items where the non-[s] words rhymed with the [s] words and in addition had initial consonants which were hard to discriminate from [s].

Following this, the child listened for words which ended in [s]. Pairs of words were again used, and a progression similar to the above was used, differing only in that final, rather than initial, [s] sounds were under consideration. After 81 items for discriminating final [s], the child was next exposed to problems of discriminating medial [s] sounds from other medial sounds. Pairs of words were again used. The same general principles of emphasis and fading out were followed here, and again the other word of each item gradually progressed toward greater and greater similarity to the paired [s] word.

Powers suggests that the next discrimination task should be that of identifying the position of the [s] sound within words. However, some transition items were included to insure that the child would listen to the whole word again, rather than concentrating on a part of a word, and to begin to establish his ability to recognize the position of sounds in words. The child was instructed that he would hear some words one at a time. Some of the words had one [s] sound in them, some had two. He was to decide how many, and push the appropriately numbered button. There are only 30 items in this part of the program. However, gradual progression was an important factor. Early items had one or two quite obvious [s] sounds. Close to the end, the items required that the child discriminate between sounds which are similar to [s] in order to count the correct number of [s] sounds.

In Phase 3, the child was asked to identify the position of the [s] within a word. The 95 items in this phase of the program forced the child to listen carefully enough to respond to the position of the [s] sound in each word. He had, by now, been trained in discriminating the [s] sound in every position in words; but now he had to respond differentially to the position taken by [s] in a given vord. We pressed the first button for an initial [s], the middle button for a medial [s], and the end button for a final [s]. The earliest items had exaggerated [s] sounds, were easily recognizable as to [s] position, and furnished systematic practice with all three positions before the words were randomized as to position of [s] within them. Gradually, the changing of [s] position in a similar word was presented, and lastly final discriminations were forced with words which have within them, in addition to [s] sounds, sounds similar to that phoneme.

Phase 4 involved discrimination of correctly articulated from misarticulated [s] sounds within words. Omission of the [s] sound, nine substitutions of other phonemes, and four [s] distortions formed the basis for the program. All were discriminable on the tape recorder. These were arranged from most audibly different from [s] to least audibly different from [s]. Three initial [s] words, three medial [s] words, three final [s] words, and three [s] blend words were assigned to each "error." There were 168 items in all.

For each item, the child heard the same "word" twice, once correctly and once misarticulated. Pressing button number one was the correct response if the first word was correctly articulated, while pressing button number two was correct if the second word was correctly articulated.

Two types of gradual progression were built into this phase. The first type was the gradual progression from most obvious to most subtle type of misarticulation. In addition, within each misarticulated segment the most discriminable items occurred first, and effort was made to exaggerate the misarticulation in early items. This was gradually faded out.

In accordance with good teaching machine technique, the program progressed through a finely graded series of more and more difficult auditory discriminations. Care was also taken throughout the program to insure that the items sampled [s] sounds adjacent to all possible vowels and all [s] blends. This follows programming technique, which suggests that we include as wide a variety of examples as possible in order to adequately establish a discrimination (6). All of the words used in the program were checked with the Thorndike-Lorge lists (16). Words which did not appear in the first 3,000 were not used unless it was clear that children would be familiar with them. Partial randomization within the items of the program determined which of a pair of words was correct. Initial, medial, and final words were also randomized for Phase 3. Restrictions were applied so that not more than six successive items were keyed to a particular button. For all items following Phase 1, the time from beginning of one item to the beginning of the next was eight seconds.

After Phase 1 of the program, every problem had at least one good [s] sound in it. This program format was chosen because such items forced the child to listen to at least one good [s] per item and furnished much more [s] stimulation than otherwise would have been available. Stimulation with good sound production is often mentioned in the clinical speech literature as important to articulation correction (7, 17), and it was thus incorporated into Program I.

Program II. Program II was just an extension of Phase I, Program I. It attempted to teach auditory discrimination by requiring the child to differentiate only between the [s] and other speech sounds when they are not embedded in phonetic context. The format was exactly like the isolation phase of Program I and differed only in that it was much longer, that it sampled all the consonants and vowels of English, and that there were a greater number of problems for each phoneme. There were 605 items in the program.

Program III. Program III, an extension of Phase 4 of Program I, was constructed in exactly the same manner, and had 588 items.

All three programs were tape recorded in a sound-proof room using the same recorder which served as the teaching machine. The tapes were recorded using the voice of a graduate student in speech pathology who was formerly a professional actor, chosen because of his excellent speech and imitative ability.

Subjects

Twenty-seven children (18 males and 9 females) between the ages of eight and eleven served as subjects. All of the children were of normal intelligence, as noted in their school records. All had been diagnosed by public school speech correctionists as having defective [s] articulation. None of the children was enrolled in speech therapy. The grade range was from the second through the fifth grades. In order to test the effectiveness of the training, a test for [s] discrimination was constructed which sampled the child's ability to discriminate sounds in isolation, to discriminate whether or not a word had [s] in it, to recognize [s] within words, and to distinguish correct from misarticulated [s] sounds within words. This test was administered before and following discrimination instruction.

Four other auxiliary tests were given before and after training. These tests were the Templin Short Test of Sound Discrimination, a test of general sound discrimination ability; a sibilant discrimination test constructed for the study in order to assess the child's ability to discriminate between sibilant sounds in similar fashion to the [s] discrimination test; a picture articulation test used to measure general articulation; and a picture articulation test designed to measure the child's ability to articulate [s] in the initial, medial and final positions and [s] blends in the positions in which they occur in English. The three discrimination tests were recorded using the experimenter's voice. The subjects wrote their answers on special answer blanks for the discrimination tests, and their responses on the articulation tests were scored by the experimenter. For each of these tests, the child's score was the number of correct responses he gave.

The experimenter's reliability in judging correctness of articulation was checked by computing a percentage of agreement between original scorings and scorings of randomly selected recordings of the three children's articulation tests. This involved 288 sounds, and the percentage of agreement was 95%.

On the basis of the test scores, three matched groups were evolved. Children in Group I worked through Program I, children in Group II worked through Program II, and children in Group III worked through Program III.

The experimental procedure for each group was identical except for the contents of the programs.

Testing Procedure

Insofar as was possible, discrimination tests were administered to small groups. The children were informed that they had been selected to participate in a listening job and that before the job began a series of tests had to be given to determine if they listened well enough. Directions for each test were recorded on the test tape. If a child wished to hear a particular question over again, he was so permitted although the other children were not allowed to change their answers. Articulation tests were administered individually.

The programmed instruction was administered individually, in most cases during school time. At the beginning of the first session, the child was taught to operate the teaching machine. Throughout the entire program, each child was responsible for all of the operations involved in playing the recorder. Each child worked as long as he wanted to at each session. He was also allowed to hear items over again if he wished. The average time per session was 40 minutes; average time for completing the Programs was 2 hours, 15 minutes for Group I; slightly less than 2 hours for Group II; and for Group III, it was 2 hours, 25 minutes.

Each child was retested within three days following his completion of the program. The procedure for the post-test was exactly like the pre-program test procedure.

Results

In order to evaluate the effectiveness of the programs, scores from the tests given before and after the programs were compared. These comparisons were evaluated for statistical significance by a t-test for matched groups (2). The comparison in Table 1 of test performance before and after the programs reveals that only Group I showed significant improvement in [s] discrimination. Scores on the auxiliary tests improved significantly for Groups I and II on the sibilant discrimination test; for none of the groups on the Templin test; for all of the groups on [s] articulation; and for none of the groups on the general articulation test. The improvement in [s] discrimination for Group I represented improvement in eight of the nine subjects; the improved sibilant discrimination represented individual gains by six of the subjects in Group I and four subjects in Group II; and improvement in [s] articulation was noted in six children in Groups I and III and seven in Group II.

Measure	Group	Mean Difference	SE Difference	t
General Articulation	I	.67	1.11	.60
	II	.44	.75	.59
	III	− .45	.86	.52
[s] Articulation	I	3.3	1.06	3.11**
	II	4.2	1.44	2.91**
	III	2.3	.66	3.48**
Templin	I	1.89	1.31	1.44
	II	1.89	1.65	1.15
	III	− .77	1.94	.33
Sibilant Discrimination	I	1.56	.76	2.04*
	II	1.30	.55	2.36*
	III	.45	.57	.79
[s] Discrimination Test	I	6.22	.98	6.04**
	II	.78	.88	.89
	III	.11	.92	.12

*t .05 = 1.86 (one-tailed)
**t .01 = 2.89 (one-tailed)

TABLE 1

Comparisons of Pre- and Post-program Performance
on the Test Battery (df = 8)

The relative effectiveness of the various programs was evaluated by comparing the degree of change in a child's scores on the two tests with that of his matched subject in each of the other two groups. These comparisons were also evaluated for statistical significance by a t-test for matched groups. Table 2 shows these comparisons. It can be seen from this table that only on the [s] discrimination test was there a statistically reliable mean change for Group I as compared to both Groups II and III.

One of the advantages of teaching machine programs is that the student's answers provide a step-by-step record of his progress, pointing up strengths and weaknesses which assist the programmer in revising the program. A record of each subject's errors was kept, and the analysis of errors in each program is summarized in Tables 3, 4, and 5.

Measure	Groups Compared	Mean Change	Difference	SE Difference	t
General	I	+ .66	.22	1.31	.16
Articulation	II	+ .44			
	II	+ .44	.88	1.47	.6
	III	− .44			
	I	+ .66	1.10	.79	1.39
	III	− .44			
[s] Articulation	I	+3.33	.89	1.70	.52
	II	+4.22			
	II	+4.22	1.89	1.49	1.26
	III	+2.33			
	I	+3.33	1.00	1.17	.85
	III	2.33			
Templin	I	+1.89	—	2.42	—
	II	+1.89			
	II	+1.89	2.66	2.87	.93
	III	− .77			
	I	+1.89	2.66	2.10	1.26
	III	− .77			
Sibilant	I	+1.56	.23	1.05	.21
Discrimination	II	+1.33			
	II	+1.33	.89	.63	1.41
	III	+ .44			
	I	+1.56	1.12	1.01	1.10
	III	+ .44			
[s] Discrimination	I	6.22	5.45	1.13	4.82*
	II	+ .77			
	II	+ .77	.66	1.46	.45
	III	+ .11			
	I	+6.22	6.11	1.40	4.36*
	III	+ .11			

*t .01 (df = 8) 3.35
Minus signs indicate a higher pre- than post-test score

TABLE 2
Comparisons of the Amount of Change in Pre- and Post-program
Test Scores on the Test Battery

Phase	Number of Items	Total Errors	Number of Items Missed by More than 1 Subject	Number of Items Missed by More than 2 Subjects
1. Isolated Sounds	62	1	—	—
2. Sounds in Contexts				
a. Initial [s]	83	35	8	2
b. Final [s]	81	25	7	1
c. Medial [s]	66	31	8	0
Transition Items	30	41	12	8
3. Position in Words	95	63	15	8
4. Correct — Misarticulated Words	168	29	7	2
TOTAL	585	225	57	21

Average number of errors 25
Percentage of errors 4.3%

TABLE 3
Error Analysis — Program I

Items	Total Errors	Number of Items Missed by More than 1 Subject
1–100	2	0
101–200	4	0
201–300	8	0
301–400	4	0
401–500	7	0
501–605	9	0
	34	0

Average number of errors 3.78
Percentage of errors .... .62%

TABLE 4
Error Analysis — Program II

Items (grouped by misarticulation)	Total Errors	Number of Items Missed by More than 1 Subject	Number of Items Missed by More than 2 Subjects
Omitted [s]	14	2	2
Glottal stop	10	1	0
(k)*	2	0	0
(t)	11	2	0
(dʒ)	8	2	0
(tʃ)	9	1	0
(ʒ)	6	0	0
(t)	6	0	0
(z)	8	1	0
(ʃ)	6	0	0
(e)	16	3	1
Snort	13	2	1
Lateral [s]	34	7	1
Whistled [s]	69	19	9
Slight frontal lisp	23	5	1
TOTAL	235	45	15

Total items 588
Average error 26.1
Percentage of error 4.4%
* had only 28 items. All others had 40 items.

TABLE 5

Error Analysis — Program III

Because both the content and the phasing of the programs differ, it was difficult to make a generalized cross comparison of the three programs. However, 168 items written for Program I were incorporated into Program III, thus making one simple comparison possible. Phase 4, Program I, discriminating correct from misarticulated [s] within words was spliced into Program III as the last 12 items of misarticulations common to both programs. These items were consecutive in Program I and were preceded by 28 items involving the same misarticulation in Program III. The comparison is shown in Table 6.

Items (grouped by misarticulation for [s])	Total Errors Program I	Total Errors Program III	Total Items Missed by More than 1 Subject Program I	Total Items Missed by More than 1 Subject Program III
Omitted [s]	0	5	0	1
Glottal stop	2	6	0	1
(t)	1	5	0	1
(dʒ)	0	2	0	0
(tʃ)	1	6	0	1
(ʒ)	0	1	0	0
(o)	0	0	0	0
(z)	1	3	0	0
(ʃ)	1	3	0	0
(e)	1	6	0	0
Snort	0	7	0	2
Lateral [s]	4	8	1	3
Whistled [s]	12	22	4	7
Slight frontal lisp	6	7	2	2
TOTAL	29	81	7	18

Average error Program I 3.7
Average error Program III 9.0
Percent of error Program III 5.3%
Percent of error Program I 2.2%

TABLE 6
Error Comparison for 168 Common Items: Programs I and III

Discussion

Discrimination of the [s] phoneme. It's not surprising to find Program I to be adequate in improving scores on the [s] discrimination test. A major reason for its success is that it makes more use of good programming principles than do the other programs. To be sure, all three were comprised of short problems to which the child had to provide a response which was reinforced if correct; all were constructed so that the density of reinforcement was high; all moved in gradual progression from easiest to successively more difficult items; and all attempted to control the student's observing behavior. However, an important basic difference between Program I and the other two programs is the way it proceeds in establishing a discrimination.

Adequate speech sound discrimination requires that the person be able to distinguish the sound in its full range of contexts. Such needs are characteristic of other situations which have been met in teaching machine work. It cannot be assumed that training in only a few representative cases in any training problem will lead to perfect transfer to the full range of cases. For this reason, an outstanding rule of teaching machine programming is to vary the examples, context, syntactic arrangement, etc., over as nearly the complete range as possible. One of the most striking features of Program I was its wide range of examples, stemming basically from this principle of program construction.

Appropriate variations were also used within each of the other programs, but the changing tasks of Program I allowed for a far greater breadth of possible examples and variations. In both Programs II and III, there was only one task in which these variations could take place.

The error analysis for the 160 items common to Programs I and III reflects this difference. These items comprise the final phase of Program I and thus were preceded by the varying tasks of the earlier phases. These items were spliced in Program III in sets of 12 for each of the 14 types of misarticulations. They followed immediately 28 items drilling on the same distortion. Despite this practice, students using Program III made many more errors on these items than did students using Program I. This provides confirmation of the worth of varied discrimination tasks like those in Program I.

The reactions of the children to each of the three programs shed some light on the question of their relative efficiency. Children in Group I enjoyed what they were doing; children in the other groups tired more easily, became bored and restless. Since it is unlikely that the groups were mismatched in enthusiasm, this too seems to be an added advantage of Program I.

Of particular interest was a spontaneous recitation, either aloud or whispered, of the items by most of the children in those phases of Program I where the items were composed of words. In the parts of Program I in which the children had to count the [s] sounds and in which they responded to the position of the [s] sound in words, all of the children recited the items. In a few instances in Phase 4, they not only repeated the correct word, but also imitated the misarticulated one as well. This behavior was noted for only a few children in Program III and was completely absent for the children working with Program II.

This spontaneous vocalization was unexpected, is at present unexplained, and might well be of considerable importance. Program I provided most of the vocalization and also gave clear-cut improvement in [s] discrimination. Therefore, we cannot overlook the possibility that vocalization as such may play an important role in facilitating development of speech sound discrimination. These vocalizations might force careful observation of auditory cues, or they might provide supplemental kinesthetic stimuli which could be useful in close discriminations. On the other hand, the vocalizations may have no direct influence in discrimination establishment, but might, rather, reflect some other factor which is itself the important variable. The close difficult discriminations might also result in vocalization, whether actually useful or not. Similarly, both vocalization and adequate training may depend upon the interest of the student. Although there is no ready explanation for the vocalization and no information as to its importance in discrimination training, the possibilities raised are of considerable theoretical and practical importance.

Program I is clearly the superior of these programs for teaching [s] discrimination. This superiority is probably a direct reflection of the varying tasks within Program I. In addition, the wide range of tasks and the careful noticing of the [s] phoneme required from students using Program I point up two of the advantages of auditory discrimination training to articulation correction. When correct production of a sound is finally achieved, regardless of whether the etiology of defective articulation involves defective speech sound discrimination, the consistent conversational use of the correct sound depends upon reinforcement for using it. This reinforcement is automatic; that is, it results from "hearing yourself say it correctly." Careful noticing of a sound, within a wide range of phonetic contexts, sets up many more occasions upon which correct sound production can be reinforced. Careful auditory discrimination training would appear to be important in establishing stable correct articulation.

Auxiliary Tests. The Sibilant test, the Templin test, the [s] articulation, and the general articulation tests formed a secondary type of evaluation for the programs. They were included in an effort to test a number of hypotheses concerning the benefits of auditory training, but are, in the long run, side effects to the teaching of [s] discrimination.

The Sibilant Test. Since the sibilant sounds are among the most difficult to discriminate from [s], many items in Program I involved such tasks. Thus, training in discrimination of [s] gave training in discrimination of the other sibilants as well. It has been the clinical experience of the investigators that when correction of one sound has been achieved, the correction of similar sounds follows easily. The increased ability for Group I to discriminate sibilant sounds reflects this observation experimentally as far as discrimination training is concerned.

The reliable change in sibilant discrimination for Group II is less clear-cut. Only four subjects contributed to this improvement, and the other five subjects showed no change. However, from the nature of the items in this program, children in Group II shared an advantage with children in Group I in that their program, too, was heavily loaded with sibilant sounds. The heightened ability to discriminate sibilants may reflect this.

Group III, whose program did not afford the increased sibilant discrimination practice noted for the other groups, showed no significant improvement. Lack of improvement on this task in addition to lack of improvement in [s] discrimination suggests that Program III was altogether inadequate in teaching speech sound discrimination.

The Templin Test. None of the three groups showed reliable changes in general speech sound discrimination as measured by the Templin Test. It is felt that this reflects the remote relationship between auditory training for a specific sound and auditory discrimination ability for a large number of speech sounds.

[s] Articulation Test. Viewed alone, the improved [s] articulation scores for all three groups is perhaps the most surprising find-

ing of the study. For this reason, it must be cautiously interpreted. It is emphasized that the test for articulation involved three [s] sounds and fifteen [s] blends in a variety of positions in English words. The child's score was the number of sounds and blends he correctly articulated. Thus, an 'improved' score on this test does not indicate that the child who could not previously articulate [s] now could do so. It means, merely, that in the 24 phonetic contexts in which [s] was tested, the child was able to articulate [s] correctly more often. In order to satisfactorily modify his [s] sound for testing purposes, a child would have had to score 24 on the post-test. No child modified his [s] to this degree; all still had [s] problems, even in the testing situation, at the end of the study.

It is well known that few persons who misarticulate sounds do so in all possible phonetic contests (14). Twenty of the children in this study initially showed such inconsistency. The significant increase in correct [s] production noted for all three groups reflects simply an ability to articulate [s] within a few more phonetic contests, not correct and stable [s] production. This gain is a beginning sign in articulation improvement and must be regarded as nothing more.

It will be remembered that no differences were shown to exist between the three groups as to their articulation gains. It is believed, however, that Group I, with its increased ability to discriminate [s], could capitalize upon the ability from these early gains.

General Articulation. The measure of general articulation ability was an attempt to gain an overall speech picture of each subject. This lack of improvement in general articulation following specific auditory discrimination training for a single sound was not surprising.

Conclusions

It seems clear from this study that techniques for improvement of [s] discrimination in children who misarticulate [s] are amenable to teaching machine programming. It is highly feasible that other sound discrimination programs can be developed following similar principles. At its most practical level, this study suggests that a clinical method is adaptable for automation. The same advantages which pertain to automated teaching in general — increased efficiency and effectiveness — also pertain here. The children in Group I, after spending approximately ten minutes learning to operate the tape recorder, worked through their program in an average of two hours and fifteen minutes and improved their [s] discrimination. With proper automation, this would involve only the student's time. Careful sound discrimination training by traditional methods usually takes considerably longer. The values of this time advantage lie, not only in accelerating the training, but also in freeing the clinician's time to work on sound production — a phase of articulation correction requiring the individual skill and knowledge of the clinician.

Challenging opportunities lie in the extension of teaching machine concepts to other areas of speech pathology and audiology. Alphasia rehabilitation, for example, may well be a promising area for automation of teaching. A library of programs for reshaping impaired language skills in adult aphasics would be an invaluable benefit to the aphasia clinician. Programs similar to this one — as well as programs for teaching arithmetic, reading, spelling, grammar, and foreign languages — should be examined and evaluated for use with aphasic adults. It is quite possible that such programs, and extensions and modifications of them, can form the beginnings of some excellent new concepts for rehabilitation of individuals with communication disorders.

Teaching machines can contribute to the field of speech pathology and audiology. The future should hold wide applications which go far beyond this simple start.

Acknowledgment

The writers are deeply indebted to James G. Holland of Harvard University for his constant help throughout this study. They are also grateful to Lawrence Bloom whose voice was used for the experimental tapes.

REFERENCES

1. Brong, C., "An Evaluation of Ear Training as a Pedagogical Technique in Improving Sound Discrimination." Unpublished doctoral dissertation, Northwestern University, 1948.

2. Edwards, A., *Experimental Design in Psychological Research*. New York: Holt, Rinehart and Winston, 1950.

3. Evans, J., L. E. Homme, and R. Glaser, "The RULEG System for the Construction of Learning Programs." Unpublished paper, University of Pittsburgh, 1959.

4. Glaser, R., "Christmas Past, Present, and Future," *Contemp. Psychol.*, 1960, 5, 24–28.

5. Holland, J. G., "Teaching Machines: An Application of Principles from the Laboratory." In A. A. Lumsdaine and R. Glaser, *Teaching Machines and Programmed Learning*. Washington, D.C.: National Education Association, 1960.

6. Lumsdaine, A. A., and R. Glaser, *Teaching Machines and Programmed Learning*. Washington, D.C.: National Education Association, 1960.

7. Powers, M. H., "Clinical and Educational Procedure in Functional Disorders of Articulation." In L. Travis (Ed.), *Handbook of Speech Pathology*. New York: Appleton-Century-Crofts, 1957.

8. Pressey, S. L., in *School and Society*, 1926, 23, 586.

9. Skinner, B. F., "The Experimental Analysis of Behavior," *Amer. Scientist*, 1957, 45, 343–371.

10. Skinner, B. F., "The Science of Learning and the Art of Teaching," *Harvard Educ. Rev.*, 1954, 86–97.

11. Skinner, B. F., *Science and Human Behavior*. New York: Macmillan, 1953.

12. Skinner, B. F., *Verbal Behavior*. New York: Appleton-Century-Crofts, 1957.

13. Spriesterbach, D. C., and F. F. Curtis, "Misarticulation and Discrimination of Speech Sounds," *Quart J. Speech*, 1951, 37, 483–491.

14. Templin, M., "A Study of Sound Discrimination Ability in Elementary School Pupils," *J. Speech Hearing Dis.*, 1943, 8, 127–132.

15. Thorndike, E. L., and I. Lorge, *The Teacher's Wordbook of 30,000 Words*. New York: Columbia University Press, 1944.

16. Van Riper, C., *Speech Correction: Principles and Methods* (3rd ed.). Englewood Cliffs, N.J.: Prentice-Hall, 1954.

14

James McDearmon

Programmed Learning Instruction in Phonics

Skinner (*1958*) has suggested, "Cannot the results of laboratory research on learning be used in education without machines? Of course they can." The present writer has applied programmed learning principles to phonics instruction on a flexible, individual basis for reading and certain articulatory disabilities. It is not the purpose of this paper to present the rationale for such use of phonics, but simply to describe and clarify the method used.

Occasionally one or more of three preparatory phases may be required: (1) speech sound discrimination; (2) visual form discrimination; or (3) letter form discrimination. These will be described briefly.

Sound discriminations are taught through successive problems of delicately graded difficulty in recognizing whether two sounds are alike or different. The work begins with gross differences, as between vowels and plosives; advances through diminishing differences, as between plosives and fricatives; and finally through the most difficult discriminations, as between unvoiced fricatives. Learning to discriminate isolated sounds prepares the child for learning to discriminate sound sequences at ascending levels of complexity in the phonics program itself.

Visual form discrimination is taught in tiny steps, utilizing the oddity problem. In successive problems the odd one of three forms is first grossly different, then gradually more similar. Concurrently, the forms progress in complexity, until readiness for letter forms is gained.

The specific teaching of letter form discrimination, which supports visual with tactile and kinesthetic associations, utilizes plastic block or cut-out sandpaper letters in the oddity problem. Early steps teach gross discriminations, as between *i* and *o;* later steps, more difficult ones, as between *o* and *u;* and still later, the most difficult, as between *d* and *b*. The letters are first taught without concern for their positions. If upper-case letters are used, they should be used throughout the program. Lower-case letters are preferable, however.

Before describing the phonics program proper, it is necessary to define a basic phonic concept, the allograph.

An allograph is a particular spelling of a phoneme. The phoneme is the smallest distinctive unit of speech sound, such as the sound of *ou* in *out* and *our*. The sound is spelled *ou* in *out*, *ow* in *cow*. Thus, *ou* and *ow* are different allographs of the vowel phoneme in these words.

Phonemes may be called the "building blocks" of spoken language. From the point of view of phonetics, allographs may be called the "building blocks" of phonetic written language. All spoken words are either single phonemes, such as "awe," or phoneme sequences. All written words are single allographs or allograph sequences, often interspersed with silent letters.

The interpretation of the make-up of an allograph in a given word is often partly subjective. In many words *o* has, or can have, the sound of *aw* in *law: broad, gone, off, ought*, etc. In such words as *ought* we may consider *o* as the allograph of the vowel, and *ugh* silent; or we may consider *ough* as the allograph.

Whenever feasible, allographs are here simplified by considering them as single letters, reducing the total number of allographs to be learned to the minimum (91 for nearly all words in ordinary reading), and increasing the frequency of letters to be regarded as silent.

Programmed phonics requires learning to identify individual allographs before learning their sequences, because individual allographs are much simpler to learn, fewer in number, and more important in terms of frequency (*Moore, 1951, pp. 28–37*), and because learning of allographs provides readiness for learning of sequences (thus: *s* and *t*, for *st; st* and *r*, for *str*, etc.).

Through the progressive presentation of allographs and their sequences, the stringent requirements of linear-type programmed learning may be satisfied. Only one new allograph is introduced at a time. At any point in the program, a word to be learned contains only (1) the new allograph, (2) previously learned allographs, and (3) silent letters. Thus, allograph by allograph, sequences and words are built up for practice, mastery, and review. Cumulative allograph learning permits progress through tiny steps of learning, based upon readiness for the new and mastery of the old.

The concept of "mastery" is important throughout the program. It means attainment of consistent accuracy of response in repeated presentations of the same practice items. Mastery, not speed, should be the criterion of progress at every point.

The phonics instruction begins with learning to identify and sound a single allograph (short *a*) when *a* and *t* are presented in random order. This is followed by learning to identify and sound *t* when both *a* and *t* are again presented in random order, then by learning to sound both allographs separately in the order in which they are presented. A connected sequence of these two allographs (*at* as in *cat*) is then presented, making a total of three items so far presented (*a, t,* and *at*). Combinations of two, and then of all three items in a single frame (stimulus-response unit) are presented next. A third allograph (*c* as in *cat*) is then presented, later followed by the sequences (*ca*), and still later by the word (*cat*).

The beginning frames are outlined. Individual frames, of course, are reviewed as often as necessary for mastery.

The sequencing of allographs and words in the entire program is given at the conclusion of this chapter.

By way of illustration, let us consider in detail a typical plan for the first lesson. Each lesson is fairly short, and begins with the presentation of a picture or object, and ends with some favored activity.

A large, colorful picture of a cat, with *cat* printed in large letters below it, is placed before the child. After informal discussion of the picture, attention turns to the word. The teacher points out that the printed letters stand for sounds, and that the sounds form the word "cat." She pronounces the word slowly and asks the child to repeat it after her. Strong emphasis is given each sound, but all

New Items Presented	Items Randomly Ordered in Each Frame	Items Identified and Sounded in Order Presented
a (as in *cat*)	1. *a t*	*a*
t (as in *cat*)		
	2. *a t*	*t*
	3. *a t*	*a t*
at		
	4. *at a*	*at*
	5. *at a*	*at a*
	6. *at t*	*at t*
	7. *at a t*	*at a t*
c (as in *cat*)		
	8. *c a*	*c*
	9. *c a*	*c a*
	10. *c t*	*c t*
	11. *c at*	*c at*
	12. *c a t*	*c a t*
	13. *c a at*	*c a at*
	14. *c t at*	*c t at*
	15. *c a t at* . . .	*c a t at*
ca (as in *cat*)		
	16. (etc. — continuing with similar sequencing, but with unnecessary review frames dropping out)	
cat		
ta (as in *tack*)		
tack		
etc.		

sounds are in connected sequence. Then teacher and child pronounce the word in unison several times. Next the teacher explains that, while the two of them together pronounce the word again very slowly, she will point to each letter just as they are saying its sound. She asks the child to watch and listen closely. After this is done several times, the teacher asks the child to join her in pointing to each letter as they continue repeating the word. Finally, she asks the child to point without assistance to each letter as sounded in the spoken word.

The teacher explains that learning to read the "letter-sounds" helps one to learn to read the words. She makes no further attempt at this point to teach perception of sounds within their sequences. Gradually the child will acquire such discriminations and differentiated responses through practice in distinguishing sounds and their innumerable sequences (as: *a, at, cat, tack*) and in sounding out words (as: *l, a, la, n, lan, d, land*).

Next, the teacher shows the child the letters *a* and *t*, each printed with felt pen on separate 3 x 5 cards. These letter-sounds are shown to be the same as those under the picture. The teacher tells the child he will first learn a sound of *a,* and she presents and sounds the *a* card several times. She then shuffles the cards and presents them together in random order. Ignoring the *t* card for the time being, she then sounds *a* three times, and the last time points to the *a* card. Next, in each frame, she shuffles the cards, sounds *a,* and asks the child to point with her to the *a*. When the child begins occasionally to point first, with accuracy, the teacher delays her own pointing. After sufficient practice, the child is allowed to point without assistance.

Next, pointing precedes sounding. In each frame the teacher shuffles the cards, presents them in random order, and points to each in turn. At this time the *a,* when pointed to, is always sounded; the *t* when pointed to is ignored. After the teacher offers several demonstrations of shuffling, pointing, and sounding, in each frame she asks the child to sound the *a* after her when she points to it. Later, the teacher asks the child to sound the *a* along with her when she points to it. When the child begins occasionally to sound the *a* first, the teacher delays her own response. Finally, the child sounds the *a* at the appropriate point without assistance. The teacher must watch carefully to insure that the child responds only to the appropriate card.

In most later frames (as in #3 in the outline above), there is active response to all the cards used, not to only one of them as in the first few frames.

The stimulus materials can be presented in many ways other than cards, while still maintaining the basic sequencing. Among the useful media available are flannel-board, plastic, cut-out, or modeled clay letters; letters filled in by the child with colors; blackboard; and Language Master. Letters may be printed on play devices: for example, on "fruit" for a flannel-board or artificial tree, or on the jackets of small puppets.

Knowledge of results is the major reinforcement programmed. The child is informed when he is correct and when he is not; by the nature of the programming, he is correct most of the time. (For practical purposes, we may say that incorrect responses are the failure of the teacher and the program, not of the child.) Correctness of response is typically communicated at once by a warm or enthusiastic "right," a nod or smile, or the like. Incorrectness is much more subtly communicated, with minimal or no "negative affect." A slight shake of the head, silence, or a "Let's try it again," may be sufficient. Slow learners are often punished enough; they should not be punished further.

Reinforcement also includes games and other play activities, particularly in the latter part of the lesson. Simple "move" games (as those using toy cars), block-building, nest-stacking, and flannel-board assemblies are a few of the types of play in which a correct response of the child is followed by his being allowed a move or turn. Another type of reinforcement is some kind of sound or sight: a bell that rings, or a Jack-in-the-box. It is important that each reinforcement be brief so that it does not distract from the learning.

The use of a favorite activity is reserved for the end of the lesson. The child may color a picture and a descriptive letter or word under it (for example, a *t* whose sound describes the clock in the picture above it). He may play a dart game, sounding the letters in the squares hit, or a variation of the "old shell game," guessing the sounds of the letters in each of several small boxes and then discovering if he is correct.

Throughout the program, each allograph and allograph sequence is always presented as part of a word which will later be learned as a whole. For example, *c* is first presented as the letter-sound in *cat,* then in *tack,* etc. Allographs are not taught as independent elements to be pieced together in a purely synthetic manner. In reality, the reader tends to attack a new word *both* synthetically and analytically. He pieces sounds together, but he also uses larger cues in interpreting ambiguous allographs. Allographs, allograph sequences, and whole words are thus mutually assisting.

For example, the child, in grappling with the word "character," is likely to begin it with the sound of *ch* as in *chair,* until some visual or acoustic stimulus related to the over-all configuration of the word suggests that he try the hard *c* sound. This cue may be assisted by other allographic cues in the word.

One important set of frames, occurring at the conclusion of the work with every newly learned word, has been omitted from the above outline for expedience. This set provides practice in:

(1) identifying and sounding out, within each syllable of the word, the sequential allographs and sequences, then the whole word. For example, the sequential frames for the word *paper* evoke the following responses: *p, a* (long sound), *pa; p, r, per; paper.*

(2) naming already learned whole words presented in random order without the help of sounding.

(3) reading already learned words in sentences, unfamiliar words being immediately told to the pupil. Thus, after *cat* and *tack* are learned, the sentence, "The *cat* sat on a *tack*" may be used.

Two essential characteristics of the program have yet to be discussed: assistive procedures to assure successful response, and the fading of the devices as the need decreases. These procedures are repetitive stimulation, initial orderliness (non-randomness) of responses, small size of groupings, and underlining of allographs.

(1) Prior to the presentation of one or more frames, repetitive stimulation with letters and sounds is provided until the child is able to respond successfully. Practice is continued until this prompt is no longer needed.

(2) Another assistance is provided through the sequencing of responses within successive frames. Ability to respond correctly with allographs presented in any order in a frame is the goal, but at the beginning, the child is assisted by a non-random order. Thus, in repeating frame #9 above, the responses for the *c* and *a* in *cat* may be ordered as follows: *c —a — c —a — c —a —c —c —a*, etc. Randomness is gradually increased, little by little, as the child responds more accurately and discriminatingly. Each frame is practiced until this assistance is no longer necessary to assure correct responses.

(3) A third variable is the number of items within a frame. It is, of course, easier to identify and name two items than three, and to identify and name three items than four, etc. Therefore, frames are at first limited to only two items. After the child responds accurately to groupings of two items, frames are enlarged to include

various groupings of three items, then of four, etc. With increasing ability, larger groupings can be used at the outset in practicing new items.

(4) A fourth prompt enables the child to distinguish allographs from silent letters. Allographs are underlined; silent letters are not. At first the underlinings are dark, but gradually, as more allographs and words are mastered, the lines are lightened and finally eliminated.

A fundamental issue in phonics concerns the desirability of teaching isolated allographs. The advantages of this in a programmed learning approach have been pointed out earlier. But such teaching has often been objected to as resulting in unnatural pronunciation and labored reading. No convincing evidence has supported this contention. Learning individual allographs before sequences and words does not appear to jeopardize the learning of normal pronunciation and reading any more than the learning of the use of the individual typewriter keys jeopardizes the later fluent and automatic typing of words, phrases, and sentences.

Bloomfield (1961, p. 28) and other linguists have complained that the pronunciation of sounds in isolation is unnatural and should not be part of the learning process. Their phonetics is correct, of course, but their learning theory is open to question. It is true that isolated sounds are rare in actual use and are articulated differently from the way they are articulated in connected speech. The same may often be said of isolated words. Yet learning to articulate either isolated sounds or words is a step in learning to articulate them in speech.

The principle of beginning with small elemental units, then adapting them in gradually accumulating combinations, is seen over and over in numerous areas of learning, and is, in fact, an essential aspect of much programmed learning. The real necessities involved in the teaching of speech and language bear this out. Most speech pathologists teach sounds in isolation before teaching them in syllables and words. Language teachers often do the same.

It has been said that non-continuant sounds, such as [k], can not be pronounced in isolation. However, according to Wise (1958, p. 66), "any sound whatever can be pronounced alone." At any rate, with a little practice, both teacher and student can eliminate enough of the excrescent voiced or unvoiced "uh" sound after the plosive sound attempted in isolation, so that useful application of the learned sound in a connected sound sequence is unimpaired.

The writer began his attempt to develop a simplified, totally cumulative method of teaching phonics more than twenty years ago. As the method evolved, he turned from its use in the schools to its application in the speech clinic. Further refinements, suggested by programmed learning methodology, were in accord with its already established basic features. The method has had favorable results with more than fifty children and adolescents, many of whom were slow learners or retardates.

These cases showed significant gains in both reading and speech. The latter appeared to result from three sources: better auditory discrimination; improved analysis and snythesis of sound sequences ("vocal phonics"); and better recall and reproduction of sound sequences. Apparently, visual association of allograph sequences provided important sensory assistance in the auditory and kinesthetic guidance of speech.

The order of presentation of allographs and words in the program is given below. The order of allographs must be maintained, but the choice of specific words is flexible, after the first four or five in a grouping. Only words that can be immediately useful for the child should be used. The unstarred words include almost all those words which lead one or more of seven frequency lists. These are all the words (excepting "Mr." and "Mrs.") in the Dale list of 769 words (1931); the Thorndike first 500 (1944, pp. 267–268); the Gates first 500 (1935, pp. 21–23); the Durrell first 480 (1956, pp. 363–365); the Mecham and Jones 412 words (1956); the Dolch 220 words (1950, pp. 507–508); and the Dewey first 300 "root words" (1923, pp. 19–21).

The Sequence of Allographs and Words

a (as in)	at
t	at
c	cat tack* act
k	tack*
p	cap tap* pat* pack*
n	an can pan pant* nap*
e	ten pen pet neck kept

b (as in) back bat* cab*
i   in it bit pick picnic kitten captain
l   let tell bell bill kill till built plan plant black apple little
o   on lot not top lock* clock
          ought* bought* nought*
r   ran rat rock bear tear brought robin rabbit
r   burn turn learn per
r   better letter cracker*
u   up upon nut but cut cup run butter until public
d   add did dead doll duck bad bed bird red end and land
          band bread build drop under dinner dollar doctor double
d   licked* ripped*
a   a ate late cake lake take day pay lay play plain tail rain
          train paint laid trade paper table cradle labor
a   air pair care
m   am man men met mill milk came name made make may
          mail drum matter middle minute number permit
e   me be bee knee peep deep keep meet need tree eat beat
          meat mean real read lead dream clean people birdie
e   ear near dear tear clear
s   us sun sat sit sick set sell less miss kiss pass loss its it's sir
          say stay same case sail see seed seem seen sea seat ask last
          sand stand class else best nest rest send sent dress press
          step sled bless lips skin silk stick still lost cost cross stop
          spot must dust space state taste sleep steel speak east least
          spread street straight answer lesson listen sister summer
          possible increase instead
i   I I'll I'm pie lie die tie tried cried nine line mine time tire
          ride side kite write mile smile like might night light right
          bright sign kind mind blind climb iron strike
f   if off fan fat fell fill fit fun fail fair feed feel feet fear fire
          fine life fight fast fact self felt left lift soft from free find
          field first friend after itself careful differ
o   O oh no so toe own know bow bowl row low slow snow
          blow oak boat coat coal road load rope note bone smoke
          stone close old told sold cold don't post most roll follow
          fellow
o   or nor for four door floor corn born sort fork form more
          store storm court course corner order board toward

g (as in) go get guess got gone God gun egg leg bag big pig dig dog game gate goat girl flag glad glass grass gray grow grain green gift gold forget

u true blue suit fruit bluebird

v give live five drive leave gave save brave serve over ever never river silver

y carry marry daddy kitty dolly funny valley body very ready baby lady tiny pony only early candy country story every family military

y eye by buy my cry dry try sky fly butterfly myself supply

y you yes yet yellow year yesterday

s as is nose rose close goes leaves please games guns easy visit scissors surprise present

a are arm car far farm farmer mark bark dark barn yard part party star start army garden grandma grandpa

a all ball call fall tall small saw law draw cause caught* talk salt also almost already

w we wet well wear went west will win wind window was want wall walk way wave wait waste wee week wife wide wild war warm were work word world water winter twelve twenty sweet always

wh why what when where wheel wheat white while

a ago away alone appear asleep across afraid America American mamma idea breakfast several important animal Christmas Indian Santa Claus

h has hat have half had hand hen head held help hid him his hill hit hot hop hall he hay high hide hope home hole whole hold horn horse hard heart hair hear here her heard hurt hunt heavy happy hurry herself himself perhaps husband

o come some none done love son money cover color does front above company wonder sometime blood govern

o today tomorrow lion crayon apron bottom person reason season second consider purpose commit

th the that than then them there their this thus though those these with within clothes either neither other another rather weather whether father mother grandfather grand-mother brother together themselves

e (as in) even often open happen seven given taken broken golden
between believe moment hardest hundred different president market government

e begin began became become because behind beside before remain result return report remember demand basket interest

e been pretty England

j jam* jar* John jump just

o do to two who whom whose move into

g edge age page large bridge danger gingerbread general

a package* garbage* orange*

oo too noon moon soon roof room broom rooster cool school food balloon afternoon

qu quite quiet quick queen square squirrel quarter require

ew new knew grew newspaper* New York

ew few mew

sh she show shoe shall ship shop shut shake shape sheep shine short dish fish wish wash fresh sunshine finish shoulder English

u use human music beautiful pupil*

u continue United States

th thick thin thought third three throw through earth bath path both cloth month forth north birthday

ou out our hour house mouse mouth south loud cloud found pound sound round ground count about around without outside mountain thousand

ow owl cow how now down town brown power flower crowd crown however

ch chair chief choose church chick chicken each reach teach teacher touch much such catch rich which watch lunch branch march change child children

ng ring king thing wing sing spring song long wrong strong young tongue hang bring among along belong being going coming nothing something everything evening morning stocking building Washington

ng finger hungry longer

n think drink bank thank monkey uncle Thanksgiving

oo book took look cook cooky wood good good-by stood foot poor

u (as in)	put pull full could would should your during pussy
oi	noise point voice
oy	boy toy
s	sure sugar
s	measure treasure* television*
c	face race place ice mice nice peace piece price cent center certain city since dance chance fence circle receive ice-cream force office produce service fancy
e	eight neighbor great break they
t	station nation national condition
a	said again against any many anything
t	picture question
o	one once
ph	elephant telephone* phonograph* photograph*
gh	laugh enough cough*
x	box fox fix six next except expect
x	exact* examination*
z	zoo* puzzle* size
i	policeman* automobile*
c	ocean machine*
o	wolf woman
o	women
f	of
d	soldier education*
u	busy business
u	figure
y	system

REFERENCES

Bloomfield, L., and C. L. Barnhart, *Let's Read.* Detroit: Wayne State University Press, 1961.

Dale, E., "A Comparison of Two Word Lists," *Educ. Res. Bull.*, 1931, 10, 484–489.

Dewey, G., *Relative Frequency of English Speech Sounds.* Cambridge: Harvard University Press, 1923.

Dolch, E. W., *Teaching Primary Reading.* Champaign, Ill.: Garrard, 1950.

Durrell, D. D., *Improving Reading Instruction.* Yonkers-on-Hudson, N.Y.: World Book, 1956.

Gates, A. I., *A Reading Vocabulary for the Primary Grades.* New York: Teachers College, Columbia University, 1935.

Mecham, M. J., and Dixie Jones, "A Nucleus Vocabulary for Use in Building Oral Language Skills of the Cerebral Palsied Child," *Except. Child.,* 1956, 22, 280–284.

Moore, J. T., "Phonetic Elements Appearing in a Three-thousand Word Spelling Vocabulary." Ed.D. Dissertation, Stanford University, 1951.

Skinner, B. F., "Teaching Machines," *Science,* 1958, 128, 969–977.

Thorndike, E. L., and I. Lorge, *The Teacher's Word Book of 30,000 Words.* New York: Teachers College, Columbia University, 1944.

Wise, C. M., *Introduction to Phonetics.* Englewood Cliffs, N.J.: Prentice-Hall, 1958.

15

Donald E. Mowrer
Robert L. Baker
Richard E. Schutz

Operant Procedures in the Control
of Speech Articulation

It comes as no surprise to a young mother when her child begins to articulate fluently between the ages of four and six, and most parents assume that verbal fluency is as much a part of the developmental process as are crawling and walking. Frequently, however, specific articulation deficiencies persist long after children have mastered speech fluency. These deficiencies are called functional articulation problems and are manifested by [w] for [r] substitutions, [s] distortions, omission of [1], and the like. Nevertheless, most non-fluencies are replaced by correct phonemes by the time the child has finished the third grade.

Some professional workers, pediatricians, and family doctors view this change as a progressive maturational process due to time alone. On the other hand, those who consider speech to be learned behavior have contended that proficiency in articulation can be accelerated by the manipulation of specified environmental and social events.

Although the family doctor holds favorable odds with respect to his predictions concerning speech maturation, the fact remains that some children do not "outgrow" their speech difficulties. Generally, it is difficult to predict whether or not a child will outgrow a speech handicap; and the child with delayed speech often experiences difficulties in communication that can create social and emotional problems. To the educator, factors that retard the child's social and educational advancement become targets for amelioration.

Identification of articulation disorders constitutes no problem for the speech therapist. Children readily reveal faulty phoneme production as the first dozen words tumble out, and therapists can usually agree unanimously as to which sounds are misarticulated.

Correction of misarticulation is a great deal more complicated than detection. For example, it may take three months to correct an [s] omission in one child's speech and eight or more months to correct the same omission in another child's speech. Of course, one generally accepted explanation is that the children are different individuals possessing different motivations, response sets, abilities, and interests; therefore, they cannot be expected to learn at the same rate. The concept of individual differences is used to provide built-in protection from criticism for speech therapists and classroom teachers. Slow progress or failure is frequently attributed to the unique characteristics of the child, and the teacher's or therapist's methodology is seldom questioned.

However, during the past decade there has been a quiet revolution among professional workers in the behavioral sciences. Instead of focusing on individual differences, attention has been given to individual similarities. Recently there has been a concerted effort to discover basic principles of learning that apply to all living organisms. B. F. Skinner (1957) has been instrumental in applying these concepts and procedures to human learning. As a result of research in this area, considerable doubt has been raised concerning both the reputed positive effects of certain procedures upon the correction of articulation and the rationale used in devising these procedures. To assist the reader with a clearer understanding of some of the problems that exist today with respect to formulating effective procedures, a brief outline of the more traditional beliefs will be presented.

The classic techniques of speech correction have been validated largely on the basis of practical experience. Proceeding on the assumption that since a child speaks incorrectly he hears incorrectly, various techniques have been designed to stimulate him with correct sounds. Van Riper (1947) was one of the first actually to formulate a method based upon auditory stimulation as a starting point for speech correction. It was his opinion that after the child had been convinced that he had a speech problem his ear should be bombarded with the correct sound in a series of auditory discrimination activities. By developing discriminative listening skills, the child should be able to monitor and correct his own verbal responses. Van Riper makes his position clear when he states, "After intensive ear training, the child should produce the sound perfectly on his first attempt." He goes on to suggest that if the child is not successful, he should be returned for additional auditory discrimination exercises. Such a technique finds little empirical support in learning research.

Even when the use of such techniques appears to result in success, the empirical researcher is forced to consider the *post hoc ergo propter hoc* fallacy. That is, it is conceivable that the change in behavior was brought about by some variable other than the one identified by the clinician. Bombarding the child's ear with correct sounds may assist the child in identifying the clinician's production of the sound, but this skill may not be related to the skills needed by the child in order to produce the sound himself.

When the "stimulation method" fails to evoke the desired response, the speech therapist uses other techniques to fit the "individual needs" of the child. West, Ausbery, and Carr (1957) state, "There will be certain individuals who, because of sensory deficiencies, will not be able to learn to recognize or discriminate between sounds through auditory discriminations." If this is the case, these authors suggest that a phonetic placement method be used to show the child where to put his tongue. This may require actual physical manipulation and/or the use of pictorial drawings. One wonders how a child with defective sensory deficiencies is detected in the first place. It would appear that the reasoning runs thus: all children who profit from ear training succeed in producing sounds correctly. Those children who do not succeed have sensory deficiencies. Such reasoning is clearly circular and actually describes little more than the already observable facts.

Other clinicians reject the analytic methodology, favoring a more realistic or "naturalistic" speech setting. Backus and Beasly (1951) draw heavily from such phenomenological and social psychologists as Lewin, Fromm, Horney, Rogers, Cansion, and Kohler in formulating their therapeutic approach. They maintain that interpersonal relations are of greater importance in speech correction than are drills, speech exercises, word lists, and the like. Their procedure consists of stimulating children to make "natural" verbal responses in a group situation. If a child misarticulates a sound, it is called to his attention and he is encouraged to repeat the word. If his attempts result in a closer approximation, his efforts are rewarded by the teacher as well as by group approval.

Backus and Beasley may be correct when they say, in effect, that many children who have the appropriate response in their repertoires often do not produce this response in a social contest. Rather than concentrating on creating a "natural" speaking situation, it might be more accurate for instructional purposes to view the speech problem in terms of extending and refining the stimulus control of the correct response. Looking at the problem this way, one would question the efficacy of group procedures, particularly during that phase when a new response is either nonexistent or weakly established in the child's verbal repertoire.

There are other therapeutic approaches that are less structured than those advocated by Backus and Beasley. When a child does not respond to the "usual" corrective methods, Henja (1960) feels that a nondirective play therapy approach is needed. The basic assumption here is that individuals possess the ability to resolve their own problems of adjustment by themselves, with only indirect assistance from a therapist. When an atmosphere is established in which a youngster feels free to express himself, Henja maintains, speech improves automatically.

Again one can ask, "What is the cause of what?" Factors other than those that occur in the play therapy settings may be responsible for subsequent articulation changes. Few will quarrel with the possibility that some children who have speech difficulties, as well as many who do not, may benefit from some kind of psychological help or counseling. However, to call play therapy and speech correction one and the same is inappropriate.

The minimal effectiveness of some speech therapy procedures in correcting articulatory problems has been reported by Irwin (1963). Articulation responses of an experimental group receiving speech therapy for seven months differed little from those responses of a matched group who received no speech therapy during the same interval. Irwin found this result quite difficult to interpret and suggested further study.

It is a well known fact that articulation problems decrease as a function of increasing age. Roe and Milisen (1942) report that by the end of the third grade few articulation problems persist, even in the absence of speech therapy. Clinicians estimate that out of every three children receiving speech therapy during the school year, one will be dismissed as corrected (Chapman, 1961). The family physician may wonder if the observed speech improvement is not the result of a maturational process rather than the result of activities that took place during speech class. However, when articulation improves, the clinician is quick to take credit for this change, and is strongly reinforced for using his current procedures.

Rigdrodsky and Steer (1961), using mentally retarded subjects, compared traditional speech therapy (stimulation method) with an adapted form of O. H. Mowrer's autistic language development theory. Their results failed to reveal any significant difference in articulation ability between the two groups after receiving different speech therapy programs. Furthermore, the control group receiving no speech therapy made the same articulation gains as did the two groups who received the eight months of speech therapy. Such studies lead one to question seriously the efficacy of traditional speech correction techniques, and indicate the need for systematically accounting for the variables involved in various clinical methods. An empirical analysis should enable one to determine why some techniques appear to succeed where others fail.

The current investigations were designed to validate speech correction procedures. Most studies comparing different procedures fail to control adequately for the effects of certain interpolated activities and variables introduced during the period treatment. The experimental treatment is usually administered to large groups of subjects over long periods of time, often six to eight months. As improved articulation often develops during comparable time periods in the absence of speech therapy, the researcher must control such effects in some manner. Many studies are not replicable due to absent or inadequate recording and specification of procedures. Conclusions drawn from procedural studies in which there is little control over relevant variables or inadequate specification of procedures are highly questionable.

One of the first objectives in the series of studies that follow was to construct a standard written instructional program with a high degree of success in bringing about changes in articulation. A second objective was to decide upon an adequate criterion measure of articulation to be administered prior to and at the completion of the instructional sequence.

The remainder of this paper addresses itself to a description of three sets of activities: (1) the development and validation of an instructional sequence; (2) an analysis of the role of several variables related to the mode of program presentation and student response to the sequence; and (3) an assessment of the need for a trained speech therapist as program monitor.

Development of the Instructional Sequence

Choice of the frontal lisp as the initial articulatory problem to attack was based on the fact that both correct and incorrect behaviors can easily be defined operationally. This was not a cowardly decision, as speech therapists devote vast amounts of time and energy to this problem. In other words, correction of the frontal lisp constitutes a practical school problem and at the same time ensures the researcher an adequate number of experimental subjects.

In constructing the standardized instructional program designed to correct the frontal lisp, heavy reliance was placed on predicted efficacy of two procedures: successive approximations and differential reinforcement. To be sure, other learning concepts are involved, but the peculiar nature of articulatory problems makes it very important that the response classes be identified and the enroute responses carefully analyzed and sequenced. The peculiarity stems from the fact that correction of a speech disorder is not just a simple matter of acquiring the correct response and subsequently producing it under all appropriate stimulus conditions. The lisping child already has a response that is produced under all appropriate stimulus conditions. The listening community does not like the response, but nonetheless the response is reinforced and is well established in the child's repertoire. To extinguish the lisping response and replace it with the [s] response requires tight control and extreme care in introducing the stimuli that, hopefully, will eventually evoke the correct [s] with high probability.

Part I of the Instructional Sequence. To elicit a relevant first response without introducing stimuli that control the lisping response was the first task. The overall strategy suggested starting with a response already in the child's repertoire and successively approximating the [s], first as it occurs in isolation, then in words and sentences, as responses to objects in the child's environment, and eventually in free and continuous verbal discourse.

Although it is a natural tendency to move quickly into the heart of things, pilot data indicated that the probabilities of eliciting a [s] were far greater if the child was asked, "Close your teeth and say [s]," rather than, "Close your teeth and say [soap]." The word "soap," although meaningful, appeared to be a strong S^D eliciting the response [θop] while the "Say [s]" stimulus, not having the same history, did not result in the automatic [θ] response. Since [s] can be operationally defined in terms of teeth closure, the first "frame" in the program consists of the verbal cue, "Close your teeth." This stimulus produced the desired [s] teeth position, and thus became the first reinforced response. The cue, "Close your teeth and say [s]," used as the second frame, almost always resulted in a correct or close approximation of [s]. By gradually fading this cue, it was found that the instruction "Say [s]," resulted in a correct [s] sound.

During this initial phase of the program, as many relevant cues as could be identified were used. In addition to the reinforcement contingency involving redeemable tokens for correct responses, visual feedback was provided the child. A mirror was placed directly in front of him. He was instructed to watch the mirror as he closed his teeth and said [s]. This provided the child with the opportunity to help monitor his own responses. The clinician's correct production of the [s] may have provided an additional visual cue. It was noted that many children carefully watched the clinician's lips as he read the instructions. However, this was not introduced as an experimental variable until later.

As soon as the child could make an appropriate [s] sound, the vowel [i] was introduced. The [i] was used because the teeth are visible and the lips are spread laterally during its production; both conditions are readily amenable to observation and have response properties similar to the [s]. The instructions were, "Close your teeth and say [i]." This was followed by, "Keep you teeth closed and say [is]." If the child said "[il]" (frontal lisp), the instruction, "Close your teeth and try it again," was given. This single-frame loop almost always resulted in "[is]". It was found that rewarding corrected responses after errors led to increased misses on first attempts. Consequently, knowledge of results without a token was awarded for correct second attempts. The child "shaped up" when the payoff came only after correct first responses.

Analysis of pilot data indicated that if a child required the additional trial with the teeth closure cue on more than 20 of the first 50 items, in almost all instances he would not be successful in acquiring the [s] in the remainder of the program. On the other hand, if he produced [s]'s on more than 30 of the first 50 frames on the first or second trial, error rate was minimal during the remainder of the program.

The objective of Part I of the program was to bring the [s] under the control of monosyllabic words as they appeared in six- and seven-word sentences, and as they were associated with pictures of environmental objects. As described earlier, the first task was to strengthen the [s] in isolation and then introduce the [s] plus vowel combinations. Up to this point, most of the responses produced by the child were echoic. That is, he simply repeated the words produced by the therapist. To approximate a less heavily cued response successfully, a picture-naming technique was used. The following series of items illustrates this transition.

"Say saw.
Here is a picture of a saw. Say saw.
You use a saw to cut wood. Say saw.
What's this? (picture of saw)
What do you cut wood with?"

No difficulty was experienced in evoking the desired response using this procedure. Other words such as *soap, suit, sun,* and *sink* were similarly introduced. They were presented first in an echoic fashion, then echoic plus the presentation of a picture, followed by picture naming, and finally a simple recall response. Once the child acquired some practice naming these pictures correctly, a variety of new pictures and words (*seal, safe, saddle*) was introduced. Within this general class of words the children soon found it unnecessary to rely on the echoic cueing function.

At this point four-word sentences in the form of, "I see a ———," were introduced. This portion of the program was designed to strengthen the [s] both in a medial sentence position and in a sentence context. The items were sequenced as follows:

> "See the sun? Say sun. (picture cue)
> Say see.
> Say I see.
> Say I see a sun.
> Here is a suit. Say suit. (picture cue)
> Say I see a suit.
> What do you see here? Say I see a———." (picture cue)

Similar practice was given with the "I see" phrase reintroducing other [s] words previously used in the program.

A final set of eight frames reviewing the pictures used throughout the program was presented next. Two new pictures, *sailor* and *suitcase,* were added. These ten items served as an enroute criterion test measuring the child's success on using the [s] in monosyllabic words included in six- and seven-word sentences.

To avoid student fatigue and reactive inhibition, only one part of the instructional sequence was administered each day. Part I consisted of 110 items or frames and required 20 minutes to administer.

Part II of the Instructional Sequence. In addition to maintaining and strengthening the Part I responses, the objectives of Part II were to: (1) strengthen the [s] in all word positions — initial, medial, and final — in polysyllabic words and (2) to elicit in continuous discourse six- and seven-word sentences containing several [s] words. Since the administration of the second part was to follow approximately 24 hours after the first part, the first 10 items were review items presented as follows:

"Close your teeth and say [s].
Say suit.
Keep your teeth closed and say sun.
What's this? (picture cue)
What do you put on a horse?"

Children who produced more than 70% of the items in Part I correctly rarely had difficulty with this type of review item.

Following the review several polysyllabic words were introduced. Also included was [s] in various consonant blend combinations such as in *lipstick, school,* and *stick.* The [s] position was varied, using such words as *bus, grasshopper, house.* Initially, the child was asked to repeat the words in an echoic fashion. Later, [s] was elicited merely by asking the child to name the picture.

The [z] was introduced at this point by using words such as *zebra, hose, zoo,* and *zipper.* This decision was based on a factor analytic study of speech sounds by Mowrer, Schutz, and Baker (*1964*), which yielded a fairly pure factor with the [s] and [z] showing as the principal variables. Pilot data demonstrated that production of the [z] at this point was not a difficult task.

Next, sentences containing more than three words were elicited by using pictures containing two nouns. For example, a picture of a sailboat in the water was shown. The frames following this picture were:

"Say sailboat.
Say the sailboat is.
Say the sailboat is in the water.
Tell me where the sailboat is. Say the sailboat is . . . ."

Similar "is" items were constructed for pictures of a car in the grass, a cat on a chair, a dog on a horse, and the like. Student responses to the "is" pictures usually resulted in six- or seven-word sentences. After two or three pictures the therapist could usually fade the first three cues and move directly to the last frame.

The final 10 items (polysyllabic words, [z] words, and six- and seven-word sentences) of this 101-item section served as the criterion test for Part II. This section also required approximately 20 minutes to administer.

Part III of the Instructional Sequence. Part III of the program was developed to extend the production of [s] to connected speech. The initial items reviewed Parts I and II. Following the 15-item review, a story was told to the child as he was shown a series of three pictures representing different phases of the story. The first story followed the following sequence:

(1) A boy named Sam was sailing his sailboat in the water. The wind blew his sailboat away and Sam tried to reach it with a stick.
(2) He couldn't reach it with his stick so he asked his dog, Spot, to jump in the water and get his sailboat.
(3) Spot jumped into the water and got Sam's sailboat.

The student was then asked questions about the story. The questions were stated in such a way as to elicit different [s] words used in the story. They were as follows:

"What was the boy's name?
What did he put in the water?
What did he use to try to get his sailboat?
What was the dog's name?"

Appropriate pictures related to the story sequence were shown as the above questions were asked.

The next step was to elicit the appropriate [s] word in sentence context. Since the story sequence might not have been clear to the child, the clinician told the story again and requested the child to fill in the correct words. There was no difficulty eliciting the correct responses if the reader paused expectantly before the blank.

One day, a boy named _____ went to the pond to sail his _____.

The wind blew his _____ away and Sam tried to reach it with his _____.
He couldn't reach it with his _____ so he asked his dog, whose name was _____ to get his _____.
The dog, whose name was _____, jumped into the water to get Sam's _____.

By this time, the child was quite familiar with the story. He was asked to tell the story by himself as he looked at the three pictures shown in sequence. The child was reinforced with tokens for each correct [s] he used in telling the story.

A second story was told using three pictures. The same procedures were used in presenting this story as were used in the previous one. A third story was presented in the same manner. Finally the child was asked to retell the "Sam and His Sailboat" story again as a criterion test for Part III. Approximately 20 minutes were required to administer this 58-item section.

Final Instructional Sequence. The three-part program in its final revision consisted of 269 frames designed to elicit approximately 300 [s] responses, provided the child moved through the program without error. Each part required approximately 20 minutes to administer. One part was given each day over a three-day period. A final criterion test, consisting of the final 10 items from each of Parts I, II, and III, was administered following the third instructional period.

Evaluation of the Instructional Sequence. Initially, eight subjects with frontal lisps between the ages of six and eight, plus three additional children with assorted articulatory problems, were brought into the laboratory. At this point, no attempt was made to maintain strict adherence to an experimental procedure or program. The immediate goal was only to work out laboratory strategies and revise the "frontal lisping" instructional program described above. Important here were thorough behavioral analyses, order and arrangement of stimulus materials, design of cueing techniques, ways and means of reinforcing the correct response, and possible techniques to bring correct articulation under the control of new stimulus conditions. During this phase the children were seen individually by a speech therapist for half-hour sessions five days weekly. The experimental sound-treated therapy room (8' by 8') contained two chairs, a table, two one-way vision mirror windows, and a toy dispenser. The therapist sat directly opposite the child while administering the program. Detailed records were kept of the child's articulation production during each session. Foot switches controlled the operation of a token dispenser and a light. The buzzer was used following an incorrect response; a token was dispensed following a correct response.

Ten kindergarten children who misarticulated the [s] were selected as subjects for a pilot study of the revised lisp correction program (*Baker, Mowrer, and Schutz, 1964*). A criterion test, which consisted of the last 10 items of each of the three instructional sessions, was administered to all subjects individually as a pre-test. Analysis of the test results revealed that eight of the ten subjects used the [θ] for the [s], one subject omitted the [s], and one substituted [t] for [s].

Part I of the program was administered on the day following testing. The first subject was escorted from his classroom to a nearby empty classroom. He was seated at a table opposite the speech therapist. The speech therapist explained that he would ask the child to say some words. If the words were said correctly, the child would be given a token. If the words were not said correctly, a light would blink and he would not get a token. Prior to the session he was told that he could exchange his tokens for small plastic toys when the lesson was finished.

The therapist proceeded to read the instructional frames. If the child missed an item, he was given four more trials in which to produce a correct [s]. A token was dispensed following first-trial success only. The visual materials were presented on 3 x 5 picture cards at appropriate times throughout the program.

Upon completion of Part I, the child was escorted back to his classroom and another child was selected. Part I was administered to all the children in this manner during the first day. During the second and third days, Parts II and III were administered. On the fourth day, the criterion test was again administered. The number of correct responses for each subject is shown in Table 1.

Seven of the ten subjects are within chance of a perfect score. A *post facto* analysis of the children revealed that subjects number four and six substituted sounds other than [θ] for the [s] on the pre-test. Parent and teacher reports indicated that subject number eight had severe emotional problems that may have inhibited his performance. In this pilot work the program demonstrated a high degree of effectiveness in modifying lisping responses, but was not quite so effective in modifying the omissions and [t] for [s] substitutions manifested by subjects four and six. It also must be recognized that severe emotional disorders can undoubtedly interfere with the efficiency of an instructional program.

In addition to demonstrating conclusively the applicability of operant procedures to problems associated with the treatment of

Subject	Correct [s] Responses*
1	30
2	28
3	30
4	22
5	30
6	23
7	30
8	0
9	30
10	30

* Highest possible score, 30.

TABLE 1

Number of Correct [s] Responses
Made on the Criterion Post-test

articulation disorders, several rather important methodological points were identified. First, the position of the phoneme in context appeared to be a significant variable. Initial position was much easier to shape than medial or final. That is, [s] as it occurs in the word "soap" is easier to control than [s] in the word "hospital". This generalization has long been recognized as appropriate for phoneme location within individual words. However, it also appears to hold true for the [s] position in a sentence. For example, in the sentence, "The boy saw the cat," the [s] phoneme was responded to differently than in the sentence, "I saw the cat," or "Saw is the name of my canary." Although this problem has yet to be explored fully, it is evident that the simple concept involving initial-medial-final position of [s] in the word is inadequate when considering total speech functions.

The use of token reinforcers that could be redeemed after the session appeared to be a great deal more practical and effective as immediate reinforcers than toys or trinkets. Pilot studies revealed that when toys were used, the subjects had a propensity to attend to the toys during the session in preference to the instruction. Tokens did not have this effect, and thereby helped to maintain optimum control over the subjects' attention.

Subject behavior was quite sensitive to specific aspects of the reinforcement contingencies. An example is the problem encountered when the subject was reinforced with a token after a corrected response following one or more errors. If the child emitted a distorted response on the first trial the item was repeated, and a corrected response on the second trial was reinforced on the same basis as a correct response on the first trial. Analysis of response patterns revealed that this reinforcement contingency was associated with an increasing number of first-trial errors, and generally careless first-trial behavior, since the only penalty for errors was a brief delay. To counteract this, the procedure was modified, and tokens were not dispensed on second- or third-trial successes. This was followed by a decline in first-trial errors.

A final observation was that great care must be taken to *teach* for *transfer*. One cannot assume that the newly learned response will be used in daily speech, especially since the competing response, i.e. [θ], has been practiced and reinforced in everyday contexts for several years. The revised program gradually shifts the stimulus control of the [s] response from echoic, to text, to text plus pictures, to pictures, to pictures alone, to pictures plus recall, to recall.

The immediately practical implications of this study seem quite clear. Although the frontal lisp is more easily identified and corrected than other articulation disorders, it still constitutes up to approximately 40% of the problems treated in the schools, and commands a great share of the speech therapist's time. If lisping can be modified using standardized procedures that do not necessitate the prolonged presence of a therapist, the therapist can be freed to devote more time to working with teachers and parents in bringing correct articulation under the control of non-laboratory stimuli. In other words, the clinician could begin to deal more effectively with the problems of transfer.

Mode of Program Presentation, Student Response, and Reinforcement

Development of an effective standarized instructional program made it possible to study systematically selected variables related to the general instructional setting. Several questions seemed warranted and worthy of experimental study:

1. Is it necessary to use manipulable secondary reinforcers (tokens) that are external to the program instead of simple feedback in the way of knowledge of response correctness?

2. Is there a criterion performance advantage in having the speech therapist verbally administer the program in full visual presence of the subject?

3. Is it critical that the subject be placed in a one-to-one relationship with the therapist and overtly (vocally) respond to the program?

The initial program employed the use of a token-type reward for each correct response. Were the programmed instructions alone responsible for articulation changes or did the reinforcement contingency significantly increase the probability of making the correct response? The role of the token reinforcers was evaluated by comparing the criterion performance of one group of subjects, which received redeemable tokens for each correct response, with another group, which received only knowledge of performance results.

In the previous studies the speech therapist was physically present during the administration of the instructional program. Visual cues produced by the therapist, such as teeth closure, were possibly an aid in acquiring the appropriate response. It is also possible that the therapist might unknowingly have provided the subjects with differential auditory cues such as word emphasis and pauses. To evaluate the possible effects of differential facial and auditory cues three treatment procedures were compared. In the first, the experimenter's face was always visible to the subject as the experimenter read the instructions and provided feedback. In the second, the experimenter was not visible to the subject, but read the instructions. In the third, the experimenter was not visible to the subject, and the instructions were all prerecorded on tape and controlled by the experimenter.

The value of listening activities in group therapy sessions has seldom been questioned. Most public school speech correction programs use group procedures. The supposition is that children in the group profit from listening to other children produce correct responses. Changes in articulation as a function of listening to and observing others respond to speech correction were evaluated by allowing one subject to respond to the program while another subject was told to simply observe.

Sample Selection and Research Design

To obtain a suitable sample of lispers for this three-factor analysis, a total of 1,201 children enrolled in the kindergarten and first-grade classes in a large metropolitan elementary school district were asked by a speech therapist to say the words "sun," "missing," and "bus" (*Mowrer, 1964*). If a child's tongue visibly protruded between his front teeth during articulation of the [s], he was defined as a lisper.

Eighty-one children were identified as lispers by this test. Subsequent to the initial screening, each of the 81 children was given the 30-item program criterion test. Results of the performances revealed that 75 of the 81 children lisped on every one of the 30 items on the test. These 75 "lispers" comprised the final sample.

Thirty-two of the subjects were girls; 43 were boys. All subjects were between five and seven years of age. Audiometric screening tests administered by school nurses three to five months prior to this study indicated that the hearing acuity of all subjects was within "normal" limits.

The subjects were assigned randomly to 12 treatment groups and a control group. Table 2 shows the number of subjects assigned to each cell in the factorial design. The no-instruction cell was appended for graphic clarity, and is not a part of the factorial model.

| | Reinforcement | | | |
| | Token | | Knowledge of Correctness | |
Presentation Mode	Participant	Listener	Participant	Listener
Therapist Visible	5	5	5	5
Therapist Not Visible	5	5	5	5
Tape Recorded Instructions	5	5	5	5
No Instruction (Control)		15		

TABLE 2
Number of Students Assigned to Each of the Treatment Cells

Each "participant" subject produced vocal responses when instructed to do so, and program progress was dependent solely on his performance; the "listener" subject was told at the outset to watch the participant, listen to the instructions, and try to respond to the instructions subvocally. Thus the participant subjects in three of the six groups were given redeemable tokens immediately following correct responses. If a response was incorrect, a buzzer was sounded. The participants in the other three groups (no reinforcement) received only knowledge of results, and were not given tokens for correct responses; nor was the buzzer sounded when an incorrect response was produced. The "listeners" in the token-reinforcement group received tokens that were equal in amount to those earned by their participant-partners and delivered at the same time.

Three methods were used to present instructions. The experimenter's face was visible to one group as the instructions were read. The second group could not see the experimenter's face as he read the instructions. In the third group, presentation consisted of playing standardized prerecorded instructions, which were controlled by the experimenter.

The control group, comprised of 15 subjects, did not receive the instructional program. They were administered the criterion test at the onset of the study and again when the experiment was completed.

During the week immediately following the initial criterion pretests, the instructional program was administered to the experimental groups. Each pair of subjects was escorted to the instruction room by the therapist. The participant was seated directly in front of a one-way vision mirror in the subject's booth. In one of the treatment groups the one-way vision mirror was removed so that the therapist was visible to the subjects. The listener-observer was seated about 14 inches behind the participant (see Figure 1). If the participant was to receive reinforcement, the following instructions were read:

> We're going to play a speech game today, tomorrow, and the next day. You can earn some play money if you say just what I tell you to say. Then, you can buy some toys with your money. See the plastic money box? If you fill it with money up to the white line, you will get one toy. If you fill it up to the black line, you will get two toys. If you fill it up to the red line, you

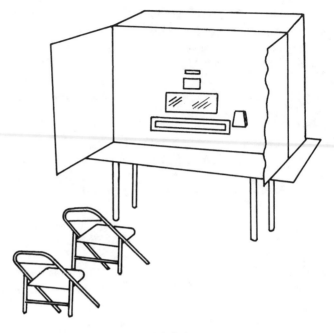

FIGURE 1
Subject's Station

will get three toys, and if you fill it up to the top, you will get four toys.

If you say the word wrong, you will hear a buzzer and you won't get any money. If you say the word right, you will get some money. Let's play the game now.

The observer-listener, sitting behind the participator who was to receive reinforcement, was told:

You are going to watch someone play a speech game today, tomorrow, and the next day. I want you to listen, but you're not allowed to say anything. If you are very quiet, you will get the same number of toys the other person gets when the game is over. He's (she's) allowed to talk, but you aren't. You will get toys if you sit in your chair and say the words to yourself. If you get out of your chair or bother the other person, you won't get any toys. Your game is to see how well you can watch, listen, and say the words to yourself correctly.

If the participator was in the group that did not receive reinforcement, then instructions given were as follows:

> We're going to play a speech game today, tomorrow, and the next day. The object is to get as many of the words right as you can. You do just what I tell you to do. Let's play the game now.

Similarly, the instructions to the observer-listeners were as follows:

> You are going to watch someone play a speech game today, tomorrow, and the next day. I want you to listen, but you're not allowed to say anything except to yourself. He's (she's) allowed to talk, but you aren't. Your game is to see how well you can watch, listen, and say the words to yourself correctly.

Immediately following the preliminary instructions, the experimenter turned the monitor tape recorder to "record" position and seated himself in the experimenter's booth. The program items were presented serially allowing four to six seconds for the subject to respond, depending upon whether or not a picture item was presented.

If a subject lisped on his first response to any of the first 50 items of section one, the experimenter read the cue, "Close your teeth and try it again." If the subject lisped a second time on that item, the response was scored as wrong and the next item was presented. If his second try was correct it was recorded as right, but in no case was token reinforcement given for the corrected response. On the remaining items, 51 through 285, the subject was not permitted to make a second response.

Following the completion of the first section of the program, both the participant-subject and the listener-subject of the reinforcement groups were given the appropriate number of plastic toys and then informed that they could return to their classroom. Those who did not receive tokens were not given toys, but were merely told to return to their classroom. The same procedure was followed during the second and third day, after administration of the second and third sections of the program.

Immediately following the completion of Part III of the program, the criterion test was again administered. Two weeks later, each subject was taken to the testing room and given the criterion test again. This completed the data collection for the subjects.

Results of the analyses of variance for the reinforcement and mode of presentation treatments for both the immediate post-test and delayed retention test scores resulted in only two statistically significant differences. Table 3 shows the analyses of variance results. F-values of 5.77 and 4.87 for the effects of token reinforcement on the immediate and delayed criterion performances, respectively, are statistically significant beyond the .05 level.

Source of Variation	s.s.	d.f.	m.s.	F
A. Immediate Criterion Test				
Reinforcement	940.8	1	940.8	5.77*
Mode of Presentation	471.4	2	235.7	1.45
Interaction	523.4	2	261.7	1.61
Error	3907.2	24	162.8	
Total	5842.8	29		
B. Delayed Retention Test				
Reinforcement	770.2	1	770.2	4.87*
Mode of Presentation	116.3	2	58.1	1.00
Interaction	777.9	2	38.8	1.00
Error	3795.5	24	158.1	
Total	4759.9	29		

* Significant beyond the .05 level ($F_{1,24} = 4.26$).

TABLE 3

Analyses of Variance and Resulting F-values for Reinforcement and Modes of Presentation of Immediate Criterion Test and Delayed Retention Test

A look at the descriptive data in Table 4 indicates that the treatment groups receiving token reinforcers achieved the higher level of performance in both cases. F-values of 1.45 and 1.00 suggest that the mode of presenting the instructional program had no differential effect on performance. Visual and auditory clues, such as facial cues (teeth closure, smiles, frowns) and verbal cues (word emphasis and intonation) played an irrelevant role in criterion performance.

Inspection of Table 4 would suggest that the performance of those subjects who were active participants is dramatically superior to the performance of the subjects who were observer-listeners. An F-value 32.6 from a single classification analysis of variance corroborates the above.

| Group | Thirty-Item Criterion Test | | | | |
| | | Immediate | | Delayed | |
	N	Mean	S.D.	Mean	S.D.
Token Reinforcement	15	20.4	12.8	13.3	14.3
Knowledge of Correctness	15	9.2	12.7	3.3	7.8
Participant	30	14.5	16.3	8.3	12.6
Listener	30	.5	3.2	2.4	.27
Control	15	.1	.5	.1	.4

TABLE 4

Descriptive Data for Immediate and Delayed
Criterion Test Scores for Treatment Sub-Groups

Table 5 shows the results of applying Dunnitt's t to multiple subgroup comparisons with the control group. Groups A and B (Reinforced and No Reinforcement) were statistically superior to Group E (Control) on the immediate criterion post-test, but only Group A was superior after a delay of two weeks. Subjects who were allowed to observe and were encouraged to silently participate did not perform any better than control subjects. As a matter of fact, Table 5 indicates that the active participants who were not reinforced did no better statistically than the control group on the delayed retention test.

The Role of the Speech Therapist as Program Monitor

Up to this point, all instructional sessions had been conducted by trained speech therapists. Data from the previous experiments suggest, among other things, that a tightly organized and sequenced instructional program might not require the physical presence of a speech therapist. Another experiment was designed to test the com-

Immediate Criterion Test			Delayed Retention Test		
Mean	Mn. Diff.	t	Mean	Mn. Diff.	t
A E	20.3	6.34	A E	13.2	4.13
20.4 .1			13.3 .1		
B E	9.1	2.84	B E	3.2	1.00
9.2 .1			3.3 .1		
C E	.1	1	C E	1.6	<1.00
.0 .1			1.7 .1		
D E	2.0	1	D E	2.9	<1.00
2.1 .1			3.0 .1		
t . 95 (70) = 2.34			t . 99 (70) = 2.86		

A = Reinforced
B = No Reinforcement
C = Observer-Reinforced
D = Observer-No Reinforcement
E = Control

TABLE 5
Dunnitt's t for Multiple Sub-Group Comparisons
with the Control Group on Immediate and
Delayed Criterion Tests

parative efficacy of using non-speech therapist school personnel to administer and monitor the program.

Twenty-five kindergarten children in a large school district, who substituted the [θ] for the [s] consonant, were identified by a speech therapist. All 25 received a score of 0 on the test for correct [s] responses. A volunteer classroom teacher was given approximately one hour of training, covering such things as the criteria for a correct [s], how to operate the equipment, and how to administer the program. The equipment consisted of a token-buzzer box, a tape recorder, and an automatic 35mm slide projector. The programmed instructions were recorded on the upper track of the tape and an inaudible signal was recorded on the second track. The signal activated the slide projector advance. In this manner, the appropriate visual stimulus was always presented automatically in conjunction with the correct audio portion of the tape. This enabled the teacher to concentrate exclusively on evaluating the child's responses. If a response was correct, the teacher pressed a green button, which activated a token dispenser, and one token was ejected. If the child produced an incorrect response, the teacher was instructed to depress a red button, which resulted in a buzzer sound.

The teacher administered the three-part program to each of the 20 subjects. Since three days were required to administer the program and only seven subjects could be scheduled during the school day, seven subjects were run the first week, seven during the second, and six during the final week. The speech therapist administered the criterion test to each of the three groups immediately following program completion.

Sixteen of the 20 subjects obtained perfect scores on the final criterion test. Three others obtained near-perfect scores and one produced no [s]'s on the criterion test. Inspection of the subjects' responses to program items revealed that the three subjects who obtained near-perfect scores (24, 20, 28) produced correct [s]'s to most program items. In this regard the program is considered successful even though criterion scores were slightly lower than absolute success.

The one subject who scored 0 on the criterion test also performed poorly on most of the program items. Further diagnosis revealed that the child had an open-bite condition. Normally the cue "close your teeth" elicits a response that inhibits tongue protrusion. Such was not the case with the child who had an open bite. Closure of the teeth resulted in molar contact but not incisor contact. Thus, when asked to say [s], the child's tongue still protruded between the front incisors.

The reader will recall that during one of the early pilot studies it was very difficult to establish control over [s] omissions and [s] substitutes, other than [θ], using this program. In the experiment above it was noted that it is equally difficult to evoke [s]'s from children who have a structural deviation such as open bite. Similar difficulties would also be experienced with children who substitute the lateral lisp for [s]. Such observations point out the importance of careful behavioral analysis in constructing relevant cue items. This program was written specifically to correct the functional frontal lisp.

Conclusions

The following conclusions may be drawn from this series of experiments:

1. The development of an effective standardized set of instructions and the establishment of well controlled school-laboratory conditions provided a set of powerful procedures for empirically studying the effects of manipulations of specified instructional variables on the correction of articulation.

2. The use of reinforcers external to the instructional program were dramatically effective in facilitating the learning of correct articulation responses.

3. The inference that group procedures in speech therapy are inefficient, at least in the acquisition stage, seems warranted. While it was possible to control and correct faulty articulation of subjects who responded actively, it was not possible to correct the articulation of subjects who were merely observer-listeners, a common condition in group speech correction.

4. Apparently the speech therapist himself is not a source of cues that facilitates program success. Permitting the subject to observe the therapist's face while the correct sound was being presented did not promote learning. It appears that it is quite possible to control articulation using tape-recorded instructions and an isolation booth, with only the stimulus materials visible to the subject.

5. The validation of a tightly sequenced instructional program and the brief training of a non-speech therapist to monitor the program and evaluate subject responses precluded the necessity of having to use a trained speech therapist for such instruction. Certainly, freeing the therapist from this particular chore should enhance his ability to cope effectively with the more difficult problems of speech.

REFERENCES

Backus, O., and J. Beasley, *Speech Therapy with Children.* Boston: Houghton Mifflin, 1951.

Baker, R. L., D. E. Mowrer, and R. E. Schutz, "Controlling Articulation through the Application of Operant Learning Procedures," *Classroom Learning Laboratory Technical Reports,* Arizona State University, 1964, No. 3, 1–7.

Chapman, M. E., E. L. Herbert, C. B. Avery, and J. W. Selman, "VI. Clinical Practice: Remedial Procedures," *J. Speech Hearing Dis.*, 1961, Monograph supplement 8, 58–77.

Henja, R., *Speech Disorders and Non-directive Therapy.* New York: Ronald, 1960.

Irwin, R. B., "The Effects of Speech Therapy upon Certain Linguistic Skills of First Grade Children," *J. Speech Hearing Dis.*, 1963, 28, 375–381.

Mowrer, D. E., R. L. Baker, and R. E. Schutz, "An Experimental Analysis of Variables Controlling Lisping Responses of Children," *De Therapia Vocis et Loquelae*, Society of International Logopedics and Phonetics, 1965, 1, 151–153.

Rigrodsky, S., and M. Steer, "Mowrer's Theory Applied to Speech Habilitation of the Mentally Retarded," *J. Speech Hearing Dis.*, 1961, 26:3, 237–243.

Roe, V., and R. Milisen, "The Effect of Maturation upon Defective Articulation in Elementary Grades," *J. Speech Hearing Dis.*, 1942, 7:1, 37–50.

Schutz, R. E., D. E. Mowrer, and R. L. Baker, "A Factor Analysis of Consonant Articulation of Children," *Language and Speech*, 1964, 7:1 16–21.

Skinner, B. F., *Verbal Behavior.* New York: Appleton-Century-Crofts, 1957.

Van Riper, C., *Speech Correction: Principles and Methods.* Englewood Cliffs, N.J.: Prentice-Hall, 1947.

West, R., M. Ansberry, and A. Carr, *The Rehabilitation of Speech.* New York: Harper & Row, 1957.

VII

Stuttering

The application of "learning theory" to stuttering has a long history (e.g., K. Dunlap, *Habits: Their Making and Unmaking*. New York: Liveright, 1932). However, recent experimental work on stuttering indicates how necessary extreme precision and careful procedures are to avoid incorrect or meaningless conclusions. For instance, many "theories" of stuttering, which attribute stuttering in some way to "anxiety" or "anxiety-reduction," assert that any increase in noxious stimuli will increase the rate of stuttering. Yet, as the following chapters by Martin and Goldiamond both indicate, various noxious stimuli, when clearly contingent upon the behavior defined as stuttering, reduce rather than increase the rate of this behavior.

A rich background of laboratory data on the operant manipulation of stuttering is currently leading to interest in more "clinical" problems, such as generalizing to other environments the reduction in stuttering that can be achieved in the laboratory setting. Both Martin and Goldiamond report recent studies on this problem, and it is interesting to note the orderly progression from the laboratory to the clinic that is occurring in this area.

16

Richard Martin

The Experimental Manipulation
of Stuttering Behaviors

In recent years there has been growing interest among speech pathologists and psychologists in studying and treating the clinical disorder of stuttering via the application of operant conditioning principles (*Shames and Sherrick, 1963*). In the main, however, the available literature concerning this topic is sparse. Moreover, there are few reported studies in which an attempt was made to modify stuttering frequency through careful manipulation of the response contingent environmental consequences in a controlled laboratory situation (*Flanagan, Goldiamond, and Azrin, 1958; Goldiamond, 1960; Goldiamond, 1962; Goldiamond, 1965; Martin and Siegel, 1966a; Martin and Siegel, 1966b*).

For the most part, operant conditioning principles were not derived deductively, but were induced from systematic observations of animal behavior in the laboratory. The extent to which these principles can be applied to the clinical treatment of maladaptive human behavior is not a question for debate, but a subject for empirical research. At the University of Minnesota Speech and Hearing Clinic, we have been conducting such a research program for

The research reported in this paper was supported in part by grants from the Graduate School, University of Minnesota, and by Public Health Service Research Grant No. MH 08743.

the past three years. The main purpose of the research reported in this paper was to explore systematically whether certain principles of operant conditioning originally developed in animal laboratories can be employed to manipulate overt behaviors of stutterers. The intent was not to devise a treatment program, but rather to arrange environmental consequences and observe their effects on stuttering behaviors in a controlled laboratory situation.

Method

The basic method of investigation was that of single subject research (*Sidman, 1960*). Each stutterer was run for several sessions of varying lengths, with the total number of sessions spanning a period of several weeks. A subject's response frequency was observed and recorded continuously throughout all sessions.

Base Rate. Initially, no experimental treatment was introduced until the frequency of the particular response under study was stable (base rate). Generally, base-rate response frequency was considered stable when the number of responses emitted by the subject during three consecutive two-minute periods did not vary by more than a given amount. If the number of responses emitted during the first of three consecutive two-minute periods was between 0 and 9, then the number of responses emitted during either the second or third two-minute period could not vary by more than one from the number emitted in the first two-minute period, in order for the behavior to be considered stable. The amount of variation allowed in either the second or third two-minute period increased as the number of behaviors emitted in the first two-minute period increased: 0 – 9 responses, variation of 1 allowed; 10 – 19, 20 – 29; 3; 30 – 39, 4; etc. One additional criterion was imposed relative to base-rate. In the initial session, a subject had to speak or read for a minimum of 30 minutes (as well as meet the frequency criteria) before the base-rate response frequency was considered stable.

Experimental Tasks. Two experimental tasks were employed in the present series of studies. Some subjects spoke in a spontaneous speaking situation. A subject was instructed to talk about anything that came to mind, but to keep talking continuously until told to stop. A list of nouns was available to the subject to help him "think of things to talk about." Other subjects were observed in an oral reading task. The reading passages were excerpted from prose materials appropriate to the reading level of each subject.

Subjects. All subjects were adult, male stutterers who had been or were at the time of the study enrolled in a speech therapy program at the University of Minnesota Speech and Hearing Clinic. All stutterers volunteered to serve as subjects; some were paid, some were not.

Apparatus. All sessions were conducted in a four-room experimental suite. In most instances the subject was placed in a sound-treated experimental room, and the experimenters were located in an adjacent control room. The experimental and control rooms were connected by both vision and sound systems.

In the experimental room the subject was seated at a table. A microphone, and, when appropriate, reading materials, words to encourage spontaneous speech, a stimulus light, and a set of wrist electrodes were also placed on the table.

In the control room the subject's microphone was connected to a tape recorder. The input to the tape recorder was also fed to an amplifier and speaker system which was used by the experimenters to monitor the subject's speech. An experimenter in the control room depressed a hand switch each time a subject emitted a stuttering response. Each depression of the hand switch pulsed the response pen of a Davis cumulative recorder and also pulsed a Sodeco printout counter. Every two minutes the printout counter printed and cleared. Thus, response frequency data for each subject were available in two forms: a continuous, cumulative graphic recording, and the total number of responses emitted in each two minute interval.

Three conditioning procedures were employed in the present experiments: response contingent shock; response contingent "good," "not good," or "wrong" delivered live-voice; response contingent "wrong" delivered from a tape recording. When programmed, a shock source was switched into the apparatus so that each depression of the experimenter's hand switch delivered a shock to the subject's wrist electrodes, "stepped" the cumulative recorder, and pulsed the printout counter. When live-voice verbal stimuli were programmed, the apparatus was so constructed that each depression of the experimenter's hand switch opened a microphone circuit long enough for the experimenter to say "good," "not good," or "wrong" into a microphone. The microphone delivered the stimuli either to earphones worn by the subject or to a loudspeaker in the experimental room. When recorded verbal stimuli were programmed, each depression of the experimenter's hand switch activated the start mechanism of a 354 Ampex tape recorder. The 354 Ampex system was specially designed so that when it was activated, the tape recorded word "wrong" was delivered to the subject's earphone, and the recorder stopped automatically — primed to deliver the same word again when activated.[1]

Reliability. For all subjects, the accuracy with which the experimenter recorded responses was determined in one of two ways. In those instances where the response class under consideration was comprised mainly of audible behaviors, tape recordings were prepared, and an independent observer counted responses from the tape recordings. The response counts made by the independent observer and the experimenter were compared. When the response class included both audible and visible behaviors, the accuracy with which the experimenter recorded responses was determined by having an observer record responses while watching the subject from a second control room.

For all subjects, there was high agreement between the experimenter and the independent observer in terms of both correlational agreement and agreement relative to the absolute number of responses emitted during a given period. In the case of Subject *O*, for example the mean numbers of tongue-protrusion responses recorded each two minutes by the experimenter and the independent observer during Session 2 (Figure 3) were 3.45 and 3.52, respectively. In addition, the correlation coefficient between the numbers of tongue protrusion responses recorded by the experimenter and the independent observer for each of the 20 two-minute periods in Session 2 was .98.

[1] For a complete description of the 354 Ampex system, the reader is referred to Brookshire (1965).

The reliability data obtained from all subjects were comparable to those of Subject O, and support the conclusion that the experimenters reliably recorded responses in the present group of studies.

Specific Procedures and Results

Subject E[2]

This subject was a 24-year-old male stutterer. The response class selected for study was defined simply as the emission of a stuttering. E's stuttering included several specific behaviors, the most frequent of which were sound or word repetitions and short, jerky holding and releasing of the breath. At times E emitted only one specific behavior during a stuttering; at other times he emitted some combination of behaviors. In either event the experimenter depressed his hand switch as soon as he observed E emitting any of the specific stuttering behaviors. Subject E was run for eight sessions spanning a period of approximately five weeks. The experimental task was spontaneous speech, and the response contingent stimulus was electric shock.

During the first session, E was run for 40 minutes without electrodes. Throughout the session, stuttering frequency was stable at a low rate of between five and six per two minutes.

Graphs of the frequency of stuttering per two minutes during Sessions 2 (50 minutes) and 3 (40 minutes) are shown in Figure 1. During the first 34 minutes of Session 2, the electrodes were attached, but no shock was delivered. Stuttering frequency during this 34-minute base-rate period was stable at a rate almost identical with that of Session 1. After 34 minutes of Session 2, and throughout Session 3 (Figure 1), shock was delivered contingent upon each stuttering response. The result was an almost complete suppression of stuttering by the end of Session 3.

In Session 4 (40 minutes), E was run without electrodes and there was a progressive increase in stuttering frequency from essentially zero at the beginning of the session to a stable rate of between five and six per two minutes for the last 20 minutes.

---

[2] Data for this subject appear in Martin and Siegel (1966a).

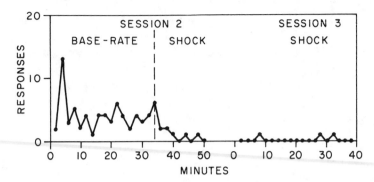

FIGURE 1

Number of stuttering responses emitted by Subject E each two minutes during Sessions 2 and 3.

Throughout the fifth session (36 minutes) the electrodes were attached and shock was delivered contingent upon stuttering. In addition, a 25-watt, blue light located in front of E was turned on during the entire session. Stuttering frequency was suppressed rapidly after delivery of the first shock and remained at essentially zero for the entire 36 minutes.

E continued to receive response contingent shock, and the blue light remained on, for the first 10 minutes of Session 6 (50 minutes). E emitted only two stutterings during the 10-minute period. After 10 minutes the electrodes were removed and the light was switched off for the remainder of the session. The result was a gradual increase in stuttering frequency — by the end of the session stuttering frequency was stable at the base-rate level (five to six stutterings per two minutes).

During the first 10 minutes of Session 7 (40 minutes) the electrodes were not attached, nor was the blue light on. As can be seen in Figure 2, stuttering frequency was very close to the base-rate level. After 10 minutes the blue light was switched on, but the *electrodes remained off,* for the rest of the session. As the curve in Figure 2 illustrates, simply switching on the blue light occasioned a rather dramatic decrease in stuttering frequency.

The blue light was on and the electrodes were off during the final 36-minute session. Stuttering frequency was low at first, but gradually increased to base-rate level by the end of the session.

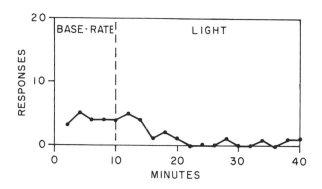

FIGURE 2

Number of stuttering responses emitted by Subject *E* each two minutes during Session 7.

Word Output. Utilizing the tape recordings prepared during each session, counts were made of the number of words emitted by *E* each two minutes of each session. *E*'s average speaking rate was close to 185 words per two minutes. Although a certain amount of variability existed from two-minute period to two-minute period, *E*'s word output rate did not vary with the experimental conditions in any systematic way.

Summary. The results obtained from Subject *E* were replicated with two additional subjects, and suggest the following general conclusions. (1) Response contingent electric shock served as a punishment in that presentation of a shock contingent upon emission of a stuttering response suppressed the frequency of that response. (2) The suppression effects of response contingent shock upon stuttering extinguished relatively rapidly; once the shock was removed, stuttering frequency returned to base-rate level. (3) Stuttering frequency can be brought under discriminative stimulus control; a stimulus light which had been illuminated during a period of response contingent shock served to suppress stuttering frequency when later presented alone.

Subject O[3]

Subject *O* was a 28-year-old male whose stuttering involved a variety of specific behaviors: protrusion of the tongue, prolongation of the initial sound of words beginning with [s], repetition of the initial sound or syllable of a word, holding of the breath prior to initiating phonation, and rapid blinking of the eyes. Typically, *O* emitted more than one behavior when he stuttered. At times the behaviors were emitted simultaneously; at other times they were emitted serially. One specific behavior, a pronounced protrusion of the tongue, was selected as the initial response class to be considered. Each time *O* protruded his tongue, the experimenter depressed his hand-switch. The response contingent stimulus was electric shock, and the experimental task was oral reading. *O* was run for nine sessions spanning approximately two months.

Initially, *O* was run for a 40-minute session without electrodes. Tongue protrusion frequency was highly stable throughout the session, averaging about 11 per two minutes.

During the first eight minutes of Session 2 (40 minutes) no electrodes were attached, and *O*'s tongue protrusion frequency was close to that of the initial base-rate session. Data for this session are presented in Figure 3. After eight minutes the electrodes were attached and shock was delivered contingent upon each tongue protrusion. As shown in Figure 3, response frequency decreased between minutes eight and 18; by minute 20 the frequency was close to zero. After 22 minutes with programmed shock, the electrodes were removed for the remainder of Session 2 and all of Session 3. During the last 10 minutes of Session 2 (Figure 3), and throughout Session 3, stuttering frequency gradually increased back to the original base-rate level.

Sessions 4 through 7 involved an attempt to bring tongue protrusion under discriminative stimulus control. For the first eight minutes of Session 4 no electrodes were attached, and *O*'s tongue protrusion frequency was at base-rate level. After 8 minutes both

[3] Data for this subject appear in Martin and Siegel (*1966a*).

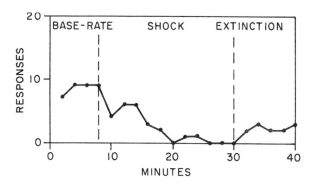

FIGURE 3

Number of tongue protrusion responses emitted by Subject O each two minutes during Session 2.

the electrodes and a nylon wristband were attached to O's left wrist, and shock was presented contingent upon tongue protrusion for the remainder (22 minutes) of Session 4. Under these conditions, tongue protrusion frequency decreased rapidly to zero. For all of Session 5 (40 minutes) both the electrodes and the wristband were removed; after 20 minutes, tongue protrusion frequency stabilized at close to the base-rate level. The electrodes and wristband remained off, and tongue protrusion frequency remained close to base-rate level for the first 14 minutes of Session 6 (40 minutes). After 14 minutes, the wristband alone was attached to O's wrist, and tongue protrusion frequency decreased rapidly to a level of approximately one per two minutes. This same situation prevailed (wristband on, tongue protrusion frequency low) for the first 20 minutes of Session 7 (60 minutes). During the last 40 minutes of Session 7, the wristband was removed and tongue protrusion frequency gradually increased to the base-rate level of about 11 per two minutes.

During Session 8 (60 minutes) a second specific stuttering behavior, prolongation of [s], was made the response class. One experimenter continued to record tongue protrusion frequency, a second experimenter independently recorded s-prolongations. Generally, both tongue protrusion and s-prolongation did not occur during the same stuttering. In this situation the two experimenters had little difficulty depressing their respective hand switches contingent upon the appropriate specific behavior. In the few instances where both tongue protrusion and s-prolongation occurred during a stuttering, there was sufficient temporal separation so that each experimenter could still respond to the appropriate specific behavior.

Figure 4 contains graphs of both tongue protrusion and s-prolongation frequency per two minutes in Session 8. For the first 30 minutes neither the electrodes nor wristband were attached. Tongue

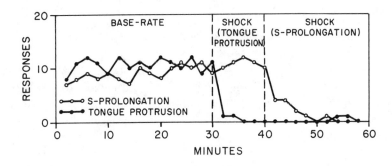

FIGURE 4

Number of tongue protrusion and s-prolongation responses emitted by Subject O each two minutes during Session 8.

protrusion frequency was stable at the base-rate level of about 11 per two minutes; s-prolongation frequency stabilized at around 10 responses per two minutes. After 30 minutes, the electrodes were attached and shock was delivered contingent upon tongue protrusion. As shown in Figure 4, tongue protrusion frequency was suppressed immediately, but s-prolongation frequency remained at base-rate level. After 10 minutes of shock for tongue protrusion, the contingency was changed and shock was made contingent upon an s-prolongation. The result (Figure 4) was a dramatic reduction in O's s-prolongation frequency.

Neither the electrodes nor the wristband were attached during Session 9 (40 minutes). There was a progressive increase in both behaviors; by the end of Session 9 both s-prolongation and tongue protrusion frequencies were at levels approaching those of the first 30 minutes of Session 8.

Word Output. In contrast to Subject *E,* the level of *O's* word output was related to the frequency of emission of the stuttering behaviors. In general, as the frequency of the stuttering behaviors decreased, word output increased. For example, during Session 1, word output level was relatively stable at an average of about 100 words per two minutes. However, during the middle 30 minutes of Session 2, when tongue protrusion frequency decreased almost to zero, word output increased to about 160 words per two minutes. This inverse relationship between word output and stuttering behavior frequency was reliable throughout the nine sessions.

Summary. The findings from Subject *O* were replicated with one additional subject, but with two different specific response classes. The following conclusions can be drawn from these data. (1) Response contingent electric shock served as punishment in that presentation of shock contingent upon specific stuttering behaviors reduced the frequency of these responses. (2) The suppression effects of response contingent shock upon a specific stuttering behavior extinguished relatively rapidly; once the shock was removed, response rate returned to base-rate level. (3) Two specific behaviors emitted during stuttering were manipulated independently. (4) The frequency of a specific stuttering response can be brought under discriminative stimulus control; after being in place during a period of response contingent shock, attaching a wristband alone served to suppress the frequency of a specific stuttering behavior.

Subject J[4]

This subject was a 19-year-old male whose stuttering included several different behaviors. One specific behavior, insertion of a prolonged "uh" prior to emission of certain words, was selected as the response class for study. The experimental task was spontaneous speech and the response contingent stimulus was the word

[4] Data for this subject appear in an unpublished M.A. thesis written by Quist (*1966*) and directed by the author.

"wrong" delivered from a tape recording. *J* was run for nine sessions of 50 minutes each.

During the initial session, *J*'s "uh" frequency stabilized at a rate of approximately 19 per two minutes. After 32 minutes, "wrong" was presented contingent upon each "uh"; by the end of the 50-minute session, *J*'s "uh" frequency was approximately eight per two minutes.

In Sessions 2 through 8 the same procedure was used — *J* was run for a brief base-rate period, then contingent "wrong" was presented for the remainder of the session. The result of this procedure was a steady decline in "uh" during the conditioning periods. Figure 5 is a graph of the number of "uh's" emitted by Subject *J*

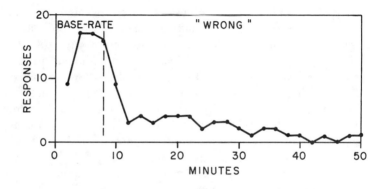

FIGURE 5

Number of "uh" responses emitted by Subject J each two minutes during Session 4.

each two minutes during Session 4. During the first eight minutes, "uh" frequency was similar to the base-rate level observed in the first three sessions. After eight minutes, and throughout the remainder of the session, "wrong" was presented contingent upon each "uh." There was a steady decrease in "uh" — during the last 20 minutes "uh" frequency was close to zero.

In Sessions 5 through 8, *J* simply spoke; no "wrong" was presented. During these four sessions the frequency of *J*'s "uh" responses slowly increased to base-rate level. After 28 minutes of Session 9, contingent "wrong" was reintroduced and "uh" frequency decreased essentially to zero.

Word Output. Subject *J* spoke at a rate of about 150 words per two minutes. Some variation in word output rate occurred among two-minute periods, but these changes were not related in any systematic way to changes in experimental conditions.

Summary. Results obtained with Subject *J* were replicated with a second subject. These results indicate that when stuttering was defined in terms of a specific response ("uh"), presentation of the verbal stimulus "wrong" served as a punishment in that it suppressed the frequency of that particular response.

Subject A

Subject *A* was a 19-year-old male whose stuttering was quite frequent and consisted mainly of short, staccato-like repetitions of the initial sound of certain words. The response class was defined simply as stuttering — whenever *A* emitted any stuttering behavior the experimenter depressed his hand switch. *A* was run for eight sessions spanning a period of approximately three months. The experimental task was spontaneous speech. Initially, the stimulus "good" (live voice) was made contingent upon 15 seconds of fluency; later the word "wrong" was presented contingent upon each stuttering.

Session 1 was a 30-minute base-rate session. No response contingent stimuli were delivered, and *A*'s stuttering frequency stabilized at approximately 18 per two minutes.

The base-rate condition was continued for the first 10 minutes of Session 2 (30 minutes), and stuttering frequency was essentially the same as in Session 1. After 10 minutes, *A* was told "good" each time he spoke for 15 seconds without stuttering. Stuttering frequency reduced by about 20% during this conditioning period.

In Sessions 3 through 6, "good" was again made contingent upon 15 seconds of fluent speech. In each succeeding session there was less reduction in stuttering frequency during the conditioning period; and by the sixth session, presentation of "good" contingent upon 15 seconds of fluency resulted in virtually no change in stuttering frequency from base-rate level.

During Sessions 7 and 8 the contingent stimulus was changed. Now, A was told "wrong" (live-voice) each time he stuttered. In Session 7 (40 minutes) A's stuttering base rate was approximately 16 per two minutes; introduction of contingent "wrong" occasioned a marked reduction in stuttering; removal of contingent "wrong" was followed by an increase in stuttering frequency to near the base-rate level.

Results of Session 8 (60 minutes) are presented in Figure 6. It can be seen from this graph that the base rate was similar to that of earlier sessions, presentation of contingent "wrong" resulted in a rapid suppression of stuttering, and removal of the verbal punishment was followed by an increase in stuttering to the base-rate level.

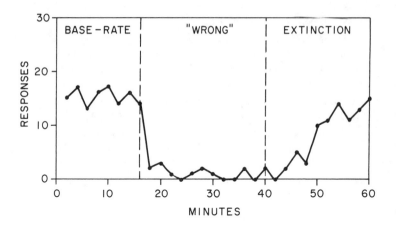

FIGURE 6

Number of stuttering responses emitted by Subject A each two minutes during Session 8.

Word Output. During the initial session A spoke at an average rate of about 235 words per two minutes. There was, however, a systematic change in word output rate accompanying changes in experimental conditions. In general, introduction of "good" contingent upon 15 seconds of fluency did not produce systematic changes in the number of words spoken by A. On the other hand, when "wrong" was made the contingent stimulus, there was a negative correlation between stuttering and word output — as stuttering frequency decreased word output increased.

Summary. Results obtained with Subject A were replicated with an additional subject. These data indicate that making "good" contingent upon 15 seconds of fluency did not result in any appreciable reduction in the frequency of stuttering. On the other hand, presentation of the word "wrong" contingent upon stuttering occasioned a marked reduction in stuttering frequency.

Subject N[5]

This subject was a 19-year-old male whose stuttering occurred frequently and involved several specific behaviors. Whenever N emitted any of these stuttering behaviors, the experimenter depressed his hand switch. Subject N was run for eight sessions spanning a period of several weeks. In all sessions the experimental task involved oral reading. Two response contingent stimuli were used. During conditioning, N was told "not good" (live-voice) each time he stuttered, and "good" (live-voice) after each 30-second interval in which no stuttering occurred.

During the initial session, N simply read continuously; no response contingent stimuli were delivered. N's stuttering frequency stabilized at the relatively high rate of approximately 50 per two minutes.

Figure 7 contains a graph of the number of stuttering responses emitted by N each two minutes during Session 2 (50 minutes). For the first 10 minutes no stimuli were delivered following stuttering or fluent speech, and N's stuttering frequency was slightly higher than the base-rate level observed in Session 1. During minutes 10 through 40 N was told "not good" contingent upon stuttering and "good" contingent upon 30 seconds of fluency. As can be seen in Figure 7, N's stuttering frequency decreased markedly during the conditioning period. After 40 minutes no more response contingent

[5] Data for this subject appear in Martin and Siegel (*1966b*).

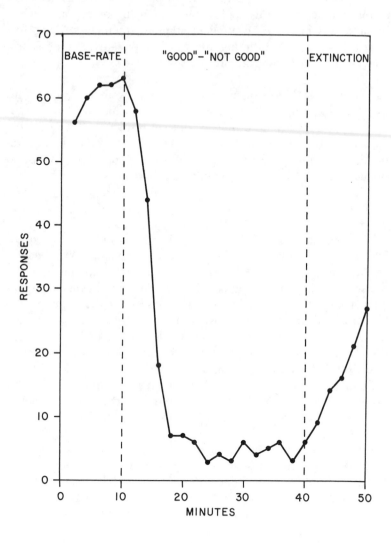

FIGURE 7

Number of stuttering responses emitted by Subject N each two minutes during Session 2.

stimuli were presented and N's stuttering frequency increased rapidly during the last 10 minutes of the session.

During Sessions 3 through 6, N's stuttering frequency was brought under control of the wristband in a manner similar to that described for Subject O. Initially the wristband was attached only during those periods when N received response contingent "not good" and "good." In Session 6, attaching the wristband alone occasioned a decrease in N's response frequency from a base-rate level of approximately 50 stuttering responses per two minutes to a new level of essentially zero stutterings.

During Sessions 7 (50 minutes) and 8 (46 minutes) N was required to read in an experimental room different from the one in which all previous sessions were conducted. In Session 7, N read to two listeners physically present in the room; in Session 8 he read into a "live" telephone. Graphs of N's stuttering frequency per two minutes during Sessions 7 and 8 are presented in Figures 8 and 9, respectively. In both sessions N's base-rate stuttering frequency was similar to that of preceding sessions; attaching the wristband occasioned a marked reduction in stuttering frequency; and removing the wristband resulted in an increase in stuttering frequency to near base-rate level.

Word Output. Subject N read at an average rate of 219 words per two minutes throughout the eight sessions. Inspection of the data revealed no changes in N's reading rate that appeared to be related systematically to changes in experimental conditions.

Summary. One subject was run in a successful replication of the findings observed with Subject N, and these data support the following conclusions. (1) Simultaneous presentation of "not good" for each stuttering and "good" for each 30 seconds of fluency resulted in a suppression of stuttering frequency. (2) Stuttering frequency can be brought under discriminative stimulus control. After training in one situation, the discriminative control of the wristband was maintained in a different environment.

Discussion

Results obtained in the present series of studies, plus results reported previously by Flanagan *et al.* (*1958*) and Goldiamond (*1960,*

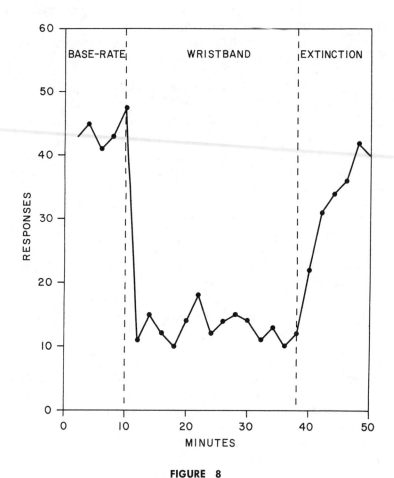

FIGURE 8

Number of stuttering responses emitted by Subject N each two minutes during Session 7.

1962, 1965), indicate quite clearly that certain of the overt non-fluent or struggle behaviors emitted during stuttering are susceptible to experimental manipulation in much the same way as are other operant behaviors. This does not necessarily mean, of course, that stuttering behaviors are instated originally by means of instrumental, operant conditioning. It is possible, and indeed probable, that the early acquisition and development of stuttering behaviors involve both classical and instrumental conditioning. Regardless of what future research reveals about the onset of stuttering, there is a growing body of evidence which suggests that the overt behaviors emitted by "chronic" adult stutterers may respond to carefully structured behavior therapy programs based on operant conditioning procedures.

The findings of the present experiments that certain stuttering responses can be brought under discriminative stimulus control (Subjects E, O, J) have particular significance for the speech clini-

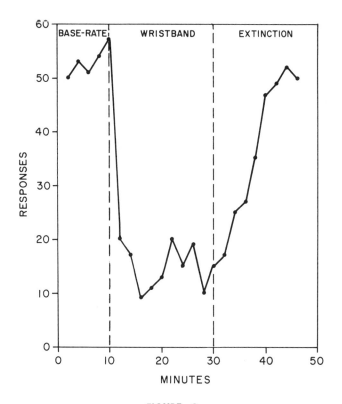

FIGURE 9

Number of stuttering responses emitted by Subject N each two minutes during Session 8.

cian. An observation reported frequently by therapists is that stutterers often experience a decrease in stuttering frequency while in a particular therapy environment, but fail in their attempts to maintain this relatively low stuttering level in "outside" situations. The demonstration that stuttering can be brough under discriminative stimulus control suggests that after the frequency of the stuttering behaviors has been reduced in one situation (therapy room or laboratory), then this reduced frequency can be extended into other environments through carefully programmed discrimination training.

Most of the published research concerning the operant manipulation of stuttering has utilized a punishment paradigm. Few, if any, studies have been reported where an attempt was made to reduce the frequency of stuttering through the application of a positive reinforcer contingent upon fluency. Presumably, stuttering and fluent responses are incompatible. That is, if the frequency of fluent responses increases, the frequency of stuttering responses decreases — assuming word output rate remains constant. In the current study, presenting Subject A with the verbal stimulus "good" each time he spoke fluently for 15 seconds produced little change in stuttering frequency. On the other hand, A's stuttering frequency reduced substantially when he was told "wrong" each time he stuttered. Although these findings are not especially encouraging relative to the effects of positive reinforcement on fluency, it may be that the use of a different reinforcer or a different response class would produce the desired increase in fluency and decrease in stuttering.

There exists at present a rather widespread notion that punishment is an undesirable means for controlling behavior in general (Skinner, 1938, 1953) and stuttering behavior in particular (Bloodstein, 1958; Johnson, 1956; Van Riper, 1954). Many speech pathologists cite the research of Van Riper (1937), Frick (1951), and others as support for their objection to the use of punishment in the treatment of stuttering. In the main, these investigations indicate that stuttering frequency increases under conditions of aversive stimulation. It should be pointed out, however, that in most of these earlier studies, presentation of the aversive stimulus was not specifically contingent upon emission of a stuttering response. In the experiments reported in the present paper, and in the studies of Flanagan *et al.* (*1958*) and Goldiamond (*1960, 1962, 1965*), care was taken to insure close temporal contiguity between emission of a stuttering response and presentation of the punishing stimulus. The invariant finding upon these conditions has been a decrement in stuttering frequency. Contrary to popular belief, there thus exists a considerable body of experimental evidence which indicates that, at least under certain conditions, the use of punishment is an effective technique for decreasing stuttering frequency.

Another objection to the use of punishment, which is voiced frequently by both psychologists and speech pathologists, centers around the possibility that continued use of punishment may lead to undesirable conditioned emotional responses on the part of the individual. Careful observation of the subjects utilized in the present series of studies failed to uncover any such undesirable behaviors. On the contrary, the word output data indicate that, if anything, the subjects' speaking or reading rates improved during the conditioning periods.

In line with the above discussion of punishment, some psychologists (*Estes, 1944, for example*) have speculated that potential therapeutic advantages might be obtained by punishing a given undesirable response and positively reinforcing, simultaneously, an alternative desired response. Presumably, the relatively rapid suppression of an undesirable response achieved through response contingent punishment would be maintained by the increased frequency of a positively reinforced, incompatible, desired response. As treatment progressed under these conditions, a subject would receive progressively more positively reinforcing stimuli and fewer punishing stimuli, thereby minimizing the likelihood that continued application of aversive stimulation would lead to undesirable emotional responses. Data obtained from Subject N ("good" for 30 seconds of fluency; "not good" for each stuttering response) in the present experiment are consonant with this simultaneous punishment-positive reinforcement notion, and suggest that such a procedure has potential as a desirable therapeutic technique with stutterers.

Finally, it should be noted that in the present paper both the reported experiments and the ensuing discussion are concerned with the specific overt responses made by the subject when he stutters. Admittedly, these responses constitute only one facet of the total clinical "problem" manifested by most stutterers. It is the opinion of the author, however, that if techniques can be devised to assist the stutterer in his efforts to speak more fluently, this alone will bring about some decrement in other aspects of the disorder. Whether additional therapy will be required to help the stutterer modify certain of his emotional and evaluative behaviors, and whether operant techniques will be useful tools in the modification of these behaviors, remains to be studied.

REFERENCES

Bloodstein, O., "Stuttering as an Anticipatory Struggle Reaction." In J. Eisenson (Ed.), *Stuttering: a Symposium.* New York: Harper & Row, 1958.

Brookshire, R. H., "The Differential Effects of Three Verbal Punishers on the Disfluencies of Normal Speakers." Unpublished Ph.D. dissertation, University of Minnesota, 1965.

Estes, W. K., "An Experimental Study of Punishment," *Psychol. Monogr.,* 1944, 57 (3, whole no. 263), 1–40.

Flanagan, B., I. Goldiamond, and N. H. Azrin, "Operant Stuttering: the Control of Stuttering Behavior through Response-Contingent Consequences," *J. Exp. Anal. Behav.,* 1958, 1, 173–177.

Frick, J. A., "An Exploratory Study of the Effect of Punishment (Electric Shock) upon Stuttering." Unpublished Ph.D. dissertation, State University of Iowa, 1951.

Goldiamond, I., "The Maintenance of Ongoing Fluent Verbal Behavior and Stuttering," *J. Mathetics,* 1962, 1, 57–95.

Goldiamond, I., "Stuttering and Fluency as Manipulable Operant Response Classes." In L. Krasner and L. P. Ullmann (Eds.), *Research in Behavior Modification.* New York: Holt, Rinehart and Winston, 1965.

Goldiamond, I., The Temporal Development of Fluent and Blocked Speech Communication," Air Force Com. Cent. Developm. Div., T. R. 60–38, 1960.

Johnson, W., "Stuttering." Chapter V in W. Johnson, S. F. Brown, J. F. Curtis, C. W. Edney and Jacqueline Keaster, *Speech Handicapped School Children* (Revised). New York: Harper & Row, 1956.

Martin, R. R., and G. M. Siegel, "The Effects of Response Contingent Shock on Stuttering," *J. Speech Hearing Res.,* 1966, 9, 340–352(a).

Martin, R. R., and G. M. Siegel, "The Effects of Simultaneously Punishing Stuttering and Rewarding Fluency," *J. Speech Hearing Res.,* 1966, 9, 466–475(b).

Quist, R., "The Effects of Response Contingent Verbal Punishment on Stuttering." Unpublished M. A. thesis, University of Minnesota, 1966.

Shames, G. H., and C. E. Sherrick, Jr., "A Discussion of Nonfluency and Stuttering as Operant Behavior," *J. Speech Hearing Dis.,* 1963, 28, 3–18.

Sidman, M., *Tactics of Scientific Research.* New York: Basic Books, 1960.

Skinner, B. F., *The Behavior of Organisms.* New York: Appleton-Century-Crofts, 1938.

Skinner, B. F., *Science and Human Behavior.* New York: Macmillan, 1953.

Van Riper, C., "The Effect of Penalty upon Frequency of Stuttering Spasms," *J. gen. Psychol.,* 1937, 50, 193–195.

Van Riper, C., *Speech Correction: Principles and Methods* (Third ed.). Englewood Cliffs, N.J.: Prentice-Hall, 1954.

17

Israel Goldiamond

Stuttering and Fluency as Manipulatable Operant Response Classes

The present paper reports a systematic series of experimental investigations of fluent speech and stuttering, and the derivation of a procedure which, when applied to chronic stutterers, has virtually eliminated stuttering and has replaced it by a fluent verbal pattern within the laboratory, with some carry-over to speech outside. Procedures for extending the behavior outside the laboratory are also being investigated. The experiments are part of a program of basic research in variables governing the establishment, maintenance, and alteration of patterns of verbal behavior, and in the experimental analysis and utilization of verbal interactions under specified conditions to alter referent behaviors outside.

The working assumption which initiated the series was the consideration of verbal behavior as operant behavior, that is, it was assumed that verbal behavior could profitably be studied using analytic procedures developed in operant laboratories. Such research has produced a body of basic knowledge in the form of functional relations between specified behaviors and conditions which has been obtained by carefully altering conditions and observing their effects on the rate or form of ongoing behavior. This research has also produced a set of generally applicable procedures which

From L. Krasner and L. P. Ullmann (Eds.), RESEARCH IN BEHAVIOR MODIFICATION. New York: Holt, Rinehart and Winston, Inc., 1965.

can be used to alter specified response patterns, or establish, or maintain them. Among the response patterns which we shall consider are those of fluent speech and stuttering.

Operant behavior manipulates its environment; it may be defined as behavior whose rate or form is governed by its consequences. The rate and form of much verbal behavior is so governed (as, for example, the slowed speech of dictation, or the altered forms of translation). Stuttering may be defined by a high rate of certain forms of speech. These include repetitions, breaks, pauses, arhythmias, and other blockages. They occur in normally fluent speech, but at a rate so low as not to define a communicative problem. The experimental question arose as to whether the rates and forms differentiating stuttering from fluent speech could be altered by using operant procedures, both within the laboratory and outside it.

In operant research, different consequences are systematically programed to different response classes. The peck of a pigeon at a disc, for example, immediately activates a food dispenser or a shock device. If this response does not occur, the device will not act. Such systematic relations between consequences and behavior exemplify *differential reinforcement,* which may be used to alter the rate and form of behavior, as well as its relationship to many features of the environment.

Where response pattern is maintained when such an event is provided, the stimulus is termed a *reinforcing stimulus* (food, in the example just cited). Where the pattern is attenuated, the event is termed an *aversive stimulus* (shock, in the case cited). The experimental procedures are defined as *reinforcement* and *punishment,* respectively. Similarly, the response may temporarily *eliminate* an ongoing stimulus (which would not be eliminated otherwise). The stimulus eliminated may be an aversive stimulus (continual shock) or a reinforcing stimulus (ongoing music). These experimental procedures are defined as *negative reinforcement* and *punishment,* respectively. Where differential reinforcement is no longer provided, the procedure is defined as *extinction.*

Differential reinforcement may also alter the *form* of the response. If the pigeon is reinforced when he raises his head, but not when he lowers it, he may respond with an outstretched neck. The process is called *shaping,* or *response differentiation.* Differential reinforcement may also define what will be responded to. If reinforcement is provided for responding when the light is green, but not when red, a green light may occasion responding which stops when it turns red. This defines *stimulus control* or *stimulus discrimination*. These simple cases may be extended to highly complex relations between the environment and behavior. Novel relations hitherto not in the organism's repertoire may be established. Precise laboratory research has often made evident or established a relationship which would otherwise be unobservable, seem capricious, or seem unobtainable.

Consideration of stuttering and fluency as behaviors maintained by differential reinforcement in complex, but systematic, relation to the environment suggested some interesting possibilities for analysis and treatment. Stuttering has often been regarded as an emotional response,[1] or as an emotionally induced breakdown, governed by the conditions which produce such upset, rather than by the way in which it (as opposed to fluency) differentially manipulates its environment. Such consideration has dictated a different approach toward its analysis and treatment.

Controlled Alteration and Instatement of Nonfluency[2]

In the first experiment in this series (*Flanagan, Goldiamond, and Azrin, 1958*), three stutterers read aloud from printed pages; E

·

[1] Emotional behavior may also be operant. Where stuttering is regarded as emotional behavior, it has more typically been considered respondent, rather than operant. Respondent behavior is governed by stimuli which elicit it (the salivation of Pavlov's dog elicited by a tone *preceding* it), whereas operant behavior is governed by the stimuli which are *contingent* upon it. Whether the emotional behavior is respondent or operant depends upon the stimuli maintaining it. If a tantrum is maintained by the attention and upset it provokes under certain conditions, it is operant. If it is maintained by conditions whose control derives from their being paired with unconditioned stimuli which elicit tantrums, it is respondent. To assess which form of behavior it is, one could manipulate the differentiating stimuli involved, and observe which altered the behavior. At the present, many treatments are based upon the implicit assumption that stuttering is respondent. The degree of acceptance of this assumption as exclusive is not matched by supporting evidence. Nothing in this paper should be interpreted to imply that stuttering may not have respondent properties. Whether stuttering is respondent or operant or some combination, or whether different types of stuttering exist, defined in this manner, is not a matter of competing ideologies, but an empirical matter of the maintaining stimuli.

[2] This research was supported by a grant from the Mental Health Fund of the State of Illinois, administered by the Illinois Psychiatric Training and Research Authority.

pressed a micro-switch for each word blocked, and recorded each page read. There were two 90-minute sessions for each S. In the *aversive* session, following about 30 minutes of recording of stuttering, each blockage definition now produced a 1-second blast of 105 decibels white noise into S's earphones. After about 30 minutes of such punishment, the noise was turned off and reading continued for another 30 minutes. The results for one S are shown in Figure 1; the stuttering curve is cumulated against pages read. Stuttering

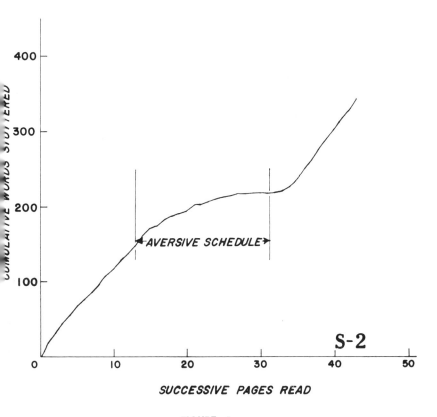

FIGURE 1

Attenuation of stuttering in a chronic stutterer upon punishment. Each word stuttered produced a 1-sec. blast of noise during the aversive period.

was almost completely eliminated toward the end of the aversive period; S read almost ten pages without stuttering. Stuttering by the other two Ss was also attenuated during this period.

In the *escape* session, following 30 minutes of recording alone, a 30-minute period was introduced during which each definition turned off ongoing noise for 5 seconds, defining negative reinforcement. Stuttering rate rose during this period, dropping when it was no longer negatively reinforced. This experiment suggested that stuttering rate could be affected by its consequences, dropping when they were aversive, and rising when negatively reinforced.

In the next experiment (*Flanagan, Goldiamond, and Azrin, 1959*), nonfluencies were increased in a *normally* fluent S (*cf. Bilger* and *Speaks, 1959,* who report similar results). He read aloud as before. After a stabilization period, a continual electrical shock was introduced via the electrodes he was wearing. Each blockage definition shut off the shock for 10 seconds; a response made during this period recycled the timer, so that by blocking at appropriate intervals, S could avert shock. Results are presented in Figure 2. Blockage rate rose dramatically during the escape period. When the shock was turned off, blockage continued for a while at its high rate: absence of shock was maintaining blockages; accordingly, turning the shock off continued to maintain it. Such persistence of avoidance behavior in the absence of its maintaining conditions is one of the characteristics of avoidance behavior which has been noted clinically. Two days later, S was run again. His blockages were now at so high a rate that he received only two brief shocks during the escape period. Elimination of the new pattern during extinction was considerably prolonged.

At the end of the second session, E interviewed S, who repeatedly attributed his nonfluencies to his anxiety and his anxiety to his nonfluencies.[3] He then attributed his nonfluencies to the slowness of his reading (which had obviously been caused by the nonfluencies). He was finally asked if a shock might have been contributory. "Oh, no," he said. "On the first day, you had a short somewhere, and

---

[3] Circular reasoning that is not restricted to this S. Where anxiety and stuttering are defined independently, it is not always clear which is causal. Among the consequences that stuttering may produce are stimuli eliciting emotional reactions.

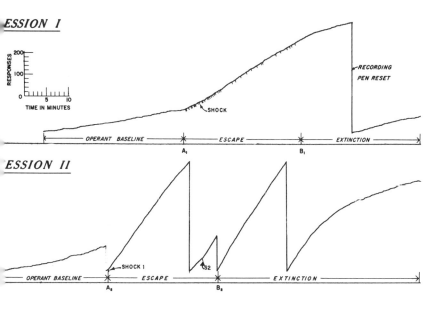

FIGURE 2

Instatement of a high nonfluency rate in a normally fluent S through presenting continual shock (during escape period), with each word blocked eliminating shock for a fixed period of time.

your equipment leaked so badly that I meant to tell you about it. You had it fixed by the second session. Shocks had nothing to do with my stuttering. I stuttered worse today, but there were no shocks at all today," which was almost true, but it was S's behavior that produced this condition of no shock. So much for S's explanation of his own behavior. It should be noted that elimination of the shock served to maintain the nonfluencies which eliminated it, just as elimination of noise did with regard to stuttering. If presenting noise during the experiment had produced anxiety, then anxiety was responsible for both the *increase* in stuttering (during negative reinforcement) and the *decrease* in stuttering (during punishment). Its explanatory value as a cause of stuttering is questionable in this case, at least.

An Experimental Analysis of Stuttering[4]

Since nonfluencies could be treated as operant response classes, we undertook a long-term experimental analysis of stuttering. In the next study (*Goldiamond, 1960, 1962a*), chronic stutterers were run daily, 5 days a week, two for as long as 9 months. They read aloud from printed material for 90 minutes a day. To get material which was uniform in style, and which was not likely to have been read before, Tolstoy's *War and Peace* was chosen; when this was completed, it was followed by *Anna Karenina*, then *The Short Novels of Tolstoy*, and a collection of short stories. Stuttering was monitored as before, with *E* reading another copy of the book along with *S* in another room; at approximately every hundredth word, a slash appeared in *E*'s copy, and *E* pressed another microswitch, thereby defining ongoing reading rate.

Obtaining generalizable data from a few *S*'s run for extended periods of time under carefully controlled conditions is, needless to say, a time-honored procedure in many areas of natural science. This point needs reiteration these days when research design is often exclusively equated with groups of Ss, run for short and equal periods, and differentiated on the basis of some variable. Obtained differences between groups are assessed statistically to evaluate their relation to the variable studied, to other variables, or to chance. While such methods are important, much of our knowledge about nerves, for example, has been obtained from single nerve fibers, stimulated over extended periods of time. The branch of psychology known as psychophysics has been characterized by controlled research (hence, the appellation "brass instrument psychology") with single organisms. In operant research, *S* may be run until a steady state pattern of behavior ensues, at which point a variable may be introduced. If response rate is, say attenuated, the variable may be reintroduced with a negative value to see if the original rate is now increased. A functional relation between dependent and independent variables may be established, and its

[4] Research performed under contracts with the Operational Applications Laboratory, Air Force Cambridge Research Center, contract No. AF 19(604)–6127, 1960, and with the Operational Applications Office, Electronic Systems Division, U.S.A. FCCDD, 1961, 1962. The author wishes to express his appreciation to Mr. Bruce Flanagan, then a graduate student in speech correction, who was research assistant under the former contract.

NO CONTINGENCIES
OBSERVER DEFINITION

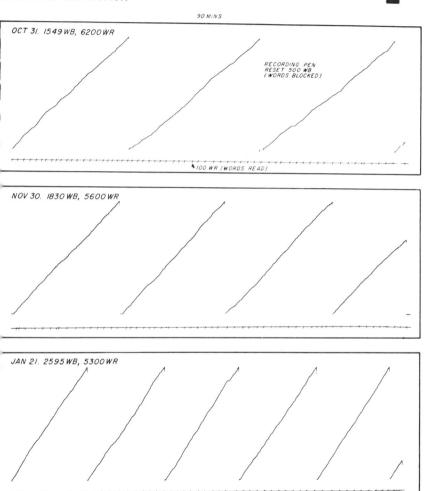

FIGURE 3

Temporal course of stuttering in a chronic stutterer reading aloud 90 min. daily. Note that stuttering rate rises over time between sessions, but decreases within sessions.

generality to other organisms may be assessed by running them (*cf. Sidman, 1960*). This was the procedure applied in this case, and it posed several problems that had to be settled first.

The Adaptation Effect

Extended investigation is called for. Consultation of literature and investigators in the field immediately brought up the "adaptation" effect. This may be related to consideration of stuttering as the product of an emotional state. A characteristic of some emo-

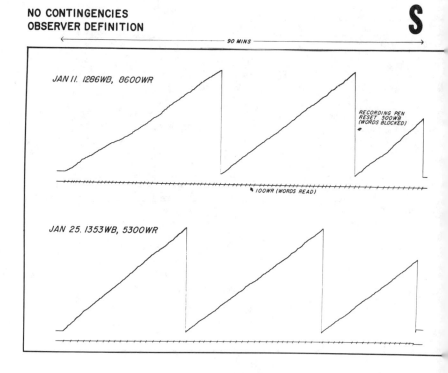

NO CONTINGENCIES
OBSERVER DEFINITION

FIGURE 4

Temporal course of stuttering in a second chronic stutterer reading aloud daily. Note that stuttering rate remains fairly constant over time between sessions, but decreases within sessions.

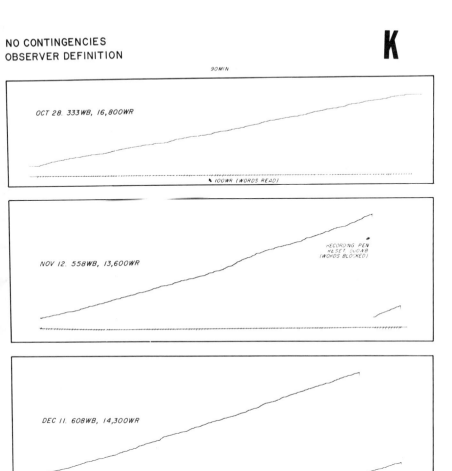

FIGURE 5

Temporal course of stuttering in a third chronic stutterer reading aloud daily. Note that stuttering rate increases over time between sessions, but tends to decrease within the session.

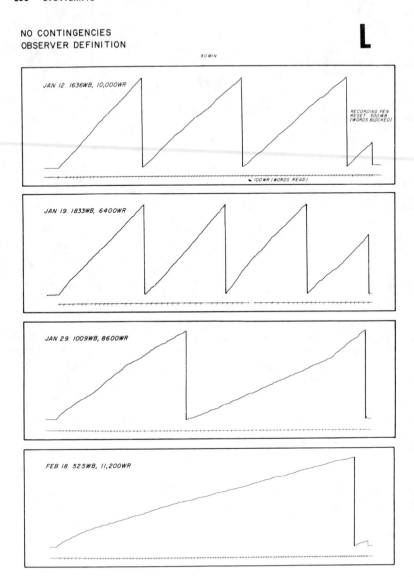

NO CONTINGENCIES
OBSERVER DEFINITION

L

90 MIN

JAN 12. 1636WB, 10,000WR

RECORDING PEN
RESET 500WB
(WORDS BLOCKED)

100WR (WORDS READ)

JAN 19. 1833WB, 6400WR

JAN 29. 1009WB, 8600WR

FEB 18. 525WB, 11,200WR

FIGURE 6

Temporal course of stuttering in a fourth chronic stutterer reading
aloud daily. Note that stuttering rate decreases over time between
sessions, and also within sessions.

tional states is that in familiar surroundings their effects are progressively lessened, and "adaptation" occurs.[5] The experimental *phenomenon* described is a decrease in stuttering rate as a session progresses. The consistency of this phenomenon poses problems for long-term research of the type described, since it may lead to disappearance of the behavior being studied. Long-term experimental analysis of stuttering of the extent used here had not been assayed before, and accordingly, Ss were first run for extended periods of time, reading aloud from the books, to see what would happen. Results for the four Ss run as indicated in Figures 3, 4, 5, and 6. As can be seen in each case, *there is an adaptation effect within each session,* that is, the terminal stuttering rate is lower than the initial stuttering rate, as evidenced by the slopes of the curves.[6] However, the stuttering of all four Ss *did not* adapt over the long run. Stability did ensue, with the steady state rate depicted at the bottom of each figure. It will be noted that two Ss, Z and K, stabilized at a *higher* rate of stuttering than their initial sessions; one, L, stabilized at a *lower* rate; and one, S, maintained the *same* rate. Apparently, the change in rate *during* a session may be independent of the change in rate *between* sessions. Adaptation between sessions has often been obtained with repetitious readings of the same passage, which is not the case here. The data also indicate that a long-term analysis may produce results different from short sessions. That transient and steady states may differ would seem to be of special concern to those dealing with long-term effects, for example, the clinician.

[5] Relatable (a) to respondent extinction: repeated presentation of the new situation without previously paired emotionally eliciting stimuli extinguishes emotional disruption; (b) to operant stimulus change: behavior disrupted by novel stimuli is re-established if old contingencies are unchanged.

[6] A word about reading the curves. These are cumulative curves, that is, the response pen goes up at each response, and stays up, going further upward at the next response. The paper, in the meantime, moves at a fixed speed to the left, producing a record which moves to the right. If there is no responding, the pen will drag, and the result will be a straight line with a slope of 0. The more rapidly it moves, the steeper the line.

The recording pen resets after 500 responses, returning to the bottom to start up again. Accordingly, a second way to compare rates is by the number of resets of the pen, since each session is constant in time.

Reading rate is indicated by closeness of slashes on the bottom line of each session. Each slash represents 100 words read.

Number of words blocked (WB), and words read (WR) per session are summarized in the upper left hand corner of each session.

Immediacy of Reinforcement

For reinforcement to be maximally effective, it must be presented concurrently with the response. Where it is not immediate, special laboratory procedures are used to make the contingency effective. If differential consequences are applied by a monitor, there may be a slight delay before he defines a pause as a blockage, since pauses also occur as normal parts of fluent speech. It was presumed that the stutterer is better informed in this matter, and, accordingly, it would be desirable to attach consequences to his definitions. Would this affect the data (*Wingate, 1959*) and introduce an artifact?

Stuttering rates before, during, and after self-definition are presented in Figures 7 and 8. The rates are those defined by the listen-

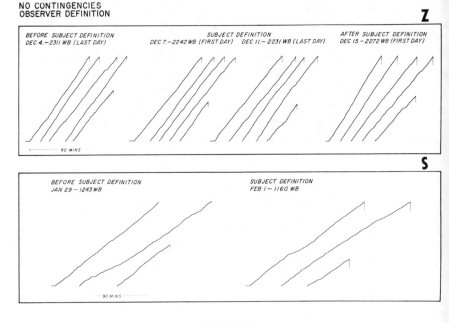

FIGURE 7

Effects upon stuttering of having S define his own moments of stuttering. Definition is by a monitor. There are no changes in rate.

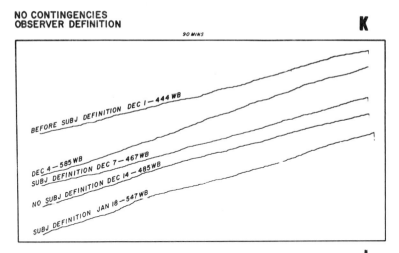

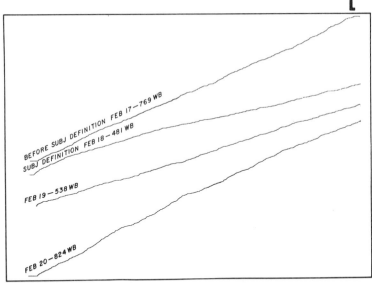

FIGURE 8

Effects upon stuttering of having S define his own moments of stuttering. For K, changes are within range without self-definition. For L, self-definition was accompanied by considerable attenuation of stuttering, which returned to baseline conditions by the third day.

ing monitor.[7] It will be noted that for Z, there are no differences in rate during these three periods. For S, only the last day prior to self-definition and the first day of self-definition are presented. There was no difference. For K, there were fluctuations, but within the rate ranges for each category. For L, self-definition resulted in a drop in stuttering rate, from 769 to 481 words. Within 2 days, however, the rate during self-definition had returned to its baseline prior to self-definition. Self-definition produced either no discernible effect or a transient change. Accordingly, when contingencies were attached, they were attached to S's definition.

Reliability of Definition

Two observers defining the same phenomenon raises the problem of reliability. (An independent third definition was included from tape recordings.) Let us assume that one observer defines 1000 responses and a second 800. A depressant variable is now introduced; the two definitions are 500 and 400. The variable is now withdrawn, and the definitions are 1500 and 1200. Similar functional relations obtain between them. They may be considered reliable, although different criteria are being used. This definition of reliability through cofunctional relations was used in this investigation, and will be illustrated in the curves shown.

Choice of Consequence

In the preceding investigations, noise and electric shock were used. Both are contraindicated as clinical procedures. Instead, we used delayed auditory feedback of S's own voice as a consequence. It was related systematically to the response classes studied: (a) it was made contingent on stuttering, (b) its elimination was a consequence, (c) it was presented continually without relation to behavior, (d) it was continually absent. Procedures c and d involve no differential reinforcement. If delayed feedback is an aversive stimulus, procedure a defines punishment of stuttering, and procedure b defines its negative reinforcement. When the switch defining a *word* stuttered was depressed, it activated a cumulative

[7] To save space, spaces between the curves have been collapsed. Slope has not been altered. Each day represents a 90-minute session.

recorder. During procedure *a*, the switch also shunted speech to a delayed feedback device for 5 seconds. During procedure *b*, the recording was shunted *from* that device to normal feedback for 10 seconds. The input delay was 250 ms from output.

General Procedure

The S sat in a small booth and was instructed to read aloud from printed pages at as rapid a rate as was consistent with comfort. His voice was presented to him through earphones, with masking noise in the booth as well as through the earphones to mask bone conduction. Each S read 90 minutes a day, and was paid. Other details will be presented with the results.

Results

The effects of making a fixed period of delayed feedback contingent upon a stuttering response (hereafter referred to as *punishment*) are presented for Subject Z in Figure 9. The upper curve of each pair is the monitor's definition; the lower is S's. The definitions are quite similar, and accord with the cofunctional reliability defined earlier. On Friday, January 22, S read 5100 words and blocked on about 2500 of them. When, on Monday, January 25, punishment of stuttering was introduced, stuttering dropped to about 1500 words, while reading rate almost doubled. The adaptation effect noted in previous sessions was reversed, with stuttering rate higher at the *end* of the session than at the beginning. This reading rate and attenuated stuttering continued for the 2 weeks of this procedure. On Monday, February 8, the baseline condition was reintroduced, and the verbal patterns prior to punishment reappeared.

Delayed feedback functioned as noise had in the first experiment; it was aversive, and its depressant effects were specific to the stuttering behavior upon which it was contingent. Attenuation of the blockages, presumably hindrances to communication, almost doubled the flow of fluent verbal behavior.

The S was run without contingencies for 2 more months. There was a slowing of reading rate (no contingencies were attached to rapid reading) to 2000 words, with 1500 of them stuttered; this was

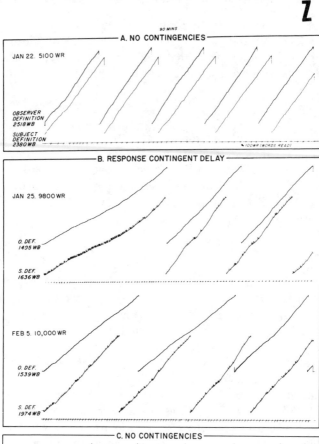

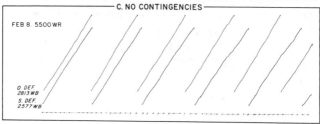

FIGURE 9

Effects of punishment upon stuttering: each word stuttered produced a 5-sec. period of delayed feedback. Note return of previous pattern of behavior when conditions prevailing prior to contingencies were reintroduced.

an absolute drop from the 2500 words stuttered during the previous baseline. Punishment was then reinstated; the new baseline and results are shown in Figure 10. The immediate effect was to decrease the rate of the punished response, which remained at a new low level, as reading rate in general gradually rose.

Did delayed feedback have to be response-contingent for its effects? Continual delay was presented for Subject *L*; results are shown in Figure 11. The immediate effect of continual (nonresponse-contingent) delay was to reduce reading rate; stuttering was not markedly affected. By the next day, reading rate had recovered, and both it and stuttering rate were similar to baseline data.

Since this S might have been insensitive to delayed feedback, *punishment* was introduced. Results are presented in Figure 12. The effects are similar to the preceding S: stuttering was considerably attenuated, dropping to about 100 words after 2 months of such treatment. The reading rate, however, also dropped, but the ratio of words read to words stuttered rose from about 30 to 1 during baseline to about 100 to 1 when aversive consequences were applied. These changes contrast to those produced by noncontingent presentation of delayed feedback. It was apparently the contingency which produced the attenuation.

For Subject S, avoidance-conditioning was instituted after stabilization. Delayed feedback was presented continually, with each nonfluency restoring normal feedback for 10 seconds. Results are presented in Figure 13. There was an immediate drop in both reading and stuttering rates. On the second day, however, both rose, with stuttering almost double the baseline rate. Delayed feedback again seemed to be functioning like shock and noise in that its elimination increased the rate of the response that eliminated it.

The hypothesis that delayed feedback is aversive appeared confirmed and, had the experiment terminated here, little new would have been learned other than such confirmation. During the next few days, however, S taught E something else. Curves from these days are presented in Figures 14 and 15. Two response patterns seemed to be competing. These were most evident on February 23. One involved both a high reading and high stuttering rate, and the other a low reading rate with almost no stuttering. The latter eventually won out, and by March 10 the reading rate was about

Z

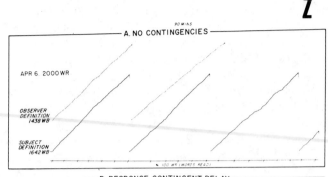

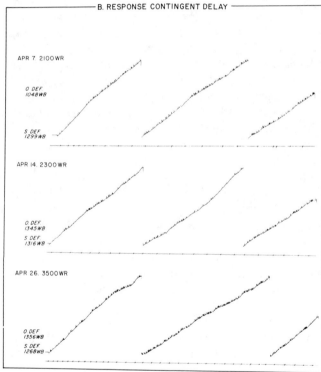

FIGURE 10

Effects of delayed feedback as punishment for stuttering upon slowed reading. Stuttering rate is somewhat lowered, but reading rate (and words read fluently per stuttered word) almost doubles.

NONRESPONSE–CONTINGENT DELAY
OBSERVING MONITOR

L

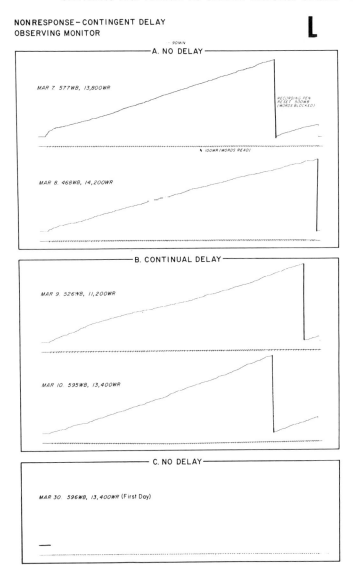

FIGURE 11

Effects of delayed feedback presented continually during both fluencies and nonfluencies. Note initial drop in reading rate, with recovery thereafter.

RESPONSE CONTINGENT DELAY

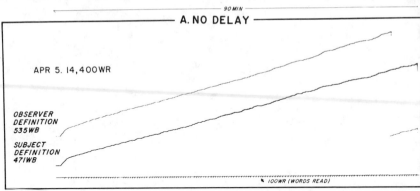

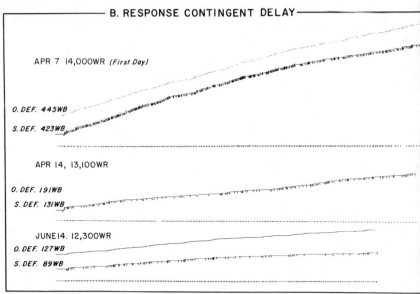

FIGURE 12

Effects of making delayed feedback contingent upon stuttering in *S* for whom continual delay had produced only transient changes. Note attenuation of stuttering.

RESPONSE CONTINGENT ELIMINATION

S

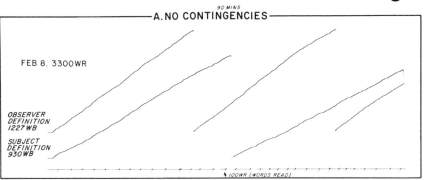

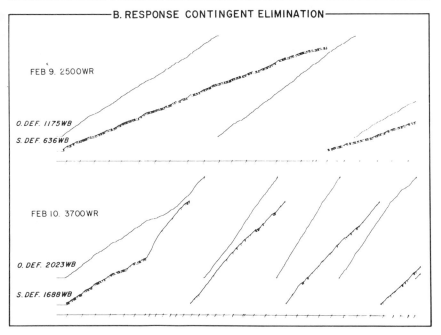

FIGURE 13

Effects of presenting delayed feedback continually, with each word stuttered eliminating it for 10 sec. Note rise in stuttering on second day.

RESPONSE CONTINGENT ELIMINATION

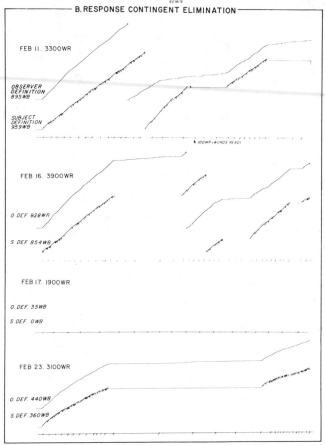

FIGURE 14

Anomalous effects of the elimination-avoidance schedule. Note existence of two competing patterns: one with high stuttering rate and high reading rate, and one with low (or null) stuttering rate and low reading rate.

S

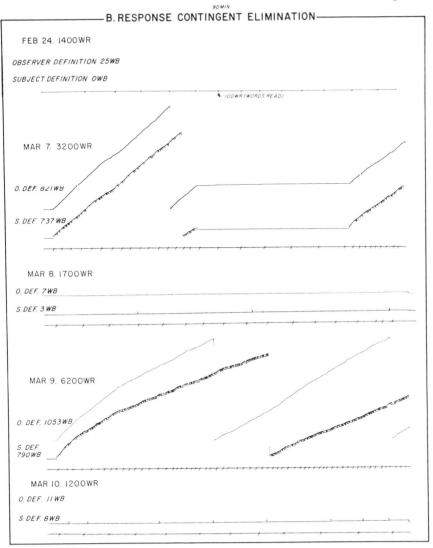

B. RESPONSE CONTINGENT ELIMINATION

90 MIN

FEB 24. 1400WR

OBSERVER DEFINITION 25WB

SUBJECT DEFINITION OWB

100WR (WORDS READ)

MAR 7. 3200WR

O. DEF. 821WB

S. DEF. 737 WB

MAR 8. 1700WR

O. DEF. 7WB

S. DEF. 3 WB

MAR 9. 6200WR

O. DEF. 1053WB

S. DEF. 790WB

MAR 10. 1200WR

O. DEF. 11WB

S. DEF. 8WB

FIGURE 15

Continuation of competing patterns under elimination-avoidance
schedule. Response pattern of Mar. 10 typified behavior thereafter.

371

13 words a minute. Two days later, negative reinforcement was eliminated, and baseline conditions of no delay were reinstated. The prolonged speech continued, without stuttering. The S was reading thus: "A-a-a-a-and whe-e-e-e-en A-a-a-a-an-na-a-a-a-a ca-a-a-a-a-ame ..." Fearful that we had substituted for one undesirable speech pattern (stuttering), something worse, we tried a variety of conditions to disrupt this behavior, but it perseverated. On June 2, an attempt was made to increase the reading rate: the number of pages S had been reading was tripled, and he was told he could leave as soon as he had read them; the total pay would be the same. He read this tripled amount in one third the time; results are shown in Figure 16. (The N, D, E refer to different schedules, which had no differential effect.) Comparison of three sessions of the speed-up (which total about 90 minutes) with the baseline session indicates that reading rate increased from 4400 words to 10,600, while stuttering dropped from about 1000 words to about 300. There was an eightfold increase in the ratio of fluency to nonfluency.

A summary presentation of procedures used for Subject K is presented in Figure 17. Punishment resulted in an attenuation of stuttering rate; the attenuation remained after the punishment was withdrawn. When elimination of delay was made contingent upon stuttering, nonfluencies were almost completely eliminated, falling within the rate of normally fluent Ss. Six weeks after the termination of the experiment, S was asked to read again under conditions of no delay. The booth maintained its stimulus control of the new pattern of rapid stutterless reading developed during the avoidance procedure.

Feedback as a Response Specific Reinforcer

If delayed feedback is an aversive stimulus (as the punishment data indicated), its elimination should have increased response rate, which it did not. Further, one of the Ss stabilized under delay. We accordingly investigated delayed feedback further. Like stuttering, it has typically been studied for short periods using groups of Ss. Eight normally fluent Ss were run for extended periods, under conditions similar to those described for the stutterers.

MIXED SCHEDULES: SPEED-UP

S

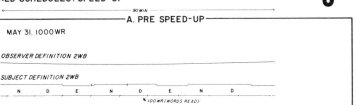

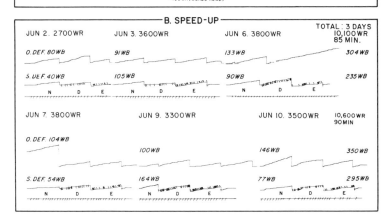

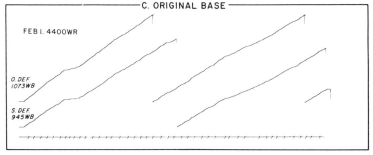

FIGURE 16

Effects of speeding up reading of S who emerged with a pattern of prolonged vocalization that persisted beyond elimination-avoidance procedure under which it was instated. Note that, compared with baseline, S is reading over twice as rapidly, with one third as many stutters, during comparable periods of time.

OBSERVER DEFINITION

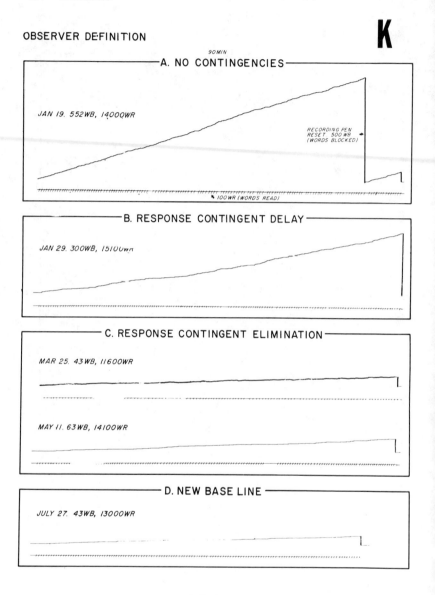

FIGURE 17

Effects of three different procedures upon stuttering. The last session was obtained after a six-week hiatus. Note persistence of pattern.

That the delay contingency was indeed aversive is suggested by Figure 18. Button presses defining nonfluency dropped from 51 to 10 when this contingency was introduced, and remained at a low level, rising to 60 when withdrawn. However, the *monitor's* corresponding definitions of nonfluency (lower half of figure) indicated no such effects upon nonfluency. The S's button-pressing response was being affected in exactly the same manner that bar pressing is affected by shock. These results, corroborated with other Ss, suggested that delayed feedback was aversive; its anomalous effects on speech during avoidance suggested the possible intrusion of additional variables during speech.

Verbal behavior produces auditory and proprioceptive stimuli, which ensemble will not be produced unless verbal behavior occurs: these stimuli are *contingent* upon verbal behavior. Since withholding them may disrupt the behavior, their presentation also serves to *maintain* the behavior. These two properties of a stimulus, contingency upon behavior and maintenance of the behavior, define a reinforcing stimulus, and the feedback produced by speech may be among its reinforcing stimuli. Other consequences include those controlled by the audience. The feedback reinforcing stimuli are specific to speech, and may have different properties when made contingent on a button press. When this reinforcement, normally immediate, is withdrawn, behavior may be disrupted. However, audience-controlled contingencies may require continuation of speech. One method of maintaining the behavior under such conditions of deferred reinforcement is to prolong the behavior so that the immediate overlap is reinstated. Figure 19 illustrates this explanation of the prolonged speech noted in Subject S. During normal speech, the verbal outputs (responses) from "then came John" become immediate inputs (stimuli). Under delay, there is an asynchrony, and response and stimulus do not overlap. By prolonging the medial units as indicated in Delay 2, the "e" output overlaps the "e" input. Asynchrony is restricted to terminal-initial units, whose relative contribution is decreased as speech is prolonged.

The maintaining stimuli are proprioceptive as well as auditory. Since temporal disruption characterizes auditory but not proprioceptive inputs, another method of reinstating immediacy of reinforcement is by switching maintenance of behavior from auditory

N3

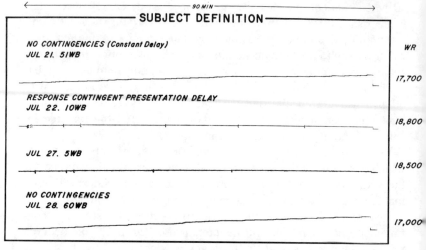

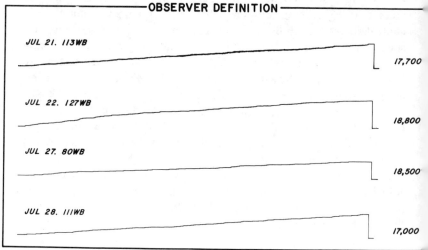

FIGURE 18

Delayed feedback as punishment of button pressing, rather than the nonfluencies supposedly indicated, in a normally fluent S.

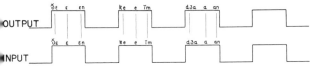

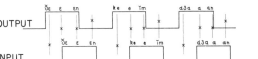

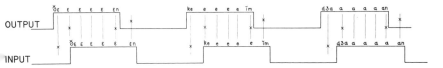

FIGURE 19

Prolonged vocalization under delayed feedback as a self-instituted procedure which restores normal overlap between speech and its auditory consequences.

to proprioceptive inputs. Results from two Ss whose reading rate had stabilized at a high rate under delay are presented in Figure 20 (*Goldiamond, Atkinson, and Bilger, 1962*). The Ss were given 10-minute reading periods. Each period was either under delayed or normal feedback. Prior to each period, S was either instructed to listen or not to listen to what he was reading. The experimental design, indicated in the key, is that of a 2-by-2 table, with the interaction of delay-listen predicted to be significant.[8] Without delay, S's speech would be controlled by usual undisturbed auditory component, whether told to listen or not, and reading rate would be

---

[8] Such a 2-by-2 design, with interaction predicted as significant, is normally designed using analysis of variance. The results demonstrate that this type of interaction can also be analyzed using an *experimental* analysis of behavior.

high. Under delay, with instructions not to listen, reading rate might be controlled by the undisturbed nonauditory components, and would also be high. But instructions to listen under delay might bring reading under control of the delayed consequences, and rate would be slowed. Two discrete response ranges occurred: one for the first three conditions, and a lower one for the fourth. The low variability of the latter condition is especially noticeable in Subject G.

The mechanisms for "tuning out" one's own verbal behavior, or the dissociation of speech, seem worthy of further exploration. We have observed that compulsive talkers, that is, people who con-

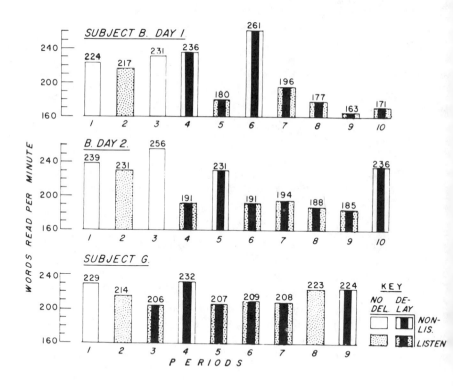

FIGURE 20

Disruptive effects of delayed auditory feedback upon reading rate when the auditory stimulus controls the response, as opposed to effects when it does not. Reading rate under delayed vs. immediate feedback, with instructions to listen and not to listen.

tinually speak without seeming to listen to themselves, are un-affected by delayed feedback.

All normal Ss run under prolonged delay stabilized their verbal behavior. The new patterns, although possibly different from normal speech, were steady states which contrasted with the perturbations when first put under delay. These patterns have been mentioned in the literature, and have been regarded as attempts to reinstate normal conditions (cf. Black, 1955), which indeed seems to be the case. Given a stimulus ensemble including both disrupted and nondisrupted maintaining stimuli, if behavior continues, the ratio between disrupted and undisrupted components must decrease over time, as presented in Figure 21. There are at least four ways of decreasing this ratio. The first involves increase of the denominator by prolonging the medial units, through prolonged speech. The second involves lowering the disturbed auditory numerator, by lowering one's voice. If the gain is then raised, the speaker may decrease the ratio by increasing the denominator through accentuating muscular movements; a tenseness is often reported in the throat. The fourth procedure is the tune-out procedure, in which whatever stimuli are involved in auditory-attentive control are decreased, while others are either increased or constant.

Outside the bounds of this set is another method for overcoming delay. This simply involves not speaking, or withdrawal: S may take off the earphones, leave the booth, etc. Our Ss, however, were paid to read; in order to read, they had to return that behavior to the control of the specific stimuli maintaining what may be called its *microstructure*. This suggests that there are at least two concurrent sets of stimuli maintaining verbal (and probably other) behaviors. Both are generated by the response and occasion its further occurrence. Verbal responses (or pigeon pecks) produce both auditory feedback (or proprioceptive feedback), on the one hand, and money-attention (or grain), on the other. Presentation of these stimuli provide the occasion for the next response, as well, producing a chain (Skinner, 1938). The difference between the two sets of stimuli does not lie entirely in their part-whole relation to the response units involved. A response unit is the response between the stimulus which occasions it (the discriminative stimulus) and the reinforcing stimulus (which maintains it) contingent upon it. Thus, the 32 words of the Pledge of Allegiance are a response

STABILIZATION UNDER DELAY

PARADIGM $\quad \left(\dfrac{\text{DISR}}{\text{NORM}}\right)_{t_1} \quad > \quad \left(\dfrac{\text{DISR}}{\text{NORM}}\right)_{t_2}$

$$t_1 \qquad t_2$$

1. PROLONGATION: AUDITORY CONTROL

$$\dfrac{\text{INIT-TERM}}{\text{MEDIAL}} \quad \begin{array}{c} = \\ < \end{array} \quad \dfrac{\text{INIT-TERM}}{\text{MEDIAL}}$$

2. MUSCULAR CONTROL A

$$\dfrac{\text{AUDITORY}}{\text{PROPR-KIN+}} \quad \begin{array}{c} > \\ = \end{array} \quad \dfrac{\text{AUDITORY}}{\text{PROPR-KIN+}}$$

3. MUSCULAR CONTROL B

$$\dfrac{\text{AUDITORY}}{\text{PROPR-KIN+}} \quad \begin{array}{c} = \\ < \end{array} \quad \dfrac{\text{AUDITORY}}{\text{PROPR-KIN+}}$$

4. TUNE OUT

$$\dfrac{\text{AUD-ATT}}{\text{VIS-PROPR-KIN}} \quad \begin{array}{c} > \\ \lessgtr \end{array} \quad \dfrac{\text{AUD-ATT}}{\text{VIS-PROPR-KIN}}$$

FIGURE 21

Mechanisms for stabilizing verbal behavior under delayed auditory feedback, involving decreasing the ratio between disrupted input under delay, and normal input not affected by delay.

unit. Each word, however, is contingent upon the preceding word and occasions the next, also defining a *word* as a response unit. We can go further into progressively decreasing constituent units, and come to those bounded by the occasioning and reinforcing properties of the auditory and proprioceptive feedback units of the microstructure, which do not necessarily end the regression. The original environmental discriminative stimulus ("Recite the pledge") may occasion a 32-word unit, which long chain is maintained by all the submacrostructural reinforcers and discriminative stimuli on the way, culminated by the final macrostructural reinforcer.[9] Since there are varying units and subunits, the part-whole relationship is not sufficient to distinguish between the two sets of stimuli (exemplified by grain and feedback) we have been discussing. The necessary difference between the two sets of stimuli may lie not so much in their part-whole relation or in their contingency upon behavior, but in the *agency that schedules the contingency.* In the one case, the agency may be the physiological and natural ecology of the response (nerves, ambient air, and bone conductors); in the other case, the agency may be the grosser environmental ecology (the experimenter, the apparatus, society, the habitat). Both sets of stimuli may control and direct the behavior and also serve as constant stimuli (*Goldiamond, 1962b*), and their relationship to each other is a fruitful field for research. For verbal behavior, there are thus at least two audiences (or agencies of reinforcement) when the person speaks: himself and the social audience. The former stimuli can evidently be conditioned reinforcers to the latter (*Kelleher and Gollub, 1962*) when, for example, a child consoles himself after a scare by saying aloud to himself, "There, there, don't cry," which input was previously produced by his mother along with other stimuli which were effective in producing comfort. These considerations suggest that the class of stimulus changes represented by delayed feedback (which can be called response-specific-reinforcers) have interesting properties meriting their further consideration in psychological research.

There is at least one other property of delayed feedback that

---

[9] Guthrie (1952) makes a distinction between an act and the movements it comprises. The foregoing discussion suggests that an analysis in terms of operant chains, derived from consideration of acts, may be fruitful in the analysis of the movements Guthrie regarded as critical.

merits its experimental interest. This concerns the logical relation between responses and stimuli. The former are the dependent and the latter are the independent variables in most psychological research. Where the reinforcing *agency* is outside the organism, the agency can program the stimuli in a variety of ways, and observe the functional relations between the independent variables he manipulates and the dependent variable of behavior. Where the reinforcing *agency*, however, is not of this kind, that is, in the case of response-produced stimuli of the microecology, the dependent and independent variables become behaviorally contaminated, that is, the independent variable (the stimulus) becomes dependent upon the dependent variable (the response) rather than being controlled by E, whose control and analysis become devious, within a behavioral framework. By using delayed feedback, E withholds the stimulus produced by the response and can manipulate it, thereby making it an independent variable, analogous to the other situation, in which he controls this variable.

For these reasons, and others related to the effects of delay upon the microstructure of speech, we decided to utilize it to attempt to develop a rapid way of alleviating stuttering as a personal problem.

New Response Patterns and the Attenuation of Stuttering

At least two alternative behavioral procedures are theoretically available to alleviate stuttering as a personal problem. One of these may be considered as *correcting* the speech pattern in which stuttering is embedded. An alternative approach involves *substituting* for this pattern some other pattern which does not contain stuttering.

With regard to correction, given some undesirable behavior, there are a variety of means to alter it to a more desirable form. These include attenuating stuttering through extinction or punishment, changing stimulus control, establishing incompatible responses, or any of the at least one dozen methods whose parameters are being investigated in operant laboratories, where modification of behavior is a tool used in the analysis of behavior. Where the undesirable behavior is embedded in more desirable behavior, the proportion of the desirable fluent components may be increased. Again, there are a variety of available procedures. In certain cases, one type of modification procedure may be contraindicated or indicated on a priori grounds, in other cases, a considerable amount of time may have to be spent in behavioral analysis and modification of the behavior to ascertain which is to be used or avoided.

On the other hand, development of entirely new patterns may not require such extensive analysis, and a procedure for the development of a pattern devoid of stuttering was the elimination-avoidance of delay procedure found to be effective in the present investigations. The fact that this pattern had unusual components, such as prolongation, does not necessarily contraindicate its use, since procedures exist which can eliminate such undesirable features.

Consideration of stuttering as an operant means that it must be considered as being under stimulus control.[10] Stated otherwise, the new patterns developed may be specific only to the laboratory, with S stuttering in his old haunts. It may also be added, however, that corrective procedures may also produce a speech pattern which is also under stimulus control, and is confined to the clinic. Accordingly, additional procedures may be required in either case to ex-

---

[10] Stimulus control rather than genetics may be involved in the observation that stuttering sometimes runs in families. At our home, the children often yell for their father. An ordinary conversation call of "Daddy" may initially have occasioned no response. The call was made continually louder until he responded. Their mother, who had answered immediately, is not yelled for. The yelling is under stimulus control, that is, it occurs under one set of conditions and not another, because of differences in systematically scheduled consequences under these different conditions. We may envisage another case, where the call of "D-d-daddy" has no immediate answer forthcoming, and so on, until a full fledged "D-d-d-d-d-daddy" provides attention. Such shaping of nonfluencies may typically not be systematic; that is, on the following day, it may be extinguished, and other behavioral patterns may be reinforced. Where, however, these is a relative who stutters, or familial circumstances exist which focus attention upon nonfluencies, differential attention may be applied to fluency-nonfluency, thereby establishing these as response classes. In this case, defining stuttering as a problem, made more probable by the existence of relatives who stutter, may actually produce the problem. Other social consequences of stuttering will be discussed in this report.

The behavior may not only be under the stimulus control of different social audiences, but also of the audience which is the speaker himself; that is, the different stimuli produced by one's own voice when one speaks in different ways. This may underlie the reports of stutterers who do not stutter when they sing or declaim on the stage (the audience, as well as the voice, may differ here), or speak to their dog (who does not apply differential consequences to fluency-nonfluency), or in a foreign language, and so on (cf. Bloodstein, 1950).

tend the behavior from the conditions in which it was established to the more general conditions outside the laboratory or clinic. It may also be, in both cases, that the establishment of speech without blockages may generate new consequences and conditions on the outside which serve to maintain it there. Interestingly, stutterers on their own often develop both procedures, developing glides and other methods of overcoming blockages, or substituting in conversation words on which they do not block for words on which they do.

Both corrective and substitutive procedures require analysis of the variables maintaining the behavior outside the clinic or laboratory, but *within* these settings, the corrective procedure requires an additional analysis which the substitutive procedure may circumvent. Accordingly, we decided to establish an entirely new verbal pattern for the stutterers, and to proceed from there. The program adhered to is presented in the following outline; the specific experimental procedures and their rationale are combined thereafter under headings paralleling the program outline.

1. Establishment of a New Response Pattern. A new pattern of verbal behavior would be established, in which stuttering had not been differentially reinforced. Optimally, such a pattern should be strikingly different from the normal pattern.

2. Altering the Stimulus Control of the New Pattern. Since behavior is under stimulus control, and the stimuli that produced this pattern are not in the general environment, the ratio of special conditions (which established the behavior) to more general conditions would be decreased in a systematically programed manner, derived from experimental research.

3. Shaping the Response Pattern to Normal Speech. This pattern, being an odd one, would then be gradually shaped to a pattern which has the formal characteristics of standard speech.

4. Self-control Procedures. Procedures would then be programed to have this speech carried out of the laboratory and used wherever the previous patterns had been used. The regular reinforcers that maintain normally fluent speech might then maintain and strengthen this new pattern, just as they do normally fluent speech. Thus, although S returns to his old haunts, it is a different environment by virtue of its alteration by an altered operant.

The program was implemented by the following specific procedures, the experimental rationale or evidence for which is given in each case:

Establishment of a New Speech Pattern

Prolongation. The new speech pattern should be one whose direction E can control, so that he can shape it into standard speech, in accord with the requirements of Step 3 in the program. Of the four possible novel patterns which may emerge under delay (prolongation, voice lowering, proprioceptive increase, tuning out), prolongation lends itself most readily to shaping, since control equipment and response definition are currently superior in this case than with the other patterns. Nevertheless, since alternative response patterns are available to S under delay, special procedures are required to produce a specified one. At least the following procedures are available:

Running S until prolongation occurs: Where prolongation occurred in the experimental analysis reported, its establishment took a great deal of time. Since other competing patterns may also be maintained by the delay, letting delay take its own course is contraindicated.

Instructing S to prolong: This depends on the degree to which S is under the control of instructions. Since instructions are discriminative stimuli, their control is governed by differential consequences attached to obedience-disobedience. Under appropriate conditions, instructions are a very rapid and efficient way to control behavior. They are both utilized and omitted in the course of this investigation.

Pacing the discriminative stimuli: Various devices exist for presenting reading material at different rates. Such rates may be compared with rates when S reads at his own pace. The author (*Goldiamond, 1962c*) has put pulses of the PerceptoScope, which present successive displays of reading material, under the control of S's button. The cumulative recorder activated presents an ongoing record of oral and silent reading rate. Figure 22 presents such data.

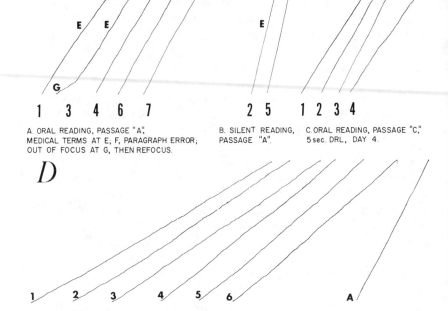

A. ORAL READING, PASSAGE "A",
MEDICAL TERMS AT E, F, PARAGRAPH ERROR;
OUT OF FOCUS AT G, THEN REFOCUS.

B. SILENT READING,
PASSAGE "A".

C. ORAL READING, PASSAGE "C,"
5 sec. DRL, DAY 4.

D. REPEATED ORAL READING, PASSAGE "D"; I-6, 9 YEAR OLD GIRL; A, COLLEGE GIRL, SAME PASSAGE.

FIGURE 22

Cumulative curves of ongoing oral (A, C, D) and silent (B) reading
rates obtained through procedures discussed in text.

Sessions at B are of silent reading of the same material read aloud
at A; other variations are depicted in the illustration. These procedures were used in the present research. Other recording devices
for the same purpose, to be assayed, are voice-operated relays and
pause or duration analyzers. In contrast to the other procedures,
pace itself can be manipulated.

Dynamic control over prolongation: The foregoing equipment
may also be used to activate devices that supply differential reinforcement for different rates and forms. Curve 4 at C in Figure 22

depicts the effects of differential reinforcement for low rates. Such control may take considerable time to establish. Neither this procedure nor aversive control was utilized here.

Delayed Feedback in the Establishment of Novel Patterns. Delayed feedback has certain properties (*Fairbanks, 1955*) which suggest its use in the development of novel speech. It interferes with the microstructure of speech and forces a new pattern. Among the nonprolongation patterns it establishes are those involving greater muscular control, which may be utilized to improve articulation. Finally, in terms of Step 2 of the program presented, it can gradually be faded out.

It will be recalled that prolonged and stutter-free speech was produced under the procedure involving elimination-avoidance of delay. Assuming that prolongation has been established, the following three possible consequences may be systematically related to verbal patterns under the elimination-avoidance procedure:

1. Normally fluent speech ———→ delayed feedback, disruption
2. Normal stuttering speech ———→ normal feedback of stuttering
3. Prolonged novel fluent speech → delayed feedback, no disruption

It will be noted that possibility 3, prolonged novel fluent speech, is the aim of the program presented in the preceding section. Regarding patterns 1 and 2, it is presumed that the depicted consequences of both patterns of speech normally available to the stutterer, fluency and nonfluency, are aversive, describing a classical avoidance–avoidance conflict. If, however, the speech pattern is prolonged, the delay is not disruptive, and this pattern is thereby established and maintained. Being a novel pattern in which stuttering was never differentially reinforced, it is free of stuttering. In effect, this pattern produces continual delay, since there are no blockages to turn off the delay. It remains to be seen if continual delay alone (without the contingency) has the same effect. Given such a novel pattern, whatever blockages occur may extinguish if no differential consequences are attached to them. The course of extinction of a response differs from its attenuation by punishment (supplying an aversive consequence upon its occurrence, the present case). Holz and Azrin (*1963*) report more rapid attenuation by the latter procedure — under different circumstances, however.

Altering the Stimulus Control of the New Pattern

Once the new pattern is established, the delayed feedback which was involved in its instatement may be gradually faded out, from 250 ms, in gradual steps to no delay. In the early cases to be reported, the delay was initially decreased in daily decrements of 50 ms; in later cases decreases occurred *within* the session. If the new behavior is then sustained without its initiating stimuli, like the grin on the Cheshire cat after the cat had vanished, the verbal behavior is transferred to the control of stimuli closer to those normally present. This procedure is borrowed from programed instruction, which initially borrowed it from animal research on successive approximations. It has been re-extended into animal research (*Terrace, 1963*) and has been adapted for the errorless establishment of difficult discriminations in children (*Moore and Goldiamond, 1964*).

Shaping the Response Pattern to Normal Speech

Where the new prolonged behavior is maintained without the delayed feedback, the reading rate may now be speeded up, by machine control of the presentations, through appropriately programed steps, to normal and supernormal rates.

Should the verbal behavior at any moment deteriorate to its previous patterns, *E* may retreat, and reinstate the supporting conditions which had been withdrawn.

Self-Control Procedures

The S may now be instructed to observe his own speech patterns, and use them on the outside, under conditions which will be discussed under a separate heading. Self-control procedures are to be distinguished from generalization procedures, in which other stimuli assumed to be more general may be introduced, or control is transferred from one set of discriminative stimuli to another through stimulus manipulation by *E* (as in Step 3). In self-control, the S is instructed to analyze the functional relations between his behaviors and the conditions under which they occur, and to change his environment in a manner likely to optimize the desired changes in his behavior. Accordingly, considerable cooperation is required from S. The author has been utilizing this procedure in counseling with regard to a variety of personal problems, such as study behaviors, obesity, and marital problems. The present paper will report their extension to stuttering.

Results

At the present writing,[11] these procedures have been applied to eight successive Ss, all stutterers with a prolonged history of stuttering, and in all eight cases there has been complete elimination of stuttering within the laboratory, with reading rate far more rapid than previously (in one case, four times as high). The speech is well articulated, and is considered pleasant by listeners, that is, there are no sing-song, delayed, or otherwise unpleasant patterns. This behavior has carried over outside the laboratory in certain of the cases. A more detailed description follows.

Preliminary Cases

The first Ss on whom the procedures were tried were referrals from the Speech Clinic at Arizona State University;[12] they had a long history of differing treatments for a perseverating problem. They sat in a specially constructed booth, their speech was monitored outside it, and from tapes thereafter, using control and recording equipment more precise than in the preceding analysis. They were run during the 1962–1963 academic year, for 3 days a week, for approximately 50 minutes a day. Initially, they read from pages projected at a rate governed by their own ad-lib depressions of the button, which successively exposed about 3.2 words per response. After a stabilization period, they were instructed to depress a second button for each word on which they stuttered. The delayed feedback elimination-avoidance procedure was then introduced. Instructions to slow down were varied. At a later period, the timer was set to pulse the reading material at the new low rate they had established ad lib, and the reading rate button was with-

[11] December, 1963.

[12] The author wishes to express his appreciation to Dr. Robert Albright, professor of speech, and chairman, who made the referrals and whose cooperation in innumerable ways made this part of the study possible.

drawn. The delayed feedback was later faded out, and the reading presentation rate was then speeded up. Instructions to extend the speech outside the laboratory were also varied.

Since these two cases were the earliest in which the procedure outlined was applied, many more sessions than later proved necessary were run. About 70 sessions extending over 7 months were run, with a change being made only after the author was assured of stability.

The author did not communicate with the Ss, but affected their conditions through instructions to the monitors after examination of the records.[13]

Subject WD. A summary of the performance and procedures for this S is presented in Figure 23. The ordinate is logarithmic. During the initial baseline period, except for 1 day of very rapid reading, the rate was about 110 (words per minute). Stuttering rate during the same period was about 15 wpm, except for the high-reading day, which was accompanied by a high nonfluency rate, as well. At session 22, self-definition of stuttering was introduced; there was an immediate but transient decline in both rates. At session 34, the elimination-avoidance procedure was introduced, with S instructed to slow his reading. Reading rate dropped to about 70 wpm, but stuttering rate plummeted to about 3 wpm, and continued to drop, remaining thereafter at less than 1 wpm, except for 1 day, when the material included difficult medical terms (MED in the illustration). At session 47, timer control of the reading rate was instituted at 78 wpm. Four sessions later, the 250 ms delayed feedback was cut to 200 ms and then in successive days to 150, 100, 50, 50, 20, 20, 20, (the 20 ms series was an unnecessary precaution) and finally it was eliminated completely. Since stuttering was still almost nonexistent, reading rate was speeded up, and then again, to 140 wpm, well above the previous baseline. Stuttering was not reinstated, but ranged between 0.2 and 0.6 wpm.

The S was informed of his progress, and was instructed to practice his new pattern of speech with his wife, with his friends, and during classes. He delivered an extensive talk in an education

[13] The research assistants were Mr. Larry Nims and Mr. Robert Moore, graduate students in the Department of Psychology, to whom the author wishes to express his appreciation. Special equipment was constructed for the project by Mr. Robert Dickie of the Physics Laboratory.

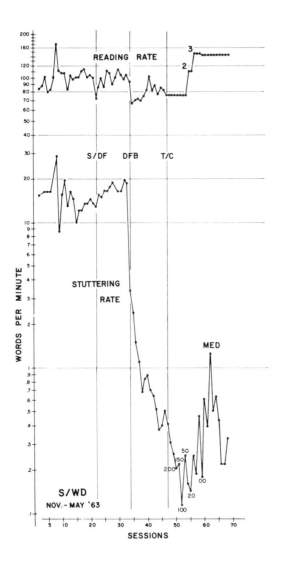

FIGURE 23

The virtual elimination of stuttering and establishment of a better-than-normal reading rate in a chronic stutterer, the first S subjected to the applied programed procedures that were derived from the preceding experimental analysis.

class, without nonfluencies, and both he and his wife reported that he was "cured."

Subject LD. Initial reading rate was about 100 wpm, and non-fluency rate 15 wpm. The results and procedures are presented in the form of fluent words read per nonfluent word in Figure 24, the ordinate of which is logarithmic. There was an initial declining trend in verbal efficiency, as defined by this ratio. At session 20, self-definition was introduced, and there was a transient drop in reading rate, stuttering rate, and efficiency. The elimination-avoidance procedure was introduced at session 31; S did not slow down, with no definite change in trend noted. At session 49, he was instructed to slow down his reading rate, and there was an immediate drop in nonfluencies (with rate between 1.5 and 2.5 wpm) and also in reading rate (between 30 and 40 wpm), but the efficiency ratio rose considerably. At session 64, reading rate was switched to the timer, at 34 wpm; nonfluencies dropped to about 0.5 wpm, and the efficiency ratio rose markedly. Delayed feedback was then faded out to 200, 150, 100, 50, and 0 ms; the low stuttering rate was maintained. Reading rate was raised in successive stages lasting 3 days each to 120 wpm. Stuttering rate continued low, and on the last day, he was reading well over 2500 words fluently for each non-fluent word read.

No instructions were given S about behavior on the outside, and he reported no changes; he volunteered the information that he should have tried his new speech pattern outside.

Later Cases[14]

The procedures described are being extended for other cases being run at the Institute for Behavioral Research. Curves from two S's will be presented.

---

[14] The research reported in this section and thereafter, on stuttering and counseling, is being performed under the contract between the Office of the Surgeon General and the Washington School of Psychiatry, mentioned in Footnote 17.

Miss Evelyn Wetzler, a speech major who spent the 1963–1964 academic year at I.B.R., served as monitor and research assistant in all phases of this project, and contributed immeasurably to its progress. The author also wishes to express his appreciation to Mr. Peter Edmondo for assistance in the instrumentation.

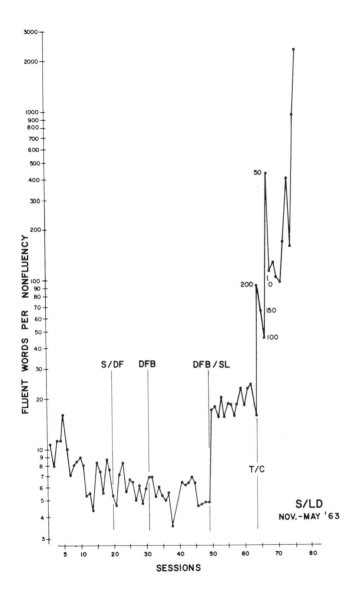

FIGURE 24

Ratio of fluent to stuttered words in the second S subjected to applied procedures, as a function of programed treatment.

Subject EZ. This S was the first run at I.B.R. He is a pronounced stutterer of long standing, as indicated in Figure 25; the ordinate presents words stuttered per minute, but words read should be multiplied by 10. Reading rate aloud averaged about 45 wpm, of which *almost half exhibited nonfluencies!* Stuttering rate rose during the baseline period with both stuttering and reading rate exhibiting a transient drop during the introduction of self-definition. At session 14, the elimination-avoidance procedure was introduced, with a resulting drop in nonfluency rate, and a slight drop in reading rate. Timer control of reading presentation was introduced on the following day; the stuttering rate dropped to zero. At session 16, the timer-controlled reading rate was dropped to 20 wpm, where it remained for 4 days, and was raised to 34 wpm the following 4 days, during which period the delayed feedback was also faded out. On session 23, the first day of no delay, three different rates were presented within the same session; S continued not to stutter at 50 wpm, the highest rate. At the next session, he was started at 72 wpm, then raised to 102 wpm, *then to 204 wpm,* a rate he reports never having attained in his life, with no stuttering.

On the following day, he was started at the same high rate, but immediately started stuttering. He was accordingly quickly dropped to 110, and the stuttering disappeared; he was then raised again, as indicated in the illustration.

This S's data indicate that merely increasing reading rate will not attenuate stuttering and can, on the contrary, reinstate it; it suggests the importance of appropriate programing and observation of S's behavior. During one of the slow reading sessions, S read each presented phrase at a fairly rapid rate, and then paused until the next presentation. He was told that if he did this, the forthcoming speedup might merely compress the pause rather than affect his speech, and was told to prolong the phrases so that he filled up all the time available, which he did.

The S's reading in the booth is at a level never attained before, and without stuttering. Articulation and intelligibility are very high. Self control procedures are in progress.

Subject JF. This S had to leave town in two weeks and, accordingly, condensed procedures were tried; there was one baseline day, 2 days under additional self-definition, and thereafter the

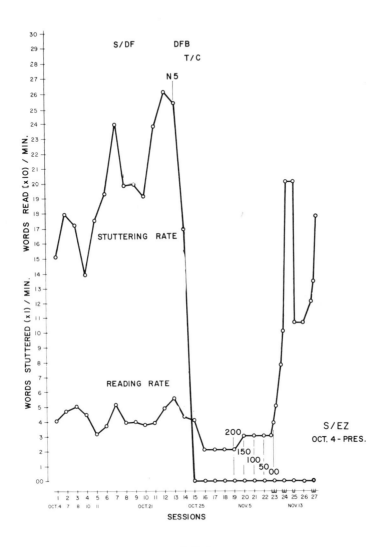

FIGURE 25

Laboratory elimination of stuttering and quadrupling of reading rate
in a very severe stutterer, the third S tried.

elimination-avoidance procedure was introduced. Fading of delay was introduced 3 days thereafter. As can be seen in Figure 26, stuttering rate became zero. On the first day of no delay, reading rate was raised twice within the session. On the second day, it was started at a lower rate (the E having learned from the preceding case), and then raised twice, *to a final 256 words per minute,* which was also sustained on the following day.

The S remained in town an extra day, during which E prescribed exercises for him at home. These involved reading very slowly for 1 minute, then reading rapidly, for another minute. His wife was then to join him and ask him questions about the material read (so that the same words might be used), and then switch to other conversation for a total of 5 minutes. During all this time he was to use his booth voice. A metronome was prescribed as a pacer, along with a hand counter for nonfluencies. These morning exercises were to be extended gradually to cover increasing sections of the day.

The S was delayed in getting the equipment, and decided to speed things up on his own (he had taken the I.B.R. course on behavior analysis). He has reported that he now sounds "like John Gielgud, without the accent" — and tapes corroborate this evaluation.

Standardized Procedure

By now, a fairly standardized procedure has emerged for behavior modification within the booth. It is exemplified by the following 3 S's.

S-A. The S is a 40-year-old male, professional, who came in three times a week after work. His schedule (reading words per minute [wpm] and nonfluency words per minute [spm] are in parentheses) was as follows: 3 days Baseline (107 wpm, 6 spm); 3 days Self-definition (112 wpm, 1.3 spm); 3 days Elimination-Avoidance Delay, Reading Rate machine-controlled (30 wpm, 0.2 spm); 5 days Fadeout Delay (30 wpm, 0 spm). On the following days, reading rate was altered within sessions, each cluster representing a day: 30–51; 102–245; 120–245; 30–185. The final rates are above his baseline ad-lib rate. There were no nonfluencies at all. On the last

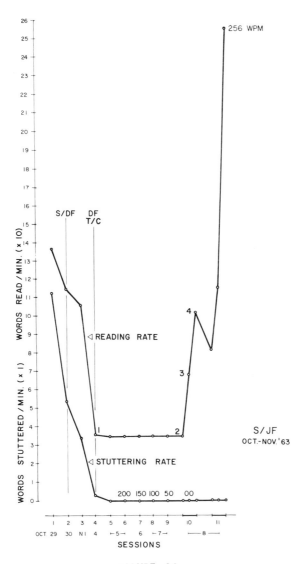

FIGURE 26

Typical results being obtained in laboratory using condensed standardized procedure developed at request of S with only two weeks
available for treatment.

day of the regular sessions, he requested a "reminder" of speech under delay, and he was given a few minutes under 200 ms delay.

The S is now on a schedule of home exercises. For the first week, he read for 2 minutes at both a slow and a normal rate, and engaged in immediate conversation thereafter for 1 minute; during the second week, the conversation was raised to 2 minutes; it is now 5 minutes, with next week's assignment scheduled for persisting in this manner all morning. Nonfluencies are recorded by S and an observer; they have averaged 1, with a range of 0–3. Reading rate per day during the ad-lib part of the first week was 112, 130, 135, 138, 130; during the second week it was 147, 148, 159, 153, 152, 148.

The S turns in his records once a week during which he and E discuss changes in procedures. He reports that his work associates have asked him what happened to his stuttering, and tapes of conversations in the laboratory and with E validate these queries, as does the referral source.

S-B.   The S is a female high school junior, whose father brings her in three times a week after work. Her schedule was as follows: 2 days Baseline (171 wpm, 5.5 spm); 3 days Self-definition (153 wpm, 2.5 spm); 3 days Elimination-Avoidance Delay, Reading Rate machine-controlled (30 wpm, 0 spm); 5 days Fadeout Delay (30 wpm, 0 spm). Reading rate altered within sessions, with each cluster a day: 30–102–204; 121–204; 51–204. Final rates were beyond her baseline, and there was no stuttering at all. The S has been given home assignments.

S-C.   The S is a college junior, majoring in foreign languages, for whom stuttering is a problem, since he also stuttered in these classes. He came daily. He was one of the earlier S's; his baseline was accordingly protracted: 7 days Baseline (151 wpm, 6 spm); 4 days Self-definition (157 wpm, 3 spm); 3 days Elimination-Avoidance Delay, Reading Rate machine-controlled (30 wpm, 0 spm); Fadeout Delay (30 wpm, 0 spm); Reading Rate altered within sessions, 51–64; 102–136–204; 102–143–224; 102–157–204; no nonfluencies within these sessions.

The S reported he was no longer stuttering in his English speaking classes, but was stuttering in his foreign-language classes. He was instructed to bring his French book into the booth, and read from that, averaging 2 spm. Accordingly, he was given the Elimina-tion-Avoidance Delay procedure, with Delay set at 50 ms. There were no nonfluencies at all during this period, nor during the next 4 days when Delay was removed. He was instructed to read from his German book in the booth; there were no nonfluencies. On the following day, he read both German and French, with 50 ms Elim-ination-Avoidance Delay, and French on the next day without De-lay. There were no nonfluencies. Two days of rapid English read-ing paced by the machine then followed, and when he read French on the third day, his nonfluency rate was 2 spm; he read 10 minutes under 50 ms Elimination-Avoidance Delay, then without it. There were no nonfluencies then, nor have there been seen any since then. His ad-lib reading rate in French is now 93 wpm. Most recently, he read *Fathers and Sons* at 186 wpm, in a section containing many Russian names. He reported that he was being pushed, felt under tension and strain — but there were no nonfluencies. He has been using his new speech pattern in such readings, in discussions with E, and reports using it at school. The new speech pattern is well articulated. He has been given home assignments.

Summary

Other cases are under way; the information they contain is redun-dant. There is an almost total elimination of nonfluencies upon in-troduction of the Elimination-Avoidance Delay procedure, coupled with machine control of Reading Rate (to 34 wpm). The non-fluency rate is maintained when the Delay is faded out. It is also maintained when the reading rate is then speeded up beyond the baseline rate. It has been possible to get Ss to use the speech pat-terns outside the laboratory, and there have been consistent reports of improvement from referral sources as well as from others. All sessions, including discussions in the office, are taped and these reveal a similar trend.

Some Questions Raised

The program mentioned follows the course of much medical research, where an attempt is made to establish and control some phenomenon within the laboratory (often with animals), to develop procedures which alleviate the problem, and then to engage in further analysis to refine and simplify the procedures so that they may be used in practice, and so that practice becomes more of an applied science, and less of an art.

Several questions with regard to the application of the procedure and its refinement for practice may be raised. Among these are: Is prolongation the most advisable new behavior from which to shape the new patterns — could others serve as well? Probably, but shaping conversational speech out of, say, singing, may require considerable skill on the part of the practitioner; in the present procedures, it is the machine which is skilled. If prolongation is used, is delayed feedback necessary in its establishment — could not instructions or other prolongation procedures, alone, or in ensemble, do the job? One consequence of delayed feedback which has already been mentioned is its control of more precise articulation. Metronomes have been used in the past, but these may produce sing-song patterns. Can explicit procedures be developed to avert this? It may very well be that for some cases, the delay is required, and that others may yield to lesser treatment. Is the Elimination-Avoidance procedure necessary or would continual delay, accompanied by instructions, do the job? Should conversation, rather than reading, be programed in the booths? Other applied questions may be raised which can be answered only by further research. Some of the basic research questions generated have been raised during the report. Nevertheless, the current procedures are effective and rapid in their control over the elimination of stuttering, and the development of fluent and rapid verbal behavior. It is our intention during the next months to refine these procedures, along the lines of the questions raised, as well as others.

Secondary Gain and Self-Control

The author has frequently been asked if he has investigated the likelihood that stuttering is supplying secondary gain, that is, that it manipulates the environment favorably some way, and that if this behavioral method of manipulation is removed, S may establish some other undesirable behavior to achieve the same results. Frequently, the question is made in the form of an assertion, namely, that some other undesirable behavior *will* develop. The assertion assumes as fact what is a model, namely, that behavior is like water filling a tightly closed container. Since water is not readily compressible, pushing in a bulge in one place to straighten out the side will only produce another bulge elsewhere. The author would like to see some actuarial data here, for example, in how many cases when stuttering was eliminated without personal therapy did, say, a tic replace it, and in how many cases not? Or, on the other hand, in how many cases did eliminating the stuttering also eliminate shyness and make the person's hold on his environment far more effective? Barring such data, the author's inclination is to view stuttering as a problem which can have considerable consequences, inasmuch as our major means of controlling our environment is through communicating with people. When S requests relief from this problem, and such relief can be rapidly provided, suffice unto the day the good thereof.

The question of secondary gain has some legitimate properties. It assumes that stuttering is an operant, namely, that it is maintained by differential consequences attached to fluency-nonfluency. It also assumes that stuttering may be a symptom. This term is currently in disrepute in behavioral research, inasmuch as it has often been used to suggest some deep, nonbehavioral state underlying the behavior. If, however, we examine the conditions of its usage, it may be a very valuable term. When, for example, the dermatologist says that a skin rash is a symptom of blood imbalance, he indicates that *rather than primarily treating the distress which brought the patient to the clinic, he will treat something else*, in this case, the blood. By this reasoning, if we state that stuttering is symptomatic, we state that rather than treating only the stuttering behavior which brought S to the clinic, we shall also go about trying to change some other behaviors in the process of treatment. The author would regard this possibility as legitimate, but would insist that it not be an article of faith. In some cases, treatment of the stuttering may make S more effective, and in other cases it may not. The author's working assumption has been that both approaches may be necessary, depending on the case.

Psychotherapy and counseling are classical approaches to behavior modification, and considerable attention has been devoted to operant control of events within the session; the verbal behavior of the patient may be affected by contingencies supplied by the therapist (*Krasner, 1958b*), and it can probably also be shown that in this reciprocal relation, the therapist himself can come under the control of the patient, a situation which is not unfamiliar to therapists. Unfortunately, very little attention has been devoted to the relation between the fine details of verbal interchanges within the hour, and the fine details of behavioral alterations outside, which is the ultimate test of the effectiveness of psychotherapy and counseling. This question was raised in the present research with reference to elimination of stuttering outside the booths. The practice sessions mentioned in the assignments given to Ss are one procedure for such carry-over.

Another procedure involves self-control. This consists in training S to recognize those behaviors of his which he wants to modify. Rather than telling him to modify them (something which he may have already told himself), he is trained in the experimental analysis of behavior, and also in the variables which maintain it, or which he can recruit to modify it. He gets regular weekly reading assignments in a private tutorial. The S's behavior is the laboratory, demonstration, or focus of discussion, along with the standard experimental animals discussed in the assigned text. The procedure may be summarized in the form of the following question: if a pigeon were exhibiting these behaviors, and you wanted to get rid of them (as in stuttering) or wanted to establish new ones (as in marital or study counseling), how would you go about programing the environment to do so? The weekly therapy sessions then become research conferences, as though between a professor and his research associate on what has to be done next to bring the organism's behavior into line. The S is the acknowledged expert in the content of the field — his own behavior and its ecology — and E brings to bear on the problem his knowledge of procedures and past effects. Eventually, as in a good professorial relation, S may become an independent investigator, capable of tending to things on his own.

The sessions start with a delineation of the problem, and S is then asked: "Under what conditions do you stutter?" He typically has a ready answer — when he is anxious, threatened, or the like. One answer was: "When my thoughts outrace my ability to put them into words." Leaving aside the referents of these answers, one must question their usefulness as research guides or as guides to modification.[15] The question may then be rephrased by *E* in a form such as: What are the environmental conditions under which you stutter (feel anxious, have thoughts outracing your words, etc.)? Are there (a) any events which occasion these responses, and (b) any particular consequences occurring in the environment as a result of your stuttering which might not occur otherwise? The answers to *these* questions not only provide a basis for further analysis and modification but are illuminating in their own right.

One S reported that he stuttered when called upon in class for an

[15] We are considering stuttering as *behavior* whose modification is an aim of the therapist. It has been argued that anxiety (for example) underlies this behavior, and that the way to eliminate it is to alleviate the anxiety, often by altering the personality structure. Indeed, patients do report seeking help because of *feelings* which disturb them. It can be argued that such disturbance is related to behavioral deficits, which, when remedied, are accompanied by altered feelings. Behaviors are observable, both to *E* and S, their consequences are observable, and alterations in both are also observable. The S may be trained in more precise observation and in procedures for altering the environment and observing its effects on behavior.

The feelings of S, on the other hand, are unobservable to *E* and it can also be argued that their definition or validity of observation by S himself raises serious questions. In the perception of color, the term "blue" may be assigned by S to his own experience by virtue of a common referent, a wave length, he shares with the verbal community which differentially reinforces the term "blue" in its presence (*cf. Graham, 1959; Skinner, 1957*). A communicable definition of color experience is taught. Feelings lack such ready common referents. Communication to *E* is hazardous, and since *E* is but a special representative of the verbal community, the referent of the verbal term when S uses it to define it to himself also becomes questionable.

A basic datum becomes S's verbal statement of feeling, which can be observed by others, but if this is considered as being an indicator of perception, or having a perceptual referent (of feeling), the author can only reiterate his previous statement (*Goldiamond, 1962b*) that credence in the verbal response is among the least valid indicators of perception. The verbal statement, however, is an operant, and may manipulate the environment, including the therapist. Conceivably, as long as such manipulation occurs, the behavioral deficit which is the major problem may remain uncorrected. And correction may require greater effort than the present control.

Focusing on behavior and its consequences may also involve long-term changes equivalent to those involved in altering personality structure. But by dealing directly with observables, their relations, and their alteration, such focus may sidestep the thorny definitional problems raised in the feelings and their alteration. And to the extent that feelings of, say, inadequacy are attributable to behavioral deficits, alteration of behavior may alter the feelings which brought S to the clinic.

immediate answer. If he stuttered, the teacher waited patiently, giving him more time to formulate an answer, something he might not get otherwise. The military adviser whose thought outraced his words stated that the stuttering provided the time for him to catch up — an answer identical to the college student's. Stuttering was also reported as serving another avoidance function, in that the stuttering student found himself called on less often. Stuttering had an even more interesting effect: when the college student stuttered and *gave the wrong answer,* he was not corrected. In his own words: "People feel that you stutter because you are nervous, and they're not going to make you any more nervous by telling you you're wrong." The military adviser said he stuttered when he contradicted himself, that is, started out with one set of statements, and wound up with opposing ones. This is under similar control by a sympathetic audience. In another case, S reported stuttering when (a) a verbal response was required, that is, its absence would get aversive consequences, and when (b) the only verbal response immediately available was one which was likely to produce aversive consequences. The stuttering then produced neither aversive consequence from the audience. Our experience has convinced us that the world can be considered as being in a conspiracy to maintain stuttering, out of ingrained decency and respect for others' tribulations. Being "indecent" in these circumstances is no help, since S may go elsewhere, where the consequences will be favorable. One S's report indicated that his stuttering was maintained by positive rather than negative reinforcement: polite attention was commanded during stuttering, and no one left the group or interrupted him while he was stuttering.

That these response patterns can come under increasing environmental control, where they start to take over increasing amounts of verbal behavior, is quite evident to Ss, hence their application for treatment. None of the foregoing should be read to imply that the secondary gain is deliberate: the behavior comes under environmental control because of differential consequences, and may, through intermittent reinforcement (*Ferster and Skinner, 1957*), occur when the consequences are absent. Where the stuttering is avoidance behavior, it will be maintained by absence of differential consequences, as in the second experiment cited, where the normally fluent S continued his nonfluencies when the shock was turned off. To attenuate such behaviors on the outside may require procedures differing from cases where it is maintained by reinforcement. Other cases, in which S has "learned to live with his stuttering," that is, commands the appropriate reinforcers despite his stuttering, may require yet other behavioral procedures.

It can be argued that in the case of the college student, the stuttering was symptomatic of his insecurity in class. Restated procedurally, to work appropriately with this S one must develop efficient study patterns and procedures for school work — in addition to attenuating his stuttering. This is precisely what is being done, with the cooperation of S, who is also displaying initiative in suggesting further leads. Where the verbal behavior is weak (as it is in children), procedures may be required to strengthen it (through acquiring mastery of the subject matter being discussed, for example). Where S's consequences are aversive for not speaking and aversive for his only available response, the procedures involved may call for making other responses available. Competing responses may also weaken speech.[16]

By this time, it will be gathered that considerable behavioral modification may be involved in treatment of stuttering, and that every step in the self-control procedure is public knowledge to S. The aims, procedures, and rationale are explicitly spelled out to S in advance of the sessions (including those in the booth), and thereafter. This explicit analysis is helpful in the self-control of this behavior, and in personal explorations of ways in which to modify it. As the author has stated elsewhere, Ss involved may have "licked their own problems and have provided their own solutions. . . . Thus, paradoxically, the application of self-control procedures derived from controlled laboratory research can supply the fulfillment of the aims of those clinical psychologists who pride themselves on effecting change through providing greater freedom for the client" (*Goldiamond, 1963*). Hopefully, such explicit analysis may provide

---

[16] The maintaining variables cited are not intended to be exhaustive, but are merely those thus far suggested by S's themselves. It should also be pointed out that continual punishment may also maintain behavior — if it is the discriminative stimulus for at least occasional reinforcement (*Holz and Azrin, 1961*).

procedures for social explorations of ways to modify stuttering behavior, and other behaviors of clinical import, of which stuttering
may be considered but one example.[17]

REFERENCES

Bilger, R. C., and C. E. Speaks, "Operant Control of Non-Fluent Speech in
Normal Talkers," *Asha*, 1959, 1, 97. (Abstract)

Black, J. W., "The Persistence of the Effects of Delayed Side-Tone,"
J. speech hear. Disord., 1955, 20, 65–68.

Bloodstein, O., "Hypothetical Conditions under Which Stuttering is Reduced or Absent," *J. speech hear. Disord.*, 1950, 15, 142–153.

Fairbanks, G., "Selective Vocal Effects of Delayed Auditory Feedback,"
J. speech hear. Disord., 1955, 20, 333–346.

Ferster, C. B., and B. F. Skinner, *Schedules of Reinforcement*. New York:
Appleton-Century-Crofts, 1957.

Flanagan, B., I. Goldiamond, and N. H. Azrin, "Operant Stuttering: The
Control of Stuttering Behavior through Response-Contingent Consequences," *J. exp. Anal. Behav.*, 1958, 1, 173–178.

Flanagan, B., I. Goldiamond, and N. H. Azrin, "Instatement of Stuttering
in Normally Fluent Individuals through Operant Procedures," *Science*,
1959, 130, 979–981.

Goldiamond, I., "The Temporal Development of Fluent and Blocked
Speech Communication," Air Force Com. Cont. Develpm. Div., T.R.
60–38, 1960.

Goldiamond, I., "The Maintenance of Ongoing Fluent Verbal Behavior
and Stuttering," *J. Mathetics*, 1962, 1, 57–95. (a)

---

[17] This paper was written under contract between the Office of the Surgeon
General, U.S. Army Medical Research and Development Command, and the
Washing School of Psychiatry, DA–49–193–MD–2448, entitled "Study of In-
terviews (Therapeutic and Interrogative) by Operant Conditioning Methods."
Supported by Grant Ns G–450, NASA. Since completion of this chapter, further research has been conducted (under NIH Grant, MH 08876–01, "Operant
Properties of verbal fluency and nonfluency") during which some of the questions raised in the discussion have been answered and new ones have been
raised. The research has led to the development of a set of explicitly specified
procedures, an outgrowth of those mentioned earlier. Our total population of
stutterers upon whom the procedures have been utilized thus far is 30. In all
30 cases, at a specified 50-minute period in the program there has emerged a
fluent pattern of reading which is well-articulated, rapid, and devoid of blockages. The pattern persists for other 50-minute periods thereafter under similar
laboratory conditions.

Goldiamond, I., "Perception." In A. J. Bachrach (Ed.), *The Experimental Foundations of Clinical Psychology*. New York: Basic Books, 1962. (b)

Goldiamond, I., "Machine Definition of Ongoing Silent and Oral Reading Rate," *J. exp. Anal. Behav.*, 1962, 5, 363–367. (c)

Goldiamond, I., "Justified and Unjustified Alarm over Behavioral Control." Paper presented to Annual Convention, American Psychological Association, Philadelphia, September, 1963.

Goldiamond, I., C. J. Atkinson, and R. C. Bilger, "Stabilization of Behavior and Prolonged Exposure to Delayed Auditory Feedback," *Science*, 1962, 135, 437–438.

Graham, C. H., "Color Theory." In S. Koch (Ed.), *Psychology: A Study of a Science*, Vol. I. New York: McGraw-Hill, 1959.

Guthrie, E. R., *The Psychology of Learning* (2d ed.). New York: Harper & Row, 1952.

Holz, W. C., and N. H. Azrin, "Discriminative Properties of Punishment," *J. exp. Anal. Behav.*, 1961, 4, 225–232.

Holz, W. C., and N. H. Azrin, "A Comparison of Several Procedures for Eliminating Behavior," *J. exp. Anal. Behav.*, 1963, 6, 399–406.

Kelleher, R. T., and L. R. Gollub, "A Review of Positive Conditioned Reinforcement," *J. exp. Anal. Behav.*, 1962, 5, 543–597.

Moore, R., and I. Goldiamond, "Errorless Establishment of Visual Discrimination Using Fading Procedures," *J. exp. Anal. Behav.*, 1964, 7, 269–272.

Sidman, M., *Tactics of Scientific Research*. New York: Basic Books, 1960.

Skinner, B. F., *Behavior of Organisms*. New York: Appleton-Century-Crofts, 1938.

Skinner, B. F., *Verbal Behavior*. New York: Appleton-Century-Crofts, 1957.

Terrace, H. S., "Discrimination Learning with and without Errors," *J. exp. Anal. Behav.*, 1963, 6, 1–27.

PART **VIII**

Conclusions

Explicit training procedures based upon a specific learning model raise, as well as answer, many questions. What are the obligations incurred by the teacher who specifically designates in advance the terminal behaviors that he hopes his client will acquire? Are these obligations any different when the goals involve what are usually called "social" or "personal" behaviors than they are when the behavior is what might be called "arithmetic"? Is there any relationship between efficacy and responsibility? Does inability (or unwillingness?) to specify goal behaviors absolve the teacher-clinician from responsibility? It is to questions such as these that Kanfer addresses himself. The final chapter, by Ullmann, is concerned with the relationship of the procedures described in this book to each other, to the overall behavior modification movement, and to general trends in behavioral-clinical areas.

Frederick H. Kanfer

Issues and Ethics in Behavior Manipulation[1]

Summary. — It is assumed that psychological techniques are now available for the modification of human behavior. This paper focuses on the implications of this technological advance for clinical psychology. The dilemma consists in the problem of justifying use of subtle influencing techniques in clinical procedures in the face of the popular assumption of the integrity, dignity and rights to freedom of the patient. The first step in the resolution of this dilemma is the recognition that a therapeutic effort *by necessity* influences the patient's value system as well as his specific symptoms. Control of behavior is wide-spread and historically not a new discovery. It was the purpose of this paper to discuss three features of the psychotherapeutic process which tend to raise ethical as well as scientific problems: (1) the particular methods of control used, (2) the domain of the behavior to be controlled, and (3) the discrepancy between personal values and cultural metavalues. It was noted that methods of psychological con-

[1] An earlier version of this paper was presented at a symposium of the Indiana Psychological Association in Indianapolis, April 1960. The revised paper was written in conjunction with research supported by Research grant MH 06922–03 from the National Institute of Mental Health, United States Public Health Service.

trol appear more dangerous to the public when they are subtle in their influence and when their methods rest on control by rewards or positive reinforcement, rather than on coercion, or physical force. With regard to the domain of behavior to be controlled it was noted that most therapeutic strategies deal with the private, personal and intimate aspects of a person's life. This choice of material results in more powerful control over a person's behavior than material which is easily accessible to the community. Finally, it is pointed out that there are numerous ways in which a person can behave without violating the metavalues of his culture. The specific changes in personal values may be heavily influenced by the therapist. The paper suggested that the social community as a whole and not just the psychologist needs to establish rules within which psychological behavior modifications can be carried out.

Whenever a science is ready to apply its principles or methods to the control of man's social and physical environment, public attention demands that the consequences of such application be carefully examined. This scrutiny often results in argumentative debates and emotional alignment of the public vis-a-vis the science, its contents and its practitioners. The merciless beam of the public spotlight has by no means been confined to psychology. In our own time chemistry, physics and biology have repeatedly provided discoveries which the public viewed and discussed with alarm. Public concern usually declined gradually as scientific contributions were absorbed into the social fabric. Nevertheless, the vigor of recent public reactions to progress in the study and control of human behavior has taken our academically-minded science by surprise. Perhaps the sudden widespread concern with test makers, public opinion swayers, and adjustment manipulators simply indicates that psychology finally may have something to offer which has applicability in everyday life. The hope for eventual development of the psychology of behavioral control also raises the problem of the ethics of manipulating the behavior of another person. The most surprising aspect of the psychologist's dilemma posed by this problem is its recency. After all, the manipulation of behavior reportedly first took place when Eve whetted Adam's appetite in the

Garden of Eden. For centuries the issues of morality and the control of one human being over another either have been kept separated or, in fact, combined in such absurd fashion that the most cruel methods of control were perpetrated under the guise of morality. The slaughter during the crusades, the elimination of witchcraft, the conquest of the American Indian, the "liberation" of Europe by the Nazis represent a few choice historical examples of human misbehavior and the use of the ultimate in behavior control through physical force and extermination. By comparison, the minor infraction committed currently when a psychotherapist subtly alters a neurotic patient's value system or his social behavior patterns seems rather mild. Nevertheless, numerous recent popular articles and books reflect the increasing public concern with the use of psychological methods in education, in industry, in the treatment of the mentally ill, and in politics.

The purpose of this paper is to discuss several issues concerning use of psychological principles in the manipulation of human behavior. These issues may arise in the context of psychology practiced in the clinic, in industry, by the military, or by governments. This paper will focus on behavior control by psychotherapy. The issues concern: (1) the methods of control, (2) the domain of controlled behavior, and (3) the selection of ends for which control is exercised.

Control by Reward Versus Punishment

With regard to the "psychology of behavior control" (*Krasner, 1962a*) in the clinic, the current sensitivity to the ethical issues stems largely from an increased proficiency in the control of behavior, and especially from a fear of one special kind of manipulation.[2] In the past, efforts toward improving control over adult behavior have mainly been directed at finding better methods of aversive control, e.g., by threat, coercion, or physical force. Currently, there is a tendency toward increasing use of control by

[2] While skeptics can point to evidence of current ignorance of even the most common determinants of individual behavior, few will doubt that rapid progress has been made in the last decade. We assume here that modification of individual behavior is feasible, though all the necessary controlling variables are not yet known.

positive reinforcement in all areas of life. This shift to promises, rewards, and seductions rather than coercion represents, in our opinion, the pith of public concern. In his discussion of methods used by controlling agencies, Skinner (1953) suggests that government, law, and religion mainly use practices of threat of punishment, withdrawal of positive reinforcers, or presentation of negative reinforcers to achieve obedience. Further, with use of these methods by social agencies the usual "effect of group control is in conflict with a strong primarily reinforced behavior of the individual" (*Skinner, 1953, p. 327*). In contrast, economic control, education, and psychotherapy rely more heavily on positive reinforcement. Recently, control by positive reinforcement has been used extensively in programs of "ideological totalism" (*Lifton, 1961*). In practice, such control is heightened when used only after achievement of complete control over the individual's environment and thought processes by force. As in laboratory animals, positive reinforcement is most effective following severe deprivation. If such deprivations can be created in human groups, success in behavior control should be markedly enhanced for the possessor of the positive reinforcers. The deliberate application of methods reserved earlier mostly for education, work achievement, child rearing and therapy, in politics and government represents a major innovation. Coupled with extension from control over individuals to control over groups, this advance in control techniques raises serious public concern. The shift in methods of control is illustrated in the history of psychotherapy by the progress from straitjackets, padded cells, and beatings to therapeutic communities, insight therapy, and counter-conditioning.

It is interesting to speculate why control by positive reinforcement might be more dangerous than control by coercion. Manipulation by aversive control creates its own hazards. The person under aversive control usually knows it. He suffers pain, experiences humiliation, anger, or other emotional discomfort. It is also likely that aversive control inevitably breeds attempts at counter-control. Even in the young child the first response to being slapped is to try to slap back. Aversive control thus motivates behavior aimed at reducing such control by annoying, teasing, or destroying the controller. Further, aversive control is difficult to maintain by a small group. To use force effectively you have to be bigger, stronger, or more numerous than your adversary. Thus aversive control by an individual over a large group, or by a small minority is doomed to failure in the long run. Finally, as Skinner (1953) has indicated, aversive control affects only public behavior. It is of limited use in "thought control" because a person can escape some aversive consequences by thinking silently or by nonconforming behavior in his private experiences.

In contrast, manipulation by positive control produces none of these disturbing by-products. By definition these methods use reinforcing stimuli which have the inherent potential for increasing or maintaining behaviors which procure these stimuli. People respond in blind faith to reward, to promises, and to reassurances. Large scale use of these methods, however, has not concerned people because the age-old deceptions of the Pied Piper have been assumed to be sufficiently transparent to allow most adults to recognize them as false promises and to resist temptation by persuasion. Recently, Browning's Pied Piper of Hamlin has become more sophisticated. He has put on the disguise of a gray flannel suit, of a human relationship expert, a psychotherapist, or a friendly interrogator in a prison camp. His pipe has turned into other instruments promising such sweet things as affection and happiness to a juvenile delinquent, money-back guaranteed satisfaction with soaps and cereals, or a political paradise for the masses, all without pain, coercion, or physical violence. This increased professionalism and sophistication in the application of psychological principles has caused uneasiness to the public because the methods have lost some of their transparency and amateurish quality. Although there is contradictory experimental evidence on the question of behavioral modification without awareness (*Eriksen, 1962; Kanfer and Marston, 1961*), these studies also clearly indicate that Ss cannot verbalize all aspects of the controlling stimuli which affect their behavior.

Certainly, the increase in psychological sophistication has also made it easier for the controller to disguise his own motives in order to mislead Ss of his controlling influence. In addition, he can manipulate conditions which would make positive reinforcement more effective. Frank (*1961*) makes this point in discussing the methods of thought reform: "the essence of the relationship is that the persuader invests great effort to bring about changes in the sufferer's bodily state or attitudes that he regards as beneficial . . . (and the setting) . . . occurs in the context of hope and potential support from the persuader and the group" (*1961, p. 95*). Since our democratic principles also uphold the right of consent of the governed, any use of control resulting in a change of behavior without S's awareness of the methods of influence and the intent of his controllers would be ethically objectionable to our society. Even though these emphases placed upon self-control, self-government, and self-determination are accepted by our culture and its scientist members, a deterministic behavioral psychology cannot disavow its implication that behavior is controlled by an organism's previous history and its environment, regardless of its ability to describe verbally these controlling variables. Regardless of ethic or social interest the fiction of the complete Rational Man as the captain of his own destiny, is as naive to behavioristic psychology as it was to Freudian psychoanalysis (although for different reasons).

In psychotherapy, social pressures or other devices attempting to manipulate the patient's behavior by coercion are rarely used as a primary method of control. Therapeutic operations are more likely to stress positive goals, to reduce tensions, to reinforce and strengthen new behaviors. The therapist is, of course, at an additional disadvantage in the use of aversive controls. When the therapist acts as a noxious stimulus the patient can counter by "resistance," by failing to keep his appointments, or by leaving the field altogether. Patients under strong aversive control by parental pressure or by court order are notoriously poor risks for psychotherapy.

Control of Private Experiences

The inevitability of mutual influence in a clinical relationship is well documented by recent research and some of its implications have been discussed by Krasner (*1962a*).

What are some of the features then which make the psychotherapeutic interaction or other similar relationships especially suited for the manipulation or control of behavior?

One factor is the distress and discomfort of the patient. The social role of the patient has been described by Parsons (*Parsons and Fox, 1958*). In our society the sick person can claim certain privileges. It is assumed that he is not responsible for his incapac-

ethics (1953). Principle 1.12–1 (p. 7) reads in part: "the psychologist's ultimate allegiance is to society, and his professional behavior should demonstrate awareness of his social responsibilities. The welfare of the profession and of the individual psychologist are clearly subordinate to the welfare of the public." Further, Principle 1.13–1 (p. 10): "The psychologist should express in his professional behavior a firm commitment to those values which lie at the foundation of a democratic society, such as freedom of speech, freedom of research, and respect for the integrity of the individual." While these statements arouse the unqualified support of all good psychologists, they do not help to resolve the conflict inherent in the problem of treating neurotic patients. On the one hand, as citizens in a democratic society, psychologists believe that every person has the right to make his own free choice about his way of life. On the other hand, as professionals they also recognize that people who are in difficulties should be helped and choices must often be made for them. The clinical psychologist is an expert in assessing and modifying human behavior by virtue of his training. Regardless of the limitations of psychological theories and methods, psychologists constitute a profession (some say the only profession) which offers extensive training in behavior theory and in methods used to assist people with psychological problems. Therefore, the psychologist is better prepared to apply his knowledge than the layman.[4] However, as noted above, there is a difference between competence in bringing about behavioral changes and in judging the desirability of the behavior and the value system to be substituted. The clinician cannot accept sole responsibility for judging the adequacy of the individual's value system, nor can he become the ultimate interpreter of cultural metavalues to the patient by psychotherapy or education. In clinical practice, the patient, his social milieu and other significant persons in his life must all be considered in selecting appropriate goals for therapy.

Nor can psychology be held responsible for the application of its principles and methods by social agencies or industry in the fields of government, economics, or education. Decisions concerning the

[4] We recognize that personality variables as yet unexplored may be important determinants of therapist effectiveness. But no scientifically grounded profession can fail to assume that additional didactic training is a necessary, if not sufficient, condition for practice.

ity, and his state of sickness exempts him from his normal social obligations. In turn, it is understood that he will attempt to get well and that he has an obligation to seek help and cooperate with others who treat him. As Parsons states, the latter implies a dependency of the sick person on the healer. The act of coming for help signifies the patient's realization that he cannot cope with the problem and that he wishes another person to take responsibility for treating it. This dependency status should tend to increase the effectiveness of the therapist's reinforcing operations (cf. research on the role of dependency, prestige, and other therapist-patient variables in verbal conditioning; Greenspoon, 1962; Krasner, 1962b).

A second feature concerns the content of the interactions. Most psychologists agree that the specific content of the patient's verbalizations in psychotherapy is far less important than was believed by earlier theorists. One common element in all therapeutic interactions is the therapist's insistence that the patient talk about those private experiences, fears, attitudes, and beliefs which are usually not shared with other people. Recent reviews by William Sargant (1957), Jerome Frank (1961) and Robert Lifton (1961) of methods of persuasion, thought reform, and therapy all suggest that the most successful methods of behavior manipulation, including magic, religion, and political coercion, share the requirement that the person publicly expose at least some of his privately held beliefs and attitudes. This accessibility to personal and private behavior, in turn, makes the person more vulnerable to control. The more behavior is exposed to the controlling agent the easier it is to set up conditions which modify behavior. Lifton (1961) points out that the admissions of guilt over minimal crimes against the state in Chinese "brainwashing" camps and universities provide the opportunity for the controller to reinforce such self-accusing behavior, to promise relief from guilt by self-punishing procedures and generally to weaken existing behavior and introduce new responses.

Privacy, the inaccessibility of much personal behavior in a democratic society, probably represents the bulwark of democracy because it allows for variability, and for divergence of attitudes and beliefs. What is jealously guarded as a right to privacy in everyday life is, in fact, surrendered in the psychotherapeutic hour. The consequences of this making accessible of the patient's private experiences have been discussed elsewhere (Kanfer, 1961). The potentials for controlling important behavioral sequences, usually not subject to control by direct social reinforcement, increase very much the extent of the therapist's influence.

Metavalues and Personal Values

Clinicians are beginning to accept the thesis that the therapist's value system tends to affect the direction of the patient's change in treatment (*Rosenthal, 1955; Schrier, 1953*). Among the many problems raised by this recognition are the methods of handling valued material (e.g., *Ellis, 1962; Meehl, 1959; Segal, 1959*), and the ethical implications of the intrusion of personal values into psychotherapy (*Williamson, 1958; Weisskopf-Joelson, 1953*). Existential analysis (*Weisskopf-Joelson, 1958*) assumes that the purpose of treatment is the realization of creative and attitudinal values and this school frankly admits its value-orientation.

Although the term "value" is difficult to define, two separate aspects relating to the problem of control in psychotherapy are worthy of mention.

There are clear cut rules for many behaviors which are common to practically all members of a given culture. These rules are usually also accepted by the therapist and his client. We will call these *metavalues* (cultural values). In addition, there is a variety of situations in which several alternate behaviors and goal hierarchies are equally tolerated by society but which differ in the degree to which they lead to satisfaction in the individual. These alternatives are determined primarily by the individual's past experience. We shall call these alternatives *personal values*. Complications arise both in the patient's value system and in the psychotherapy relationship because of the inconsistencies between metavalues and personal values. Interpretation of the cultural metavalues further varies as a function of membership in a subgroup such as a socioeconomic, religious, or geographic affiliation. The outcome of therapy should provide a wider choice of alternative behaviors for the patient with the only restriction that the new behaviors must also be compatible with the metavalues of the patient's cultural environment. The problem lies mainly in producing those changes which lead to socially acceptable behavior even while they result in sweeping changes in the life pattern of the patient. For example,

therapists generally do not disagree whether to manip havior which may avert a suicide, but they *do* disagree client's vocational or marital choice should be modified. plete absence of standards for such personal and private behavior the therapist's judgments are based mainly on his ical orientation, on his own experiences and on his own values. These therapist experiences then become the stand selecting the goals for a particular patient in psychotherapy

In most cases the neurotic patient can be of little help ciding what personal values need changing and what range natives would be tolerated both by him and by his envir When a patient *is* able to do this, the therapist's job does volve the problem of values. The patient might indicate wishes to improve his study habits or seek technical help in a vocational choice. In these cases technical skills by the p ogist may be applied directly to a problem with an outcome clearly by the client himself. Unfortunately, therapists som become suspicious even in these cases and the desirability patient's stated goal is often questioned by therapists fro viewpoint of their own personal value systems. Endowed tradition of depth-probing, many a therapist is tempted to s tute his own goal for that of the patient. Instead of rend technical assistance in a circumscribed area, the therapist may attempt to change the patient's total pattern of living.

Rules for Co

The most heated arguments are generated by the question, " establishes the legitimacy of means and ends in behavioral contr The writer does not presume to have a solution to this quest but wishes to present a few thoughts designed to stimulate furt debate.

The APA attempted to indicate the limitations of appropri means and ends for psychological practice in its early code

[3] If all mental health workers were to share a single set of values their inf ence would carry with it the same dangers as any system of total control. requirement of strict conformity to the mores and values set up by the ther pist's model of behavior is also tantamount to the complete subservience in posed by totalistic control systems.

legitimacy of means and ends in use of behavioral control methods are no more the responsibility of the psychologist than is the question whether to use atomic weapons in a war in the area of competence of the physicist, or the decision to adopt sterilization procedures with some humans in the domain of the biologist. In the absence of any specific mandate from the social community through its legal, political, religious, or social agencies psychologists will continue to use methods of control which are sometimes not acceptable to the public and use these for purposes about which there is some debate.

There has already been some indication that psychological knowledge is gradually becoming incorporated into the legal system, providing some standards of behavior which are more consistent with our knowledge of man than many current laws. There is, however, a considerable lag between mores and their incorporation into the legal structure of a society. During this lag professional groups will have to provide leadership in working out rules which describe the goals for which individual human behavior may be manipulated, and the restrictions upon methods under which this purpose is to be accomplished.

When the psychologist leaves his immediate work setting, his conduct falls under the rules by which other social groups operate. A social scientist who publicly gives opinions about the implications of behavior control techniques for international politics, education, or consumer behavior must expect the same treatment as other public figures who champion controversial issues. It is probably this change in the accustomed reaction from student or patient audiences which has made psychologists so reluctant to participate in public debate and to provide information and guidance to social groups. An additional problem, of course, lies in the thin line of distinction between fact and opinion, between researcher and reformer.

From these considerations it seems that several specific contributions can be made by psychologists to further public recognition of the social implications of recent advances in psychology.

(1) In their role as scientists, continuing research on behavioral control methods and on factors limiting their effects to special circumstances should provide clearer understanding of the extent of the problem in practical situations. Research findings already exist

which tend to suggest that total behavioral control requires a totally controlled environment; that verbal (and attitudinal) behavior can be influenced by a variety of variables toward maximal or minimal change; and that self-control training can modify the effect of incentives, thereby reducing greatly the utility of many conditioning procedures. Knowledge of these factors should permit a better estimate of the actual threat inherent in practical methods to which objections are currently raised. If recently described methods turn out to be no more effective than previous controlling devices, or if easy countermeasures are available, no further concern or action would be warranted.

(2) With no special prerogatives to dictate to society the rules by which its members should be educated, controlled, or changed, psychologists as educated citizens can make a contribution as resource persons to established social agencies. These activities demand of the consultant that he explicitly distinguish between facts, interpretation of facts, and his personal opinion.

(3) Our discussion suggests that continued public awareness of the growing effectiveness of psychological techniques may present the best safeguards against their misapplication. Ultimately, the products of any science become public property and only the informed public can wisely regulate their use.

(4) If psychologists have a service to perform in society's effort to evaluate itself, it is the scientific analysis of current psychological practices, embedded in our social matrix. Among those are many which appear to have relevance to the control of *individual* behavior, i.e., practices in education, in law-enforcement, in treatment of emotional adjustment, in consumer persuasion, and industrial personnel procedures. Contributions to each of these fields lie not only in suggestions for changes but also in a thorough analysis of the present practices and their consequences.

REFERENCES

Ellis, A., *Reason and Emotion in Pychotherapy*. New York: Lyle Stuart, 1962.

Eriksen, C. W. (Ed.), *Behavior and Awareness*. Durham: Duke University Press, 1962.

Frank, J. D., *Persuasion and Healing: A Comparative Study of Psychotherapy.* Baltimore: Johns Hopkins Press, 1961.

Greenspoon, J., "Verbal Conditioning and Clinical Psychology." In A. J. Bachrach (Ed.), *Experimental Foundations of Clinical Psychology.* New York: Basic Books, 1962. Pp. 510–553.

Kanfer, F. H., "Comments on Learning in Psychotherapy," *Psychol. Rep.,* 1961, 9, 681–699.

Kanfer, F. H., and A. R. Marston, "Verbal Conditioning, Ambiguity and and Psychotherapy," *Psychol. Rep.,* 1961, 9, 461–475.

Krasner, L., "Behavior Control and Social Responsibility," *Amer. Psychologist,* 1962, 17, 199–204. (a)

Krasner, L., "The Therapist as a Social Reinforcement Machine." In H. Strupp and L. Luborsky (Eds.), *Research in Psychotherapy.* Washington: APA, 1962. Pp. 61–95. (b)

Lifton, R. J., *Thought Reform and the Psychology of Totalism.* New York: Norton, 1961.

Meehl, P. E. "Some Technical and Axiological Problems in the Therapeutic Handling of Religious and Valuational Material," *J. counsel. Psychol.,* 1959, 6, 255–259.

Parsons, T., and R. Fox, "Illness, Therapy and the Modern Urban Family." In E. G. Jaco (Ed.), *Patients, Physicians and Illness.* (New York: Free Press of Glencoe, 1958. Pp. 234–245.

Rosenthal, D., "Changes in Some Moral Values Following Psychotherapy," *J. consult. Psychol.,* 1955, 19, 431–436.

Sargant, W., *Battle for the Mind, a Physiology of Conversion and Brainwashing.* New York: Doubleday, 1957.

Schrier, H., "The Significance of Identification in Therapy," *Amer. J. Orthopsychiat.,* 1953, 23, 585–604.

Segal, S. J., "The Role of the Counselor's Religious Values in Counseling," *J. counsel. Psychol.,* 1959, 6, 270–274.

Skinner, B. F., *Science and Human Behavior.* New York: Macmillan, 1953.

Weisskopf-Joelson, E., "Some Suggestions Concerning Weltanschauung and Psychotherapy," *J. abnorm. soc. Psychol.,* 1953, 48, 601–604.

Weisskopf-Joelson, E., "Logotherapy and Existential Analysis," *Acta Psychother., psychosomat. Orthopaed.,* 1958, 6, 193–204.

Williamson, E. G., "Value Orientation in Counseling," *Personnel Guid. J.,* 1958, 36, 520–528.

19

Leonard Ullmann

Some Implications of Current Research

Operant procedures in remedial speech and language therapy represent an important aspect of a more general trend in current theory and clinical practice. The common thread in this approach is the training of the individual in the emission of more socially favorable responses in situations in which he had previously emitted responses that were considered inadequate, unexpected, or deviant. Such direct treatment of behavioral difficulties is at present an empirical strategy rather than a well developed theory. In pursuing this strategy, however, data have been obtained that have led to the abandonment of conceptions of people and personality that dominated American psychology during the last generation.

The first change that is illustrated throughout these papers is methodological. It is frequently presumed that people are complex and that any procedure dealing with them must be complex, intricate, prolonged, and indirect. This has led to a dichotomy in research approaches and eventually among professionals. A psychologist either used a clinical method to do justice to the complexity of the subject or he used an experimental paradigm of rigor great enough to match its triviality. These two procedures may be exemplified by citations from two recent books.

Surveying clinical practices, Ford and Urban (*1964, p. 17*) were led to write:

It seems legitimate to characterize psychotherapy as, in part, a "healing art," rather than primarily a "healing science." It is an art in the sense that the consequences of psychotherapy vary extensively from therapist to therapist, from patient to patient, and for the same therapist in frequently unexplained fashion; there are few scientifically verified principles which govern its practice; major portions of the treatment procedures depend on the character of the therapist and must be learned largely by practicing therapy under the guidance of more experienced practitioners; procedures effective in the hands of one therapist are frequently ineffective in the hands of another; and the therapist is often unable to specify the treatment procedures that produced observed changes.

Chapter after chapter in the present book specifies procedures and not only indicates the derivation of these procedures from a body of empirical evidence, but in following a clinical program extends the domain of empirical evidence. The presumption of complexity is not false; it merely involves asking incorrect questions. The questions that the authors in this book ask start with the word "what" rather than with the word "why." For example, the questions are, "What is the person currently doing?" "What behaviors should be increased in frequency?" "What conditions differentially reinforce current behaviors and can be altered to foster new ones?" "What" questions focus the worker's attention on measureable and manipulatable aspects of the situation. "What" questions have a distinctly different impact than "why" questions, which lead to unobservable constructs whose loci are within the individual. The greater fruitfulness in clinical practice of the procedures illustrated in this book do not necessarily invalidate inferential theories; they merely make such theories unnecessary.

In contrast to the clinical approach stands what might be called the psychopathological approach. The psychopathological approach confuses the concepts of *control* and *experiment* with the physical location and hardware of the *laboratory*. For example, Buss (*1966, p. viii*) writes that "progress may be marked by advances from the clinic to the laboratory. . . . Similarly, we favor facts obtained in the controlled context of the laboratory over observations made in the less controlled context of the clinic." While the reaction against the clinical method exemplified by psychoanalytic theories is understandable, both the emphasis on the laboratory rather than the clinic and the concept of control used differ considerably from the functional analysis of behavior as it is manifested in the present volume. The result of the psychopathological approach has been a multitude of laboratory analogues that have theoretical, explanatory and descriptive interest and that have been as successful in creating cluttered psychological journals as they have been useless in leading to effective professional behavior in the clinical setting. In the psychopathological approach very small segments of behavior are taken completely out of context and observed for differences between groups of people during brief periods of time. Differences between the groups significant at the .05 level are then used to define the disease. The principal methodological objection to such studies is that generalizations are not limited to people in artificial situations performing limited tasks but are made to the very clinical settings that the laboratory technician eschewed.

It is in this important methodological realm that the chapters of this book illustrate and forward one of the most useful trends in current research: the behavior to be altered is altered. Throughout the book there are examples of experimental probes and differential reinforcement of other behaviors (DRO). Throughout, the chapters help the practitioner and research worker answer such questions as, "What should I do?" The work presented in this volume illustrates an alternative to the clinical and psychopathological approaches.

The chapters in this book illustrate a number of trends in practice. Perhaps the most striking single element is the repeated illustration of the development of the conditions and subject repertoire necessary for further progress. For example, imitation is not presumed to exist, but rather techniques for its development and later use are offered. Attention is a vital condition and throughout the volume there are examples of the shaping of attentive responses. Higher order concepts are operationally defined and broken down into their component parts, and methods for their development by subjects are described. The stereotype of operant conditioning as not making use of such concepts is belied throughout this book.

Perhaps the most frequently repeated practical concepts are the contingency of reinforcement upon a behavior and the necessary gradual shaping of behavior. Compared to the typical individual, many aspects of the repertoires of the people described in this book either were not previously developed or had been extinguished. That these behaviors are not emitted should not lead to the error made by the psychopathologist, who compares "normals" and "schizophrenics" under exactly the same (controlled) conditions. As Orne (1962) has pointed out, college students will comply with instructions (or presumed instructions) to which no schizophrenic in his right mind would respond. If, under these conditions, the hospitalized subjects will not emit what the experimenter considers the "right" response, it is incorrect to infer the presence of schizophrenic or other defects. Repeatedly, the chapters in this book illustrate that under appropriate training (of which shaping and response-contingent reinforcement are major ingredients), the target performances will be emitted. Many of the so-called "subject defects" are probably experimenter and psychotherapist defects.

Work of the type presented in this volume has as much of an effect on formulations of therapists as it has on conceptualization of patients. Just as there is a decreased interest in official diagnostic categories when dealing with clients, so attention is placed on therapist behaviors rather than therapist personality traits, motivations, or professional affiliations. Throughout, procedures are outlined that by virtue of their very explicitness may be taught to and be applied by parents, attendants, and even machines. The focus on "what" rather than "why" or "who" leads to a great increase in the number of people who can, and, for generalization to be most effective, must be taught appropriate responses contingent on the subject's behavior. In a larger professional and societal context, the effectiveness and teachability of operant procedures makes possible a consultant role dealing with principles that will replace the one-to-one traditional professional role limited to the specifics of a particular case.

In various chapters throughout this book there is evidence that using operant procedures not only changes the theoretical formulation of the individual but also has a direct effect on the practitioner. This is as it should be, for the same set of principles should apply to both the patient and the practitioner (*Ullmann, in press a*). Specifying the behaviors that should be emitted by both therapist and trainee leads to a more mature relationship. With the ability to specify comes the opportunity to quantify and obtain feedback both in specific cases and across cases to the procedures themselves. Just as the person receiving treatment may learn to learn, so the therapist learns to teach. The procedures detailed in this book are outlines and guides. With practice, the teacher gains skill in techniques such as shaping, fading, and chaining. This skill is as much an accomplishment as the smooth articulation of a sentence, and during treatment both the therapist and subject grow.

A major effect of direct procedures of retraining, in remediation of speech and in the treatment of functional psychiatric disorders (see, for example, the materials presented in anthologies such as those edited by Eysenck, 1960, 1964; Franks, 1964; Krasner and Ullmann, 1965; Ullmann and Krasner, 1965; and Wolpe, Salter and Reyna, 1964; and experimental studies such as those by King, Armitage, and Tilton, 1960; Meichenbaum, 1966; and Ullmann *et al.*, 1965, with schizophrenics; and by Davison, in press; Lang, Lazovik, and Reynolds, 1965; and Paul, 1966, with phobics) is optimism on the part of therapists. This optimum is based on observing gains by patients who were previously considered difficult or impossible to change. Such changes reinforce the therapist behavior as much as termination of an aversive stimulus reinforces behavior of the child. In operant procedures, the practitioner is very dependent on the subject: if the subject or his defect cannot be blamed for lack of success, the therapist's involvement increases. Just as the therapist becomes an acquired reinforcer for the patient, so the patient, because of his changed behavior, becomes an acquired reinforcer for the therapist. The patient's changed behavior shapes the particular program, and the progress of many patients maintains the professional in his use of operant principles. Rather than a cold and mechanical relationship, as critics who have not applied such procedures argue, the explicit interdependency between teacher and trainee results in a warmly personal interaction. The entire thrust of a direct-treatment approach is toward responses to behavior emitted by particular individuals. Direct treatment moves from the undeviating emission of one type of behavior in response to patients, even if such responses are called unconditional positive regard, to behaviors that are responses (i.e., patient) contingent.

Because these new procedures orient patients and therapists in new ways, new ethical formulations have become necessary. The need for serious consideration of these issues has been pointed out by Kanfer in this book, and by authors in anthologies by Nunokawa (*1965*) and Ulrich, Stachnik, and Mabry (*1966*). The limitations placed on therapists who would deny their responsibility are illustrated by Szasz (*1965*) in his description of autonomous psychotherapy. While there would seem to be little ethical involvement in whether or not to help an individual improve a basic social skill such as speech, the implications of an effective set of procedures increase the therapist's responsibility in deciding whether to treat the individual as well as increasing responsibility within the treatment itself. The therapist cannot disregard this responsibility and must search for new and more satisfactory ethical models (*Ullmann, in press, b*).

In summary, operant procedures in speech remediation provide a body of information that in itself is consistent and remarkably valuable, and that enriches a larger body of theoretical and clinical material. The effect of this work changes the formulation of both the people giving and the people receiving treatment. The future, as many of the writers in this book point out, will see a refinement of present techniques, the incorporation of additional techniques, and the extension of the procedures to a wider population. The practice of operant treatment fosters a humane, positive regard by the therapist both for the subject and for himself as effective, worthwhile members of the community. Operant procedures such as those presented in this book contribute a vitally needed research methodology, valuable data, helpful and hopeful treatment programs, and a challenging new formulation of the professional role. As such, operant procedures appear to be the most likely way in which the professional person will provide service based on science and, in so doing, service to science.

REFERENCES

Buss, A. H., *Psychopathology*. New York: Wiley, 1966.

Davison, G. C., "Systematic Desensitization as a Counterconditioning Process," *J. abnorm. Psychol.*, in press.

Eysenck, H. J. (Ed.), *Behaviour Therapy and the Neuroses*. Oxford: Pergamon Press, 1960.

Eysenck, H. J. (Ed.), *Experiments in Behaviour Therapy*. Oxford: Pergamon Press, 1964.

Ford, D. H., and H. B. Urban, *Systems of Psychotherapy*. New York: Wiley, 1964.

Franks, C. M., *Conditioning Techniques in Clinical Practice and Research*. New York: Springer, 1964.

King, G. F., S. G. Armitage, and J. R. Tilton, "A Therapeutic Approach to Schizophrenics of Extreme Pathology: An Operant-Interpersonal Method," *J. abnorm. soc. Psychol.*, 1960, 61, 276–286.

Krasner, L., and L. P. Ullmann, *Research in Behavior Modification*. New York: Holt, Rinehart and Winston, 1965.

Lang, P. J., A. D. Lazovik, and D. J. Reynolds, "Desensitization, Suggestibility, and Pseudotherapy," *J. abnorm. Psychol.*, 1965, 70, 395–402.

Meichenbaum, D. H., "Effects of Social Reinforcement on the Level of Abstraction in Schizophrenics," *J. abnorm. Psychol.*, 1966, 71, 354–362.

Nunokawa, W. D. (Ed.), *Human Values and Abnormal Behavior*. Chicago: Scott, Foresman, 1965.

Orne, M. T., "On the Social Psychology of the Psychology Experiment," *American Psychologist*, 1962, 17, 776–783.

Paul, G. L., *Insight vs. Desensitization in Psychotherapy*. Stanford, Calif.: Stanford University Press, 1966.

Szasz, T. S., *The Ethics of Psychoanalysis*. New York: Basic Books, 1965.

Ullmann, L. P., *Institution and Outcome: A Comparative Study of Psychiatric Hospitals*. Oxford: Pergamon Press, in press, (a).

Ullmann, L. P., "Behavior Therapy as Social Movement." In C. M. Franks (Ed.), *Assessment of Behavior Therapies*. New York: McGraw-Hill, in press (b).

Ullmann, L. P., R. G. Forsman, J. W. Kenny, T. L. McInnis, Jr., L. P. Unikel, and R. M. Zeisset, "Selective Reinforcement of Schizophrenics' Interview Responses," *Behaviour Research and Therapy*, 1965, 2, 205–212.

Ullmann, L. P., and L. Krasner (Eds.), *Case Studies in Behavior Modification*. New York: Holt, Rinehart and Winston, 1965.

Ulrich, R., T. Stachnik, and J. Mabry (Eds.), *Control of Human Behavior*. Chicago: Scott, Foresman, 1966.

Wolpe, J., A. Salter, and L. J. Reyna (Eds.), *The Conditioning Therapies*. New York: Holt, Rinehart and Winston, 1964.

NAME INDEX

See also References at ends of chapters.

Albright, R., 389n
Anderson, D., 245, 253
Allen, E., 88, 161n
Appel, J. B., 25
Argo, E., 19n
Armitage, S. G., 428
Atkinson, C. J., 377
Ault, M., 78n
Ausbery, M., 298
Ayllon, T., 126, 238
Azrin, N. H., 325, 350, 352, 387, 405n

Bachrach, A. J., 238
Backus, O., 298
Baer, D. M., 63, 65, 66, 68, 219n, 222
Baker, R. L., 257, 305, 308, 296–321
Bandura, A., 71
Bayley, N., 122
Beasly, J., 298
Beavers, J., 78n
Bellugi, U., 199
Bensberg, G. J., 126
Bigler, R. C., 352, 377
Bijou, S. W., 19n, 20, 77, 77n
Birch, J., 197
Birnbrauer, J. S., 19–39, 20, 21, 126

Black, J. W., 379
Bloodstein, O., 344, 383
Bloomfield, L., 289
Brackbill, Y., 20, 36
Bradway, K. P., 122
Brady, J. P., 238
Bricker, A. *See* A. B. Harris
Brooks, L. O., 21
Brookshire, R. H., 328n
Brown, R., 199
Brown, S., 78n
Browning, R., 415
Buchanan, D., 109, 114
Buss, A. H., 425

Cansion, 299
Carr, A., 298
Chapman, M. E., 300
Chomsky, N., 68
Church, J., 158
Church, R. M., 70
Coffroth, J., 206n

Dale, E., 290
Dameron, L., 186
Davison, G. C., 428
Dewey, G., 290
Dickie, R., 390n
Dmitriev, V., 78n

Dolch, E. W., 290
Dollard, J., 70, 71
Dumont, D., 154
Dunlap, K., 323
Durkin, K., 36
Durrell, D. D., 290

Ebner, M. J., 243, 254
Edmondo, P., 392n
Edwards, A. E., 197, 281
Ellis, A., 418
Eriksen, C. W., 415
Erwin, W. J., 238
Estes, W. K., 345
Evans, A. J., 206n, 281
Eysenck, H. J., 428

Fairbanks, G., 387
Falconer, G. A., 197
Ferster, C. B., 25, 128, 404
Filby, Y., 197
Finley, J. R., 21
Flanagan, B. I., 325, 341, 345, 350, 352, 354n
Ford, D. H., 424
Fox, R., 416, 423
Frank, J. D., 415, 417
Franks, C. M., 428
Frick, J. A., 344
Fromm, E., 299
Fuller, P. R., 238
di Furia, G., 221n

Gates, A. I., 290
Gewirtz, J. L., 67
Glaser, R., 263
Goldiamond, I., 126, 220, 222, 323, 325, 341, 345, 348-407, 350, 352, 354, 377, 381, 385, 388, 403n, 405
Goldstein, K., 3
Gollub, L. R., 85, 381

Gordon, E. J., 206n
Grab, J., 19n
Graham, C. H., 403n
Greenspoon, J., 417
Guthrie, E. R., 381n

Hamilton, J. W., 126
Harris, A. B., 195, 197-216, 205
Harris, F. R., 40-60, 77-100, 161n, 163
Hart, B., 157n
Hayes, C., 132
Hebb, D. O., 3
Heid, W. H., 21
Henja, R., 299
Henke, L., 78n
Hewett, F. M., 69, 126, 148, 186
Holland, A. L., 195, 197-216, 257, 259-281
Holland, J. G., 260, 280
Hollis, J. H., 36
Holz, W. C., 387
Homme, L. E., 84
Horney, K., 299

Irwin, R. B., 299, 300
Isaacs, W., 126, 132, 220, 221, 238

Jack, D., 20, 36
Jenkins, J., 198n
Jiminez, Pabon, J., 198n
Johnson, W., 344
Johnson, G. O., 20
Johnston, M. K., 40-60, 77-100, 78, 161n, 156, 185-194
Jones, D., 290
Jones, M. C., 222

Kanareff, V. T., 71
Kanfer, F. H., 411-423
Kelleher, R. T., 85, 381

Keller, F. S., 126
Keller, H., 150
Kennedy, W. A., 36
Kidder, J. D., 19–39, 19, 20
King, G. F., 428
Kirk, S. A., 20
Kohler, 299
Kolb, D. A., 126
Kosowski, I., 20
Krasner, L., 348n, 402, 413, 417, 428

Lang, P. J., 428
Lanzetta, J. T., 71
Lazovik, A. D., 428
Learned, B., 65
Lehtinen, L. E., 122
Lewin, K., 299
Lewis, M. M., 66
Lifton, R. J., 414, 417
Lind, D. L., 238
Lodge, E., 206n
Long, N., 192n
Lovaas, O. I., 76, 125, 125–154, 149, 155, 159, 186
Lowell, F. E., 122
Lowler, J., 21

MacAulay, B. D., 3–18, 102–124, 195, 242
McDearmon, J., 282–295, 257
Mabry, J., 429
Marks, J. B., 221n
Marston, A. R., 415
Martin, C. H., 19n
Martin, R., 323, 325, 325–347, 329n, 339n
Matthews, J., 197, 257, 259–281
Mecham, M. J., 290
Meehl, P. E., 418
Mees, H. I., 159, 238
Meichenbaum, D. H., 428

Metz, J. R., 63, 68, 69
Michel, D. E., 65
Milisen, R., 300
Miller, N. E., 70, 71
Minke, K. A., 21
Mohr, J. P., 238
Montessori, M., 20
Moore, J. T., 283
Moore, O. K., 20
Moore, R., 222, 388, 390n
Mowrer, D. E., 257, 296–321, 305, 308, 312
Mowrer, O. H., 65, 300

Nieman, E. W., 206n
Nims, L., 390n
Nonnenmacher, J., 19n
Nunokowa, W. D., 429

Orne, M. T., 427

Parsley, N. B., 126
Parsons, T., 416, 417
Patterson, G. R., 218, 243, 255
Paul, G. L., 428
Pavlov, I., 350n
Peterson, R. F., 61–74, 63, 65, 66, 68, 69, 156
Pines, M., 20
Porter, D., 20
Powers, M. H., 263, 265, 266
Premack, D., 84
Pressey, S. L., 259, 260

Quist, R., 355n

Reed, G. R., 243, 254
Reynolds, D. J., 428
Reynolds, N., 157n, 161n
Rheingold, H. L., 67
Rigdrodsky, S., 300
Rimland, B., 128, 185

Risley, T., 65, 67, 69, 77, 96, 126, 148, 155, 157–184, 159, 195, 186, 238
Robinson, H. B., 122
Robinson, N. M., 122
Roe, V., 300
Rogers, C., 299
Rosenbaum, M. E., 71
Rosenberg, B., 197
Rosenthal, D., 418
Ross, D., 71
Ross, H. W., 67
Ross, S., 71

Salter, A., 428
Sargent, W., 417
Schramm, W., 206n
Schrier, H., 418
Schuell, H. J., 198n
Schutz, R. E., 21, 257, 305, 308, 296–321
Schwitzgebel, R., 126
Segal, S. J., 418
Shames, G. H., 325
Sherman, J. A., 63, 65, 66, 68, 69, 126, 132, 219–241, 217, 220, 222, 238
Sherrick, C. E., 328
Sidman, M., 183, 220, 326, 356
Siegel, G. M., 325, 329n, 339n
Simmons, J. Q., 125n
Skinner, B. F., 20, 68, 84, 161, 259, 260, 261, 282, 297, 344, 379, 403n, 404, 414, 415
Skinner, H., 259
Sloane, H. N., 3–18, 77–100, 77, 242
Smayling, L. M., 254
Spacks, B., 206n
Speaks, C. E., 352
Staats, A. W., 21
Staats, C. K., 21
Stachnik, T., 429

Standing, E. M., 20
Steer, M., 300
Stolz, S., 157n
Stone, J. L., 158
Strait, R., 243
Straughan, J. H., 218, 242–255, 242, 244
Strauss, A. A., 3, 122
Stuckless, R., 197
Sullivan, A., 150
Szasz, T. S., 429

Tague, C. E., 19, 19–39
Taylor, M. L., 198
Terrace, H. S., 222, 388
Terrell, G., 36
Thomas, J., 220
Thorndike, E. L., 126, 290
Tilton, J. R., 428
Tolstoy, L. N., 354
Tosti, D. T., 206n
Tucker, I. F., 71
Turbitt, T., 161n

Ullmann, L. P., 348n, 409, 427, 428, 429, 424–430
Ulrich, R., 429
Urban, H. B., 424, 430

Valentine, C. W., 66
Van Riper, C., 104, 298

Walters, R. H., 20, 71
Webb, P., 19n
Weisberg, P., 67
Weisskopf-Joelson, E., 418
West, R., 298
Wetzler, E., 392
Wiesley, M., 36
Williamson, E. J., 418
Wilson, F. S., 70, 71
Wing, J. K., 125n

Wingate, 360
Wise, C. M., 289
Wolf, M. M., 19, 19–39, 20, 21, 126, 155, 159, 195, 238, 240, 243
Wolpe, J., 428

Yerkes, R. M., 65

Zaborska, M., 206n
Zimmerman, D. W., 65

SUBJECT INDEX

Ability. *See* IQ

Abstract or relational terms. *See* Concepts, Generalization and generality, Intraverbal behavior, Meaning, Prepositions, Pronouns, Symbols

Achievement, 2, 128

Acquired reinforcer. *See* Conditioned reinforcer

Adaptation effect, 356, 359

Adding stimuli. *See* Fading and adding stimuli

Addition. *See* Arithmetic

Alphabet, synthetic, 76, 102, 104, 105, 106, 111, 113, 115, 118, 121, 123

Anna Karenina, 354

Anticipation procedure, 160

Anxiety, 4, 5–6, 150, 323, 352, 352n, 353, 403n

Aphasia, 117, 121, 195–216

Arithmetic, 22, 126, 199, 280

Arizona State University Speech Clinic, 389

Articulation, 77, 79–80, 92, 94, 110–121, 123–124, 186, 190, 257–320

Assessment, 40–60
  of behavior, 41
  of procedures, 41, 184, 187, 194
  of progress, 41–42, 184, 187, 194

in training program, 78–79, 99, 149, 158, 217, 248, 269–270, 297, 308, 312, 427. *See also* Recording verbal behavior

Atresia, bilateral, 111

Attending behavior, 15–17, 88–89, 122, 133, 135, 138, 168, 188, 244, 262, 309, 426

Auditory discrimination, 110, 113, 118, 123, 257–320

Auditory memory span, 201–203, 213

Auditory stimulation. *See* Stimulation

"Autism" theory of language, 65, 67, 300

Autistic children, 76, 94, 114, 124, 125–254, 158–159, 161, 185, 243. *See also* Psychotic children

Aversive stimuli. *See* Negative reinforcer *and* Punishment

Avoidance, 352–353, 365, 375, 387

Behavior, definition of, 4–5

Behavioral theory, 4–7, 125, 151, 220, 409–430, 416. *See also* Reinforcement theory

Behavior theory. *See* Behavioral theory *and* Reinforcement theory

Biological reinforcer. *See* Unconditioned reinforcer

Blending, 80–81, 104, 108, 120, 267, 269, 279, 283–284, 286

Blind children, 161, 175

Brain damage. *See* Retarded children *and* Aphasia

Bureau of Child Research, University of Kansas, 157n

Cerebral Palsy, 94

Chaining
analysis, 14–15
attending behavior as a response chain, 16–17
definition, 14–15
of sounds, 75, 80–81, 94, 123, 284, 286, 288
teaching response chains, 16–17
of words, 75, 82–84, 94, 118, 123, 156, 177–182, 189, 194, 187, 190, 199, 230, 381

Childhood Autism, 125n

Classical conditioning. *See* Respondent behavior *and* Respondent conditioning and stuttering

Classroom behavior, 19–39

Codes to record verbal behavior. *See* Recording verbal behavior

Color-coding. *See* Synthetic alphabet

Communications theory, 4

Comprehension, 22, 201, 203–204, 207

Concepts, 137, 140, 144–145, 147–148, 152, 160, 188, 262, 426

Conditioned emotional response. *See* Emotional behavior

Conditioned reinforcer, 9, 64–67, 76, 127, 128, 131, 146–147, 150–151, 243, 249, 307, 308, 311, 381

Conversation. *See* Spontaneity

Cross-modal language usage, 199

Crying. See Disruptive behaviors

Cue. *See* Discriminative stimulus

Deaf. *See* Hearing impairment

Delay of reinforcement. *See* Delayed reinforcement

Delayed auditory feedback, 362–383, 387, 388–399, 400

Delayed reinforcement, 8–9, 22, 77, 104, 131, 260, 360–362

Delayed speech, 77, 79–80, 111, 124, 245. *See also* Speech sounds, Speech-free child *and* Mute child

Developmental Psychology Laboratory, University of Washington, 78, 161

Diagnosis. *See* Assessment

Differential reinforcement, 10–11, 157, 301, 349, 384, 387. *See also* Shaping

Differential reinforcement of low rate. *See* DRO

Discriminative stimulus 11, 104, 105, 106, 109, 132–135, 137, 140–144, 147, 155, 156, 190, 195, 222, 257, 262–263, 266–271, 274–280, 282–286, 292, 302, 311, 312–316, 330, 331, 332, 333, 341, 343, 350, 375, 381, 383, 383n, 384, 385, 388, 403–405

Disruptive behavior, 22, 75, 76, 89, 99, 111, 112, 122, 131, 157, 159, 161–169, 171, 176, 179, 187, 193, 276

Disturbed children, 248

DRO, 172–173, 183, 223, 226, 229–230, 234–235, 237, 239, 426

Dysarthria, 117

Echoic behavior, 12–13, 155–156, 185–186, 201, 212, 262. *See also* Echolalic speech *and* Imitation

Echolalia. *See* Echoic behavior, Echolalic speech *and* Imitation

Echolalic speech, 111, 114, 115, 139–140, 152, 154–194. *See also* Echoic behavior *and* Imitation

Electric shock, 327, 329–335, 344–345, 352–353, 362, 375

Eliciting stimulus, 350n

Emotional behavior, 345, 346, 350n, 356, 414–415

Escape behavior, 352, 362. *See also* Reinforcement *and* Reinforcer, negative

Ethics, 409–430

Evaluation procedures. *See* Assessment

Extinction, 9, 22, 133, 139–140, 149, 152, 157, 166–167, 187, 189, 190, 222, 236, 249, 254, 302, 349. *See also* Punishment, recovery from

Fading and adding stimuli, 11–12, 81, 123, 130–131, 134, 138–140, 142, 144, 146–147, 152, 155–160, 170, 178–180, 188–190, 203, 219, 221, 222–223, 225–227, 230, 232–233, 237, 261, 265, 266, 288–289, 302, 307, 388

Familial retardation. *See* Retarded children

Fathers and Sons, 398

Feelings, 403n, 405

Generalization and generality, 11, 139, 143–144, 152, 156, 179, 182–183, 189, 220, 221, 223, 228, 235–237, 238, 239, 253–254, 255, 276, 310, 344, 348, 354, 402

Generalized imitation, 64, 79, 169, 222, 237

Generalized reinforcer, 10, 85

Goals (of treatment), 409–430

Gradient of reinforcement. *See* Delayed reinforcement

Grammar, 68, 180–182, 186, 199–200

Group vs. individual sessions, 99, 121, 180, 189, 311, 320

Hearing impairment, 75, 76, 110, 111, 114, 117, 121, 197

Hyperactivity, 243–244, 245, 253–254. *See also* Disruptive behavior

Illinois Psychiatric Training and Research Authority, 350n

Immediate reinforcement. *See* Delayed reinforcement

Imitation
conditions influencing, 70–72
development of, 62–64
echoic control, 12–13
generalized imitation, 64
and language development, 64–68, 127–128, 155–156
and language structure, 67–68, 180–182
and model, 61, 70–72
and "new" behavior, 11, 61, 132
and observational learning, 61
and reinforcement, 65–67
and remedial speech training, 68–70, 79–80, 130–131, 132–136, 149, 152, 155–161, 166, 168–171, 176–182, 219, 221–226,

230, 232–233, 237, 238, 240, 426

review of, 61–73

and similarity, 61, 128, 132

teaching imitation, 62–64

and shaping, 65

value of, 62

See also Echoic behavior, Echolalic behavior *and* Generalized imitation

Imitative behavior. *See* Imitation, Echoic behavior *and* Echolalic behavior

Individual differences, 297

Individual vs. group sessions. *See* Group vs. individual sessions

Information theory, 4

Institute for Behavioral Research, 392, 392n

Intelligence. *See* IQ *and* Retarded children

Intraverbal behavior, 13, 137, 145–148, 152, 155, 187, 188, 190, 228, 229–230, 239, 261, 325

IQ, 21, 99, 103, 122, 199, 243, 244, 268, 297

Knowledge of results, 23, 122, 128, 129, 200, 201, 202, 214, 264, 287

Laboratory Preschool, University of Washington. *See* Developmental Psychology Laboratory, University of Washington

Language. *See* Verbal behavior *and* Speech

Library of the Committee on Programmed Instruction, Harvard University, 206

Love, 88

Mand
definition, 12
in training, 81–82, 92, 145–147, 152, 155, 186, 187, 188, 193

Mannerisms. *See* Disruptive behaviors

Mathematical models, 4

Maturation, 296–297

Meaning, 84, 104, 108–110, 201

Mental Health Research Institute, Fort Steilacoom, Washington, 221n

Minnesota Test for the Differential Diagnosis of Aphasia, 208

Model. *See* Imitation

Modeling. *See* Imitation

Mongoloid. *See* Retarded children

Motivation. *See* Motivating operations

Motivating operations
definition, 9–10
and conditioned reinforcers, 10
and generalized reinforcers, 10
motivation, 20, 88, 85, 131, 151, 164, 297, 414

Mute adult, 132, 217–241. *See also* Mute child

Mute child, 75, 111, 114, 124, 130, 147, 155, 217–218, 242–255. *See also* Delayed speech, Mute adult, Speech sounds *and* Speech-free child

Naming objects, 75. *See also* Tact

Neurological models, 3

Neurosis, 150

Noise, 351–352, 362

Novel stimulus effect, 359n

Novelty, 128

Nonvocal child. *See* Mute child

Noxious stimuli, 80. *See also* Reinforcement, negative

Observation. *See* Recording verbal behavior

Operant behavior, definition, 7

Operant conditioning. *See* Reinforcement theory

Organicity. *See* Retarded children *and* Aphasia

Parents, 78, 90–91, 96–100, 151, 161, 182–183, 186, 193

Partial prompt. *See* Fading and adding stimuli

Peer reinforcement, 242, 245–246, 253–254

Perseveration, 112

Perseveration of speech. *See* Echolalic speech

Personality theory, 3, 99, 150–151, 254, 298–299, 416, 424, 426

Phonetic placement, 79–80, 105, 123, 298, 302

Phonics, 22, 257–320

Phrases. *See* Chaining

Play therapy. *See* Psychotherapy

Positive reinforcement. *See* Reinforcement, positive

Positive reinforcement, time out from. *See* Time out from positive reinforcement

Positive reinforcer. *See* Reinforcer, positive

Premack principle, 84–85

Prepositions, 137, 141–142, 147, 148, 152, 200, 201, 211

Prerequisite behaviors. *See* Progressions

Primary reinforcer. *See* Unconditioned reinforcer

Programmed instruction
classroom, 19–39
and IQ, 21

and treatment, 151, 152, 195, 197–216, 222, 257–295

Progressions, 17, 78–84, 151–152, 195, 257, 261, 265–268, 283–286, 288, 290–294, 301–307, 384, 388

Prolongation, 332–335, 383, 385, 386–388, 400

Prompt. *See* Discriminative stimulus

Prompting. *See* Fading and adding stimuli

Pronouns, 137, 141–145, 147, 148, 152, 160–161, 186

Psychoanalytic theory. *See* Personality theory

Psychodynamic theory. *See* Personality theory

Psychotherapy, 129, 149–150, 217–218, 221, 248, 254, 299, 289, 401–402, 411–423

Psychotic adults, 126, 132, 219–241, 427

Psychotic children, 76, 94, 99, 125–154, 159, 185, 245

Punishment, 8, 127, 131, 133, 248, 261, 327, 329–339, 341, 344–345, 349, 351, 362, 365, 372, 387, 413, 416, 417

Punishment, recovery from effects of, 329–339, 351–352, 372

Rainier School, 19n, 21, 103

Rapport, 88

Readiness, 4

Reading, 22, 76, 102, 104, 110–114, 121, 123–124, 126, 140, 200, 207, 280, 282–320

Reassurance, 133

Recording verbal behavior, 40–60, 214–216
codes for, 48, 50–52, 55, 88

collecting data, 44, 51, 88, 183–
184, 187, 223, 327, 333–334,
351, 363
forms, 46, 52, 55
items to record, 42–44, 183, 249
observers, 48, 57–59, 88, 187
reliability, 55–57, 223, 269, 328–
329, 362
sampling observations, 59
scheduling observations, 59
tabulations, 49–50
tape recorder, 47, 88–89, 183, 223
therapist as observer, 45
time intervals, 49–50
trials, 49–50
Reinforcement
definition, 7–8
and imitation, 65–67
negative, 7, 349
positive, 7, 349
in remedial speech training program, 84–85, 104–105, 121,
131–132, 150, 152, 155, 158,
168, 170, 175, 182, 183, 189,
193, 195, 200, 219–227, 231,
232, 234, 237, 242, 248, 257,
260–261, 287, 299, 307, 310,
311, 313–317, 320, 344, 345,
381, 382, 412, 413–416, 417,
425–427. See also Differential
reinforcement, Knowledge of results, Peer reinforcement, Premack principle, Reinforcement
theory, Reinforcer, Social reinforcement, Time out from positive reinforcement and Token
reinforcement
Reinforcement schedule. See Schedule of reinforcement
Reinforcement theory, 3–18, 125–
129, 152, 260–263, 349–350.
See also Behavioral theory

Reinforcer
negative, 7, 127, 349, 362, 365,
372, 375, 387
positive, 7, 127, 349
in remedial speech training program, 84–85, 99, 120, 132–133,
149, 160–161, 163–164, 168,
170, 171–173, 188, 224, 225,
228, 230, 231, 232, 244, 245,
249, 250, 287, 309, 320, 349,
350n, 403–405, 415
See also Conditioned reinforcer,
Generalized reinforcer, Knowledge of results, Peer reinforcement, Reinforcement, Social
reinforcement, Token reinforcement and Unconditioned reinforcer
Reinforcing stimulus. See Reinforcer
Research in Behavior Modification,
348n
Respondent behavior, 350n, 359
Respondent conditioning and stuttering, 343, 345
Response chain. See Chaining
Replication (direct and systematic).
See Generalization and generality
Retarded children
brain damaged, 21, 76, 94, 96, 98,
99, 158, 159, 161
classroom behavior, 19–39
familial, 21, 91, 92, 99
mongoloid, 21, 86, 112, 116
and remedial speech training, 76–
124, 158, 159, 161, 185, 244,
248, 300

S^D. See Discriminative stimulus
Schedule of reinforcement
definition, 8
continuous, 8–9

intermittent, 8–9
in training program, 85, 231, 236–237
Schizophrenic children. *See* Autistic children and Psychotic children
Schuell classification, 198
Secondary gain, 400–401
Secondary reinforcer. *See* Conditioned reinforcer
Seizures, 117
Self control, 384, 388–389, 402–403, 405, 416
Self-destructive behaviors. *See* Disruptive behaviors
Self-help behaviors, 126
Semantic reversals, 204
"Senses" task, 204
Sentences. *See* Chaining
Session
    frequency, 78, 103, 121, 132, 135, 188, 199, 224, 270, 307
    length, 89, 103, 132, 135, 187, 188, 199, 224, 270, 307
Setting, 78, 132, 161–163, 223, 307, 308, 312, 327, 363
Shaping, 10–11, 105, 106, 349
    and imitation, 65
    in training program, 79–80, 131–132, 157, 158, 217–225, 228, 231–233, 237, 240, 261, 265, 282, 299, 301, 302, 384, 400, 427
Shock. *See* Electric shock
The Short Novels of Tolstoy, 354
Sibilants, 269–272, 278
Smith, Kline and French drug company, 148, 154
Social behaviors, 128, 159
Social reinforcement
    definition, 9
    with retardate, 22
    and imitation, 63–67

in training program, 85, 105, 127, 129, 170, 176–177, 188, 224, 228, 231, 232, 249, 254, 327, 328, 337–338, 339, 341
Speech. *See* Verbal behavior
Speech correctionist, necessity for, 317–320. *See also* Parents
Speech-free child, 75, 102–104, 111, 115, 120, 121, 124. *See also* Mute child *and* Speech sounds
Speech readiness, 4
Speech sounds, 79–80, 86–87, 91, 94, 103, 111, 114, 115, 116, 117, 121, 123, 124
Spelling, 201, 205–206, 280
Spontaneity, 84, 137, 145–148, 152, 173–176, 182, 185–194, 187, 207
Stimulation, 88, 124, 201, 202, 268, 288, 298, 300, 311, 313–317
Stimulus generalization. *See* Generalization and generality
Structural models, 3
Stuttering, 5–6, 126, 323–407
Substitute symptoms, 400–401
Successive approximations. *See* Shaping
Sullivan Programmed Reading, 113, 114
Symbolic rewards. *See* Conditioned reinforcers
Symbols, 127, 128, 137
Symptom, verbal behavior as, 3, 4, 401, 403n

TO. *See* Time out from positive reinforcement
Tact
    definition, 12
    teaching, 75, 81, 86–88, 94, 108–110, 114, 118, 121, 137–140, 145–146, 152, 155, 160, 170–

177, 187, 188–189, 225–228, 233, 235

Teaching machines. *See* Programmed instruction

Templin Short Test of Sound Discrimination, 269, 271–272, 278

Textual verbal behavior, 13. *See also* Reading

Time concepts. *See* Concepts

Time out from positive reinforcement, 8, 22, 25, 35, 86, 89–90, 99, 131, 133, 139, 157, 165–168, 171

Token reinforcement
"back-ups" for, 19, 20–21, 24
definition, 1, 9
and retarded children, 19–39
and classroom behavior, 19–39
check marks as, 19, 20, 24
effectiveness, 19–39, 21
and IQ, 21
procedures for, 24
results, 27–37
in training program, 85, 86, 104–105, 106, 112, 120, 122, 245, 250, 307–311

Training of staff, 23, 103, 122

Trait theories and tracts, 6

Transfer. *See* Generalization and generality

Type-token ratio, 207

Unconditioned reinforcer, 9, 127, 150–151

Unintelligible speech. *See* Articulation

University of Minnesota, 325, 325n, 327

University of Washington, 219. *See also* Developmental Psychology Laboratory

Values, 409–430

Vanishing stimuli. *See* Fading and adding stimuli

Verbal behavior, analysis of, 3–18

Verbal behavior, development of, 64–68

Verbal behavior and imitation. *See* Imitation

Verbal behavior, recording. *See* Recording verbal behavior

Verbal behavior as symptom, 3, 4

Verbal behavior, theories of
behavioral, 4–7
communication theory, 4
information theory, 4
mathematical theories, 4
neurological theories, 3
structural theories, 3
trait theories, 6

Violet project, 126, 154

Vocabulary, 22, 104, 108–110, 122–124, 140, 148, 152, 188, 199, 201, 207

Vowelized speech. *See* Articulation

War and Peace, 354

Western State Hospital, Washington, 221n

White River School District, Buckley, Washington, 19n, 102n

Writing, 22–23, 126, 200, 208, 210